Mitchell Symons was educated at Mill Hill and the LSE. After working at BBC TV as a researcher and director, he co-wrote early British editions of Trivial Pursuit before becoming a full-time journalist and writer. He has written regular columns for the *Sunday Times*, *Punch* and the *Evening Standard*, and has devised many print and television formats. He has written twenty-three non-fiction books. *All In* is his first novel.

He lives with his wife and two sons on the coast in Sussex.

ALL IN

MITCHELL SYMONS

review

First published in 2000
by Review

An imprint of Headline Book Publishing

10 9 8 7 6 5 4 3 2 1

ISBN 0 7472 7316 2

Typeset by Palimpsest Book Production Limited,
Polmont, Stirlingshire
Printed and bound in Great Britain by
Clays Ltd, St Ives plc.

Headline Book Publishing
A division of the Hodder Headline Group
338 Euston Road
London NW1 3BH

www.reviewbooks.co.uk
www.hodderheadline.com

To Bill Massey, my editor, and Rhian Bromage, his assistant,
for their skill and warmth.
To Luigi Bonomi, my agent, for his kindness and support.
And to Penny, my wife, for everything.

To Penny, Jack and Charlie . . . and The Boys

MONDAY, DECEMBER 28

I've had enough. I've had enough of not having enough. Of not being able to cope. Of dodging bills. Of Maggie's questions. Of my lies. Of the children's nagging. Of Dad and his misplaced pride in me. Of work. Of the fear of losing my job. Of stewards' inquiries. Of prices shortening when I don't take a price or lengthening when I do. Of feeling bad about gambling. Of hiding my gambling from Maggie. Of losing. Of winning even (why didn't I have *more* on?). Of the thought of stopping. Of not wanting to stop.

So if this year turns out to be yet another losing year then that's it, I'm checking out. I'm going to make a note of how much I'm worth on January 1. Then I'm going to keep a record of all my wins and losses over the next twelve months and if I'm worth *more* on December 31 next year, then I'm going to live. If I've lost money over the year, then I'm going to kill myself and the family will win.

The £200,000 life insurance policy I took out before I went to work in Saudi in 1980 expires on January 14. If I die before that date – even (and I've checked the small print) by my own hand – my family will get £200,000.

But what if I win? One year's success won't entirely purge years of losing but it will draw a line underneath it all. And if it does, if I win, then I'm going to get a life. A real life. I'll quit my job and travel or study (this time something *I* want to study, not what Dad wants me to study). I'll stay with Maggie and the kids but they'll have to accept me on my terms. That's the least they can do when I'm prepared to die for their financial security.

I've lost so much in the past few years: money, respect, self-respect, that I can't take any more beatings. But if I can win over the period of a year, then I will have achieved something extraordinary: I will have beaten the odds.

Otherwise, what's it all been for? I haven't exactly achieved anything. This isn't self-pity, just cold hard fact. Eight Os, three As, a 2.2 from Bristol, (approx) forty lays, one wife, two children, seven jobs (excluding temporary jobs), one breakdown, eight cars (nine if I include Mum's Allegro), two driving bans, one hospital operation, any number of foreign holidays And, if my sums are right, about £150,000 down the Swanee.

Not that I regret a single penny. It's the greatest thrill there is, the only thrill there is. When your train-fare home is riding on a maiden running in a bumper at Fakenham, when more money than you can afford to lose is on a ball ricocheting around a roulette wheel, when everything you have is being loaded into a trap at Monmore, then you know what excitement is – what fear is. Then you know that you're alive. It reminds me of the time when I tried to take up golf and I was having these lessons. Before a putt, I said for a laugh, 'And it's Steve Ross with this shot for the U.S. Masters.' And the pro – a nice guy – said, 'If you really want to put pressure on yourself, say that you need this putt to get your playing card for next year otherwise you'll be working in a fish-and-chip restaurant.' *That's* pressure.

THURSDAY, DECEMBER 31

I really can't wait to start. The annoying thing is I won £150 at the bookies yesterday but it doesn't count towards the bet. Actually, it doesn't matter, I'll add it to my stake money.

I've worked out to the precise penny (all right, pound) my entire net worth and here it goes:

Assets
The house: worth £160,000
Salary: £3,700 per month after tax (given average bonuses)

I'm not going to count the value of Maggie's car or her Halifax shares (though I wish she'd bloody sell them) and I'm not even going to *think* about the kids' savings accounts.

Less
Mortgage on the house: £90,000
Finance company loan (i.e. second charge): £40,000 (I hope Maggie doesn't find this diary! I'm being stupid: she can't possibly find it. I'm hiding it in the secret drawer – which Maggie doesn't know about – of Gran's old desk to which I have the only key. Besides, Maggie's not exactly over-burdened with curiosity which is what makes her the sort of person she is.)
Credit cards: approx £8,000 owing at any one time
Bank overdraft: £10,000
Amount owing to Dad: £10,000

So, if I don't count my salary which I need to live on and gamble with, I am worth precisely £2,000. Given that interest on my loans is increasing at a higher rate than the value of my house, I'm entitled to start this gamble at par – that's to say at zero. So if by next December 31 I'm worth more than zero, I'll live; if not then . . .

FRIDAY, JANUARY 1

11.00am. I'm getting old. This was the first time since 1969 that I've slept through New Year's Eve. Even the children stayed up. But I was so cream-crackered that I fell asleep watching a vid. in bed. Maggie says she tried to wake me up but I was dead to the world. She tells me that I let out a huge fart on the stroke of midnight. Sounds about right.

I need my sleep though. I feel like a boxer in training for the big fight. I know that *spieling* is never far from my thoughts but 'the bet' has really concentrated them. I feel so intensely aware of the stakes involved.

Tonight's the first round. I'm sure that I'm going to do really well.

I've resolved not to tell anyone about this bet – even Douglas. I don't want anyone gifting me hands or, worse, taking advantage of me in a big pot.

4.00pm. Fuck, fuck, fuck, fuck. Tonight's game is off. That's the first Friday night poker sesh we've lost since October and I'm completely fucked off. Nik phoned to say that his kid's not well and his wife's expecting any day (fair enough). Douglas says he's completely wasted from last night (sort of fair enough). I rang Ben to check he was still on but he thought that there wasn't a game because it was a bank holiday (as if) and Tanya has arranged for them to see friends. He's on a three-line whip. When I rang Jake to tell him, he said that he wouldn't play three-handed with me and Gerard – there had to be at least four players. He was absolutely implacable (the cunt).

I tried to get hold of some of the other guys, the non-regulars, but, needless to say, they'd all made alternative arrangements – even Kerry the Rat whose wife refuses to let him out even though they're doing nothing tonight, just because it's a fucking bank holiday. And she never stops going on about how much she hates him. I'm sure Moulinex (so called because he shakes like a blender every time he's got a good hand) would be free, but I've only got his work number. Rain Man (so called because he can work out the precise total of the pot just by looking at it) is on holiday. Worst of all, I just can't get hold of Gerard. How can a guy have six numbers like the Bad Man (Gerard) has and still not be contactable? There's a jealous husband or, much more likely, a conned 'client' on the warpath.

All of which doesn't help me. I feel like topping myself now and saving on a year's agony if this is how it's going to be for the next twelve months. Don't the guys know what's at stake? No, of course they don't. But even so. If Friday-night poker isn't precious, what is? I played the day after Jonathan was born. I've played with a 103 degree temperature. I once even played standing up when I'd put my back out. If only the other guys had my fucking dedication.

7.00pm. The Bad Man called! He's completely up for it. So I'm going round to his place (which is now in Earl's Court) to play backgammon and maybe some two-handed poker which can be surprisingly exciting – except when the Bad Man suggests high-low which more often than not ends up with the two of us splitting the pot!

SATURDAY, JANUARY 2

It was a great night. I won £400. These two sentences might just be connected.

Gerard's place was even more grotty than I expected. It's a one-bed (just) ground-floor flat with a prostitute (he showed me her card – BEAUTIFUL NEW 18-YEAR-OLD – which he says is wrong on all three counts) beneath him and a drug dealer (or so he says) above him. The decor is minimalist as the Bad Man hasn't yet got round to conning a catalogue company out of any furniture but he had proper poker food (tortilla chips, peanuts, Maltesers) and drink (cold Buds) so I wasn't complaining.

We started off with some backgammon. Just £1 a point but, with Gerard going mad with the doubling dice, we were playing for £32–£64–£128 a game.

By the time we switched to blackjack, I was a clear £300 up. We took it in turns to be the house and Gerard ended up about £1200 down! Needless to say, I hadn't actually seen any *money*. I paid cash for my chips while Gerard just helped himself ('If I agree to cover the chips you win, how can you complain?'). I don't mind Gerard ripping me off (well, I do) but I wish he didn't always sound so aggrieved when I point it out.

Then we played poker. Gerard plays poker manically when he's winning and even more manically when he's losing and here he was losing big time. So he was making incredibly outrageous bets: one pot got up to £500 before I backed out holding trips (three 9s) in a game of seven-card stud (nothing wild). He had a pair of 4s – in the hole!

Actually, that was one of the few seven-card games we played without wild cards. The Bad Man does like his wild cards. The truth is that I do too. We even played that Willy-Wanky-Woo game where *all* the spades are wild and *all* the diamonds are worthless. As I recall, his five queens beat my four aces. I wonder why it is that gamblers like wild cards so much when it's the same for all the players: i.e. it's just a form of poker inflation. Maybe it's our constant need for excitement; maybe by the time that 'ordinary' nothing-wild poker doesn't thrill us enough, we're beyond redemption.

We finished at four in the morning (I think: my brain isn't functioning too well after four hours sleep. Bloody Jonathan woke me up by firing his toy gun in the bedroom next door. And I was having such a wonderful dream about Cathy). I won £400. Gerard gave me £80 and an IOU for £320. True, the chances of him honouring his marker are slimmer than Kate Moss on a forty-eight-hour fast but how many people leave Gerard's with money? Especially his money.

MONDAY, JANUARY 4

First day back at work after (the best part of) two weeks off and I have to say I'm not in the mood.

I was at Head Office and said as much to Jayne, Phil's secretary. 'Welcome to the world, Steve, wake up and smell the coffee.'

I fancy Jayne – not big time, but enough. She's got fantastic tits and sparkling eyes which always seem to be challenging you (the eyes, not the tits). Trouble is, she's got a bit of a spotty boat and just the hint of a 'tache. And if there's one thing I can't stand on a girl, it's a 'tache. I take the (not unreasonable) view that if I can be bothered to shave, why can't they? I remember Bob who used to grade girls' moustaches on the scale of G1-G7 (based on the Gillette G2) with G7 as the most hirsute. On that basis, Jayne is maybe only a G1, but it's enough to put me off *really* trying. I think we're talking a soapy tit-wank and nothing more.

I did my paper work (boring), flirted with Jayne and a couple of other bits of office crumpet and then sneaked out, on the pretext of meeting a supplier, to a betting shop.

There were three races starting within five minutes of each other at the sort of courses that even the people who live near them have never heard of. Each race had an even money – or thereabouts – favourite. Last year, I'd have done a fifty-quid treble on the three favourites and watched at least one of them fail to come in.

Not now. I'm no longer interested in multiple bets. Multiple bets are mug bets. That's why bookies often offer tax-free yankees. Sure they're great when they come in but how often do they come in? I think I've had maybe four yankees come off at anything better than odds against for each of the four selections in the past twenty-five years. Every mug punter – i.e. every punter – has his successful yankee story (mine was over £1200 for a £33 stake) but, for every success, there are a thousand failures.

It's a bit like that time Frankie Dettori went through the card at Ascot. Bookies moaned that they lost a fortune from punters who backed Frankie for a seven-timer. What those lying bastards didn't say was that there are punters backing their favourite jockeys through the card every day of the week, every week of the year without ever seeing a return on their investments. That's why they call them accumulators: the bookies accumulate the punters' money.

But not mine because, from now on, I'm only going to do single bets.

So I backed each horse for £50 and two of them duly obliged. Typically, the only one I paid the tax on (because it was the shortest price) lost. Even so, I finished about £50 up and where I would once have simply ploughed it all on to the next horse, I walked out, taking my profit.

WEDNESDAY, JANUARY 6

What I won on Monday, I managed to lose (and more) yesterday.

I got a call from Jim (in accounts) who gets some serious information from time to time. He told me that he'd heard a whisper for Treetops in the 2.30 at Wincanton. I was going to phone Hill's with my switch card but then I thought, 'No, the stake money and the winnings will appear on the bank statement and Maggie might get to see it' which was totally illogical because she *never* opens my bank statements but that's Stevie Fuckwit.

By the time I got to a bookie's, the race had already started but that was OK because it was a chase and they take bets after the off. What I hadn't reckoned on was the sodding pen not working. Why it is that betting shop pens only work if you're not in a hurry? And how could I, as a veteran twenty-five years' punting, rely on a betting-shop pen?

So I missed out on a fucking 5–1 winner on which I'd planned to punt £250 (i.e. as much cash as I could get my hands on).

Instead, I frittered it away on a string of dumb bets. I found myself backing horses on the basis that their sequence of races seemed to be improving (e.g. 'F432', rather than '234F'). Obviously it's good to back a genuinely improving horse but these are just the headline results and don't take into account the proper form. For example 'F432' might actually indicate a horse with its best form *behind* it. It might have fallen at the last fence when in the lead, and then finished fourth, third and second in fields of, respectively, twenty, nine and three runners.

To use a criterion like that is plain suicide – perhaps literally in my case. I'd have been better off just handing the money straight over to the bookie and telling him to keep it and saved myself the torture of watching animals even dumber than me losing it.

FRIDAY, JANUARY 8

Tonight sees the first *proper* poker game of the year and I just can't wait. Maggie made some (very mildly) threatening noises about me not staying out too late but I merely gave her my 'breakdown' face and she backed down instantly.

The (only) great thing about the breakdown is that it was so genuinely horrific that just the thought of a relapse sends Maggie (and Dad) running for cover. It's been eleven years now and they're still terrified of me going doolally again. This of course gives me a licence to do pretty much as I please. I love them and I try not to take advantage of their good will but sometimes it's hard not to.

It was Mum's death that made Dad so indulgent. I still feel bad about borrowing that ten grand off him for my 'business idea'. He must *know* that I haven't got a big business idea. I'm not a businessman, for fuck's sake. I'm a sales rep. And why am I a sales rep? Because I failed as a teacher.

No, that's not fair. I didn't fail as a teacher. I was a good teacher: I failed as a human being. I just couldn't hack it in front of the kids. I couldn't stand having all those eyes looking at *me*. I could feel them boring into my soul. I had to get away from them. I took all the (generous) sick leave they gave me but I knew I was never going to go back. They didn't believe me until I actually had my breakdown.

And now all I can do is sell. I'm a good sales rep – I meet my targets with ease – but I'll never be anything more than a rep because there's no way that I could ever stand up again in front of a group of people and speak. So that's it. I'm a sales rep for the next twenty years or until December 31 this year. No golden watch for me, not even a silver bullet. Just a jump or a swallow. Actually, I wonder how I'll do it if I lose the bet. I think it would have to be pills as the alternatives are just too horrible to contemplate. Or I could start winning some dosh.

SATURDAY, JANUARY 9

I hate it when non-Irish people use the word 'crack' to describe a great time but last night was a great crack, begorrah.

We played at Nik's place as his wife and kid are out of the country at the moment – in Venezuela visiting her folks, which led to more than a few Caracas/crackers jokes. Cue Douglas who's got a new expression which he trots out every time someone comes out with a joke that falls flat. 'That's a bit like a joke – without that funny bit at the end that makes people laugh.' Very quickly we all adopt it and adapt it so that it becomes the phrase of the night. 'That's a bit like a bet, Jake, without that putting your money into the pot bit that makes other people put their chips in.' 'That's a bit like a spread, Nik,' said Ben to our host who had neglected to provide for his guests' inner needs, 'without the food and drink bits that people eat and drink.'

I didn't win last night but I lost less than any of the other losers did. I think I did about £60, which is nothing for a good evening out. The trouble is it's so very hard to establish who won or lost what. The winners are pretty reliable but all the losers will say is 'I'm about even.'

Gerard couldn't honour (funny word to use in connection with the Bad Man) any of his debt to me because he had prior commitments to Douglas and Ben. 'This is a bit like an IOU,' I said to Gerard holding up his marker, 'without the O and U bits at the end.'

SUNDAY JANUARY 10

I was eating breakfast. 'Why don't you do something with Jonathan today?' Maggie asked me just a tad reproachfully.

'What do you suggest?'

'Take him to mini-rugby training. Other fathers do.'

'He doesn't like rugby,' I replied, keeping cool in the face of her provocative questioning though I was finding it harder than holding in a fart.

'How do you know?'

'He came into the lounge yesterday while I was watching the rugby international and I told him he could stay if he wanted but he just left the room.'

'Why don't you take him to the zoo?'

'Because I'm not divorced.'

'All right,' she said, starting to look flustered, 'what about a car-boot sale?'

'I *hate* car-boot sales. You know I hate car-boot sales. Do we really need more junk?'

'OK, Steve, do whatever you want. He's your son.'

How dare *she* accuse *me* of being a lousy father? I love my kids – absolutely dote on them. It's true that I don't have as much time for them as I'd like but that's how it goes. Better for them to have a busy dad who they know loves them than a dad who tries to live his life through his kids. Like my dad does, Godammit.

I'm not a bad dad. I spent a fortune on Christmas presents just a couple of weeks ago. I'm not afraid to give my kids a cuddle and I never hit them (well, not Melanie at any rate).

The truth is I'm not really cut out for this fatherhood lark. I'm a free spirit. Putting me in the straitjacket of 'family man' would just send me stark raving mad. So, no, I don't know the name of my children's teachers or friends – as Maggie found out when she quizzed me last summer – and I don't take them out as often as I should. But I love them and what other dad would make the sacrifice that I'm prepared to make at the end of the year?

WEDNESDAY, JANUARY 13

I've settled back into the groove at work. I'm not only meeting my targets, I'm actually exceeding them which should mean some welcome extra dosh. Phil told me – strictly in private – that for the month of February they're going to run a special promotion in which we can either opt for a lower target and get a flat-rate extra bonus for every machine sold above target or opt for the higher target and double all bonuses for the whole month. The downside of the higher bonus is that if you don't meet it – even if you exceed the lower target – you don't get an extra penny. Obviously, I'm going for the higher target as it sounds like a good punt to me.

I had a few bets on Monday and Tuesday without really troubling the scorers. I really can't be bothered to record *every* bet if the end result of a day's *spieling* is plus/minus less than fifty quid. To go into the minutiae any more than keeping a note of the figures for the bottom-line figure at the end of the month (which I intend to do) is a bit like counting your stools after a crap.

It's Maggie's birthday tomorrow. Fucked if I know what to buy her. To be fair to her, she's the least acquisitive person I know. I think that's what attracted me to her in the first place. Especially after Cathy, after Saudi. I know I'll never be as wealthy again as I was then with that double whammy of no tax and no living expenses. And Cathy was so unselfish in helping me to spend it all.

But it wasn't just Maggie's lack of materialism that attracted me; it was also her innate decency. For as much as she pisses me off sometimes, I have to admit that she's genuinely *good*: like a person who has sweet breath without ever brushing their teeth.

Proximity was also a big factor. When I first started teaching at St Margaret's, she was one of only two or three eligible women there (discounting the girls of course – though some of the fifth-formers were unbelievably ripe and luscious, especially Mandy Crichton. I wonder whatever happened to her?) so we gravitated towards each other.

And then when I had my breakdown, she was so incredibly supportive that marriage became inevitable – notwithstanding her mother's dire warnings.

Now, ten years and two kids on, I wouldn't exchange her for

the world and I know that whatever I buy for her for tomorrow, she'll accept with grace and gratitude. So I think I'll have a bit of fun. I'd earmarked thirty quid for her present. Instead, I'll put aside £10 and gamble the other twenty (besides any other bets I might have today). So she'll get a present worth anything from £10 to, say, £100.

THURSDAY, JANUARY 14

Maggie's birthday. Cards, tea in bed, presents from the kids (organised by her mum) and then my offering.

A beautiful necklace. Sure, it was just costume jewellery but it still cost me eighty quid. Which means, of course, that I managed to turn Maggie's twenty quid into eighty. All thanks to an obliging horse named Rumandraisin which crucified the rest of the field over a mile on the all-weather at Southwell. It also helped me turn in a profit for the day of £90.

I don't really know what made me back the nag – sorry, did I say 'nag' when I meant to say 'thoroughbred' – in the first place. Actually, I do. In the bookie's, they have the racing press plastered over the walls. For each meeting, there is a table of selections which lists the newspaper tipsters' selections for all the races.

Rumandraisin won the last race of the day. By that time, I could see how well each tipster had fared. My starting point is that no tipster is going to select *every* winner at a meeting – that's to say, go through the card (well not more than once in a lifetime). Similarly, on an average afternoon with, say, two favourites, three horses priced between 3–1 and 6–1 and one outsider winning the six races, a tipster might reasonably expect *one* winner.

By the last race, four favourites out of five, plus one outsider, had won. Eight of the fourteen (or so) tipsters had picked three or more winners. Five tipsters had selected two winners. One tipster, however, hadn't had a single winner all afternoon and he alone of all of them had selected Rumandraisin. So I piled in and cleaned up.

FRIDAY, JANUARY 15

7.00pm. Last night should have been really good. I took Maggie out for dinner to this wonderful new Chinese restaurant.

Everything was going fine when, out of the blue, Maggie asked me if there was anything she should know.

Shit. 'No,' I said, feeling the chicken and cashewnuts in a yellow bean sauce rising in my gorge, 'should there be?'

'It's just that the building society wrote saying that we haven't paid the mortgage for three months.' Double shit. 'I phoned them to query it because I thought that we – or you – paid it by direct debit but they said no, you've been paying by cheque for the past six months and that this isn't the first time you've fallen behind with the payments . . .'

She let the sentence drift and then went silent awaiting my reply. Maggie does that sort of thing. I played for time by calling the waiter over and asking for some more egg fried rice.

'It's an oversight, darling, nothing more sinister than that. I'm sure I told you that I was dropping the direct debit because I didn't like the idea of anyone being able to help themselves to my money.'

'You didn't, Steve,' she said quietly but confidently.

'Didn't I? I'm sure I did. Well, anyway, that's the way it is. I pay them by cheque once a month. Sometimes I forget but it's no problem, I'll just send them a cheque for three months' worth.'

I thought she was going to say something but she did something worse and more effective: she stared at me with her head cocked to one side as though she was sizing me up. Once again, it was up to me to break the silence.

'Look, sweetie, you work for the education authority not the building society so what's with the third degree? I made a mistake. I'm sorry. I'll rectify it in the morning. Now can we get on with our meal?'

'I've eaten enough,' she said in such a way that it was

impossible for me to tell whether she was genuinely full or just (in her own quiet way) angry with me.

We did talk – chit-chat really – some more in the restaurant and on the way home but there was definitely a chill in the air and we didn't, as we'd intended, 'get it on.'

She knows though, doesn't she? She *knows* that there's something wrong. She *knows* that on our joint incomes, we should be pissing on such a small mortgage. She *knows* that I'm spending money – our money – on things I shouldn't be spending it on.

She *thinks* that it might be another woman; she *fears* it might be drugs; she *suspects* it's gambling.

I phoned the building society this morning and apologised for the delay which was due to bollocks . . . Christ knows . . . fucked if I give a damn. They told me I owed them £1800 plus change. I told them they'd get a cheque on Monday.

I endeared myself further to Maggie tonight by going to poker. Usually, she doesn't object but Melanie's poorly – very poorly, in fact, with a temperature of 104 – and Maggie's mum, who she'd ordinarily phone for support on such occasions, is out tonight (at *Starlight Express*, God help me).

I felt torn, I have to confess, but I told myself that although little Mellie has a high temperature, it can go down again in the time it takes her to digest a spoonful of Calpol and, also, I'm at the end of a mobile if anything goes seriously wrong. For Christ's sake, there's any number of single mothers who'd *die* for that sort of support.

Midnight. Came home early. Maggie really grateful and thanked me for being thoughtful. Didn't tell her the truth which is that I was the victim of a real Sketchley's job – i.e. they took me to the cleaners. I lost £300 in cash, I used up *all* the money the Bad Man owed me and I borrowed a further £300 off Ben which I also lost.

I can't believe how unlucky I was. It was four gigantic pots which did for me. Two high-low where I went low with a 7 and lost both times, a four-card Omaha where I had the nut flush until the full house appeared on the final card and a five-card stud where, incredibly, Douglas's unbelievably well-concealed trips beat my aggressively bid two pair.

Melanie's much better but I'm feeling as sick as a bulimic after a visit to a chocolate factory.

SATURDAY, JANUARY 16

Maggie has thawed a little. She's obviously very relieved about Melanie (who's woken up feeling fit and fine) but she also thinks she might have over-reacted towards me.

Here's a laugh, though. She told me she's misjudged me and that it's clear that I'm not an 'inveterate gambler' (her words). No, I didn't lie to her about last night's losses: she doesn't ask and I don't tell. *She* wanted to have a bet and *I* talked her out of it.

We were going to my father's for tea but needed to get some petrol on the way.

When Maggie spotted the National Lottery till, she asked whether we should buy some tickets. I reminded her that we have a standing entry into every draw, Wednesdays and Saturdays.

Ah yes, says she, but that's just one ticket – why don't we buy some more tickets and increase our chances?

At this point I pulled rank as a mathematician and explained the odds to her. If you buy one ticket for the Lottery, you have approximately one chance in fifteen million of winning. If you buy two tickets, you don't halve the odds to one in seven-and-a-half million as so many people think, you merely give yourself *two* chances in fifteen million. Similarly, if we did as Maggie wanted and bought ten tickets, we wouldn't have one chance in one-and-a-half million but, merely, ten chances in fifteen million.

What this means, as I explained to Maggie, is that instead of having 14,999,999 chances of losing, you reduce that to 14,999,990 chances of losing. It's the statistical equivalent of jumping from the 119th floor instead of the 120th: it's meaningless.

Maggie now thinks she's married to Captain Sensible and who am I to disabuse her? Especially, when the reality is that I lost a grand total of £400 today on the football fixed odds (bloody Liverpool – if they'd fucking won, I'd have made £3,000).

N.B. Wish I didn't have to get up early *every* day of the week just to be able to get to the post first so that Maggie doesn't see all the red bills.

SUNDAY, JANUARY 17

A weekend of best behaviour enabled me to slip out late this evening on the pretext of 'just going out for a drink.' Lucky Maggie doesn't check my car's speedo.

I went to the casino – one I joined a couple of years ago when Maggie and I were taken by Nicky Thompson and his wife. It's OK. Bad taste has been lavished everywhere, so it's as gaudy as a pimp's bedroom but it's discreet, anonymous, functional. The punters are the sort of international trash one finds in casinos. And, like all casinos, there isn't a clock or a window in sight so punters have no idea of the time.

I did what I usually do in casinos when I'm on my own. I decided to play for one hour or until I'd lost £300, whichever came first. That way, I protect the upside.

I started off playing blackjack. I play properly – that's to say if the dealer's hole card is 2, 3, 4, 5, or 6 then I 'stick' on twelve and above. If the dealer has a 7 or above (including the ace), then I draw on sixteen and below. That's it, not a difficult concept to grasp, and yet it's amazing how many people refuse to draw on, say, fourteen when the dealer's showing an 8.

I was actually two hundred quid or so up until such a civilian pitched up at the empty chair next to mine. Within a dozen hands, he helped to halve my stash by drawing when he shouldn't have done and, more importantly, *not* drawing when he should have done, thereby diverting cards which would have busted the dealer. Worse still, he actually split a pair of jacks!

I went from there to the casino poker game. This isn't a poker game against other players but against the house. You put up an ante and then decide after seeing your cards whether to bet (double the stake of the ante) or fold. Your bet only applies if the dealer's hand 'qualifies' (with ace-king high or better). If the dealer's hand qualifies, ordinary poker rules apply (although you get more for two pairs or better); if the dealer's hand doesn't qualify, you win but only get paid up for your ante. It's a vicious game which, unlike blackjack, is heavily stacked in the house's favour. Only a complete wally would even *think* of playing. Or, indeed, a Stevie.

Some players bet on nothing (which means they're paying three times the ante to win even money on the ante). I'd rather sacrifice my ante and only play on a pair of 6s or better, so there's a chance that if the dealer qualifies, I might still win.

I frittered away about a hundred and fifty quid before being dealt a straight which *didn't* fucking count because the dealer's hand didn't qualify. That did me in and I retreated to the roulette table with just ten minutes or a hundred quid to go. It looked like it was going to be a tight-run thing.

In the event, I turned that hundred into *five* hundred by betting on 26 and all the possible chevals, splits, streets, corners around it. On the very second spin, 26 itself came up. It was a wonderful moment. Nevertheless, I dutifully left after ten minutes (all right, fifteen minutes) and returned home feeling very pleased with myself.

The trouble is, at this time of night, who can I tell?

Not bloody Maggie, that's who I can't tell. There's no time of day or night when I can tell her. Why can't she be like other wives and be happy for her husband and support him?

WEDNESDAY, JANUARY 20

We were sitting on the sofa watching TV when Maggie snuggled up to me. 'Darling,' she said, 'have you always been faithful to me?'

'Yes, Maggie,' I answered nervously.

'On the children's lives?'

Shit. I couldn't cross my fingers because she was holding my hands. 'Yes, I've always been faithful to you.'

'On the children's lives?'

'On the children's lives.' But as I said those words I quickly redefined the word 'faithful' to mean that I've never 'betrayed' her to another woman – that's to say that, unlike my mate Rick, when I go with other women, I never slag off my own wife. Maybe that's loyalty rather than fidelity but there's no doubt in my mind that it's better to have a one-off screw but always talk well of your wife than it is to never have sex with anyone else but to always go around slagging off your wife.

'Are you sure, on the children's lives, you've never made love to another woman?'

Easy one that. I've screwed other women but I've never made love to them. 'On the children's lives, I've never made love to another woman.'

'On the children's lives, have you ever been given a blow job since we've been married by anyone other than me?'

I don't recall too many marital blow jobs but I didn't think that now was the best time to mention it as I was still on the back foot, so to speak. 'One hundred per cent,' I replied.

'On the children's lives?'

I pulled away from her and sat bolt upright. 'Look, Maggie, I really don't like these games. I've given you my word – on the children's lives – and that should be good enough for you. I'm off to bed. To read.'

And, with that, I stormed off. Better to have a tantrum than a divorce.

THURSDAY, JANUARY 21

I'm in a bookie's in Guildford and there's this punter – shabby bloke, smoking roll-ups – just behind me at the counter. It turns out that we're both betting on the same dog race. I got on just as they said, 'The hare's running' but he was too late. I managed to sneak a look at his betting slip as he shouted and swore at the girl and he wanted to bet £200 on trap three.

Trap three lost. So was this bloke relieved at having saved £200? No he was not. He was still furious. Not furious at the girl who hadn't taken his bet but furious with himself for not having got on sooner. He genuinely regretted the fact that he hadn't put his two hundred quid on a losing dog. Does that make him a nutter?

And yet haven't I felt precisely the same when I haven't managed to get a bet on in time? Sure I feel relief on a rational level but I still feel a sense of loss. Somehow, if I'd have had my money on, the race would have/might have turned out differently. I guess it's existential: the real race only exists if I'm involved with it. Meanwhile, I lost £260 in half-an-hour.

While waiting for an appointment, I phoned the insurance company which sold me my term insurance just to check – absolutely-for-certain-no-fucking-about-honest-injun – that they pay out in the event of suicide. After much umming and ahing they confirmed that they did and when they started to ask me nervously about why I was calling, I told them that the mobile was cracking up and cut myself off.

FRIDAY, JANUARY 22

11.00am. It's *really* annoying. We're due to be playing poker at Ben's tonight. Douglas phones me on my mobile to say we'll have to find another venue because Tanya won't let Ben have the game at their place. Or rather she will let Ben have the game at her place but not if Gerard attends. Apparently, she hates Gerard. And the extraordinary thing is, *she's never met him*.

Gerard made just this point when he phoned up for a wail. 'How can she hate me,' asked the Bad Man, showing off his well-honed sense of injustice (though he has absolutely no sense of justice), 'when she hasn't even met me?'

'It saves time, Bad Man, it saves time.'

SATURDAY, JANUARY 23

3.00am. Too tired to write an account of the night. Game eventually took place at Douglas's. Ben was big winner (£400). I lost about £200 (all right, £240). Not bad. Fun time. Wish Jake didn't smoke. Wish I hadn't eaten so many tortilla chips. Wish I hadn't drunk that last lager. Wish I hadn't drunk that last but one lager. Wish I didn't have any responsibilities. Wish Maggie didn't put cream on at night. Wish Cathy was here. Wish I'd never been born. *Man of The World*. Peter Green. Genius. He's a genius and I'm a cunt.

MONDAY, JANUARY 25

It wasn't a great weekend. Maggie's bothering me about money again. She wants to know how much we've got in our savings. I sort of deflected her questions but there's no getting away from the fact that we haven't got any savings. I closed the savings account two years ago although it's entirely possible that I neglected to tell her.

'We've got a few bob, darling, why do you want to know?'

'Oh, I was thinking about buying some new carpets.'

I thought on my feet and, answering only the substantive question, told her that there was absolutely no need as she keeps the house so beautifully that even the carpets (which are, I admit, a little threadbare) look magnificent. Like Basil Fawlty with the Germans and the War, I think I got away with it.

WEDNESDAY, JANUARY 27

I had to go to Chiswick to check on a dealer when who should I spot sitting in the window of a Cafe Rouge but Gerard. I went in to say hello. He was lunching with this rather dodgy-looking character with a pony-tail and dark glasses. Both of them had their mobile phones on the table.

Reluctantly, Gerard introduced me to his lunchtime companion. 'This is Mike. He's come down from Norwich and we're having lunch. It's not just because we're doing a computer deal.' Gerard is the Billy Bunter *de nos jours* – 'No, Mr Quelch, I didn't snaffle Coker's tuck and I didn't eat the delicious strawberry jam tarts.'

Mike scowled and buried his head in the menu.

'I bet both of those phones will go off when the bill arrives,' I said.

THURSDAY, JANUARY 28

Phil has let me know – off the record – that I might be given Reading as part of my patch in the spring.

I can't stop thinking about her, I really can't. There aren't many nights I don't dream of her. And then there are the things that never fail to remind me of her: Bob Seger records, Georgette Heyer books, sunsets, whist, Paris, spare ribs, shaggy dog stories, *Rive Gauche* perfume, long scarfs, dimples and Maltesers because she loved them. And cricket because she hated it. In fact, there isn't much that doesn't remind me of Cathy.

I can see her now, blowing upwards to take her fringe out of her eyes. And that great body. A three-ply wet dream, Dave Simpson called her.

I would give *anything* to be with her but even if she could forgive me for '83, I know she would never forgive me for '87.

I did one of my speciality bets at the bookie's. This involved backing the three outsiders in a forecast combination in each dog race through the card at one meeting (Bristol). This means twelve races multiplied by six bets in each race or a total of seventy-two bets. I did a unit stake of £5 so it cost me £360. If only two out of twelve forecasts had come off at odds of, say, 6–1 twice, I'd be in profit but not *one* single fucking forecast came in.

SATURDAY, JANUARY 30

11.00am. A funny thing happened last night. The game was at Douglas's and – wrongly, because he hadn't checked it with Douglas – Gerard brought this kid Toby along. No harm done except this kid doesn't call Gerard 'Gerard', he calls him 'Marcel'. 'What's this, Bad Man,' says I, 'why is this youth calling you "Marcel"?'

'Because that's my name.'

'But your name's Gerard,' says Nik.

'Or Bad Man,' adds Ben.

'Marcel is my middle name and sometimes I use it as my first name.'

'But why, Bad Man?'

'It's a business matter,' said Gerard, as though that explained everything.

Fade to black: fade up again.

I was telling the assembled company about my encounter with Gerard – sorry, Marcel – in Chiswick and this inspired Gerard to unburden his conscience (as if . . .) about his 'business deal'.

'Mike is my business associate,' says the Bad Man without a trace of irony (the Bad Man doesn't do irony: where other single blokes get someone in to do the ironing, Gerard has to have help with the irony), 'and, as such, is able to let me have a consignment of brand new computers at an amazing price.' He goes on to list the computers' amazing spec. and then asks us to guess the price: £500.

'That's right,' says Gerard triumphantly, 'these computers retail for £2,000 each but I can get them for £500.'

My cries of 'but they must be hot' are drowned out by the other guys clamouring to be allowed to buy them. Oh well, if you can't beat them . . .

It was a successful night for me. Apart from all the laughs, I turned in a profit of £80. Douglas won £600, Ben won £100, Toby lost £40, Jake lost £50, Nik lost £250, Gerard lost £400. I know it doesn't add up, so someone's lying. Gerard, obviously.

8.00pm. This afternoon, I went to Henry's. I really like Henry: he's the only bookie I know who takes no longer to pay out than he did to accept your bet.

There were the usual suspects littering the premises. The Asian bloke with the skin complaint who always wears his motorcycle crash helmet; the hospital sister who smiles whether she's winning or losing; Nigel, the ex-squaddie, who insists on telling you after each race how you should have known all along that the winning horse was going to win – betting-shop wisdom is always *after* the event. Then there is any number of sad old gits for whom betting shops are homes, refuges, therapy and misery all rolled into one.

There's also my mate Tim. I call him my mate but we only ever see each other at the bookie's. For all I know, he lives there; for all he knows, I live there.

Tim is an exception to the rule that only losers go to betting shops. Notwithstanding the tracksuit and trainers he always wears, Tim's a successful lad. He's the only bloke I know who probably wins more than he loses. Or at least he breaks even.

This afternoon, Tim had a tip. The horse's name was Fireman Nick and, needless to say, the whole shop was on it.

With Henry's help (i.e. credit), I had my biggest-ever bet on a single horse race: £300 to win.

Fireman Nick went off as 11–10 favourite in a nine-horse race. The only other horse in the betting was the 6–5 shot, Constantinou.

Constantinou beat Fireman Nick by a length.

The whole shop was devastated. No one said anything to Tim. Betting folk are far too used to losing to blame one of their own – they'll scream at the TV screen, they'll shout at the cashiers, they'll tell each other that a trainer's bent, a jockey's lazy and a horse deserves to become pet food but they'll understand that a man who passes on – passes on, not sells – a tip has only done his best. Besides, they knew that Tim had lost more than any of them and, despite the bad tip, they didn't want him not to share his next piece of information with them. If you're in the desert, you'll accept any water so long as it's wet.

After the shock waves had died down, I took Tim to one side and asked him about the provenance of his tip.

'I don't understand,' said he, 'for the last six weeks, they've given me the winners of six races.'

'Who's given you these tips?'

'They came by post from this bloke. I don't know his name. For three weeks, he gave me these winners for no cost at all. Then, he sold me one tip a week for £100. I paid him by cheque. An outfit called Top Man Racing or something. They were always evens – or thereabouts – but I thought it was still good value.'

'Tell me, Tim, were all the races like this one? Basically two-horse races. One horse at evens, another at 6–4 and the rest of the horses at 10–1 or more?'

'Now you mention it, Steve, they were. Why?'

'Because, my son,' I said putting a hand on his shoulder, 'you and I have been done up like a kipper. We've been stung. As a mathematician, I know how they've done it. Do you want me to explain?'

The scam's simple. The con man always chooses races with

only two possible (to all intent and purpose) winners. He then sends out, say 8,000 letters on spec to known punters (bookmakers' clients, racing newsletter subscribers etc.). For the first race, 4,000 letters tip Horse A and 4,000 tip Horse B. If Horse B wins, he forgets about the 4,000 people he wrote to tipping Horse A. Next week, he writes to the 4,000 people who were on Horse B. To 2,000 of them, he tips Horse C, to the other 2,000, he tips Horse D. If Horse C wins, he then concentrates on those people to whom he sent the correct tip. And so on. By the time he gets to charging for his tips, he's likely to get a nearly full take-up from about 400 salivating punters (half of whom will get the winning horse), then 200 and then 100. At this point, he'll probably give it up, having made over £70,000. Nice work if you can get it.

'You see, Tim, this guy didn't know anything about racing: he just understood maths.'

SUNDAY, JANUARY 31

I'm £1,700 down on the month. About what I expected.

TUESDAY, FEBRUARY 2

Last night I was having sex with/fucking/making love to Maggie. Just before we got right down to it, I decided to stake today's betting money on how long it took me. I was going to spend £250 today but wagered with myself to take off £10 for every minute I took. That's to say, if I took ten minutes, I'd take ten x £10 off today's stake money, fourteen minutes, £140 etc., more than twenty-five minutes, I wouldn't have a bet today.

In the event, I came in *eight* minutes which meant that I had £170 to bet with today.

I did the lot in just twenty minutes: a ton on a horse called Maggie's Dream (it seemed indicated) and I got no return on a ten quid win patent on three favourites across three meetings. So much for no more multiple bets.

Wish I'd taken twenty-six minutes now.

WEDNESDAY, FEBRUARY 3

Douglas took me along to this casino where he's a member to play poker. I've never played poker – against other punters – in a casino before and it was quite an education.

We were playing in a Hold 'Em tournament – £20 to play with unlimited buy-ins.

I sat down with six other guys and I disliked each of them. The guy immediately on my left was quite possibly the most unfriendly man I've ever met. I tried introducing myself – like you do – but he just didn't want to know. The only time he did talk to me was to tell me off for not putting in my ante. To his left was a bloke I nicknamed (to myself) Art because of his resemblance (physical, not vocal) to Art Garfunkel. I don't think he smiled once the whole evening. Next to him was a bloke who I initially thought was friendly until I realised that he couldn't stop smiling because that's the way his jaw had been set – a bit like The Joker.

Next to The Joker sat some sort of Iranian/Greek/Turkish man who was forever shouting across the room at his 'friends' – as if anyone could ever make friends in such a godforsaken place. When he wasn't chit-chatting, he was making a nuisance of himself with the waitresses. 'Tina,' he would bellow, 'fill my glass!' And Tina would duly scamper off to obey her master's booming voice. And he smoked the whole time. Little cigarillos, like the baddie in a spaghetti western.

On his left was a young guy I came to think of as Bandwagon as he just wanted to agree with everything everyone said – which was fine when it was non-contentious but fucking annoying when it wasn't. For example, when the bastard on my left told me off for the non-putting-in-of-ante crime, he was the first to support him, piping up, 'He's right, you know, that's not the first time someone's had to tell you.' The cunt.

Finally, there was Mr Poker Pro who'd been there, done that and split the pot. He simply couldn't resist telling us all about his gambling acumen and all the tragic poker tournaments in which he'd reached the final table ('and now, the end is here, and so I reach the final table') as though this were an achievement comparable to splitting the fucking atom. Physically, he was repulsive: I've nothing against men with nasal hair but do they have to pick it at the poker table? Also, if there's one thing worse than someone using the arm of their glasses as a cotton bud to forage for ear wax, it's that person going on to eat what they've collected.

The thing is that for me, poker has always been about fun. That's why we talk about *playing* cards. Our Friday night poker sessions are the absolute highlight of my week, of my *life*. Stripping away the fun from the game – as these creeps were doing – takes away the point of it.

I could have won the poxy tournament – I really could – but I just wanted to get away from there, so I gifted a couple of hands to Art (who wasn't such a bad bloke if truth be told), said goodbye to Douglas and buggered off. I could have played in a cash game but I could feel a wave of panic coming over me just at the thought of staying with those creeps.

FRIDAY, FEBRUARY 5

Tonight's game was at Douglas's poky poker pad.

'Where are our computers, Gerard?' we asked the Bad Man.

'Ah, I'm glad you asked me that,' he replied sounding very much like he wasn't glad that we'd asked him that. 'My supplier's let me down.'

'What do you mean by "let you down"?' asked Jake.

'What do you mean by "supplier"?' asked Ben.

I said, 'He means Mike but he isn't a "supplier", is he, Gerard? At least not in the sense of legitimate computer supplier? He's a thief and my guess is he's ripped you off too.'

Gerard looked peeved. Whether it was because I was suggesting – heaven forbid – that he would deal with anyone who wasn't kosher or whether it was because I was calling him a con man's mark, I couldn't tell but he wasn't about to go down in our estimation. 'Don't worry, boys,' he said pulling out a roll of fifties, 'you'll all get your deposits back and we'll say no more about it. Now I can't say fairer than that.'

Just before we found out whether, indeed, he *could* say fairer than that, his mobile rang. It was one of the mothers of one of his many children. From the two-minute screamfest which ensued, it was possible to discern that a) Gerard had not been paying his child's maintenance and b) he wasn't going to be allowed to see his child until he did so. In as much as you can slam down a mobile phone, Gerard did so with the valediction 'Fuck off, you bitch'. Being hidebound chaps rather than touchy-feely chicks, we didn't refer to this extraordinary interruption, although Douglas was heard to mutter – to no one in particular – 'You shouldn't internalise your feelings so much, Gerard.' Douglas is, of course, also divorced or separated – one doesn't like to enquire too deeply.

The call came at an opportune time for Gerard as it allowed him to switch from the embarrassing topic of conned man to the (for him at least) fascinating subject of his love life. 'Look at this little beauty, boys,' he said pulling out a picture of a (nearly) naked Scandinavian lovely. She looked impossibly gorgeous and I said so, stressing the word 'impossibly'.

Once again, Gerard looked peeved. 'Steve, how can you *imply* that Sylvie' – apparently the name of his *inamorata* – 'doesn't exist?'

'Oh, I'm sure she exists, Bad Man. It's not her existence I'm doubting. It's her existence in your life I'm doubting.'

Gerard grinned in that (one has to say) engaging, boyish just-been-found-out way of his which actually made me wonder if I'd wronged him. The thing is with the Bad Man that some of his claims really are true: indeed, the more extraordinary the story, the more likely it is to be true. For instance, Gerard told us that he served with the French Foreign Legion. Obviously, none of us believed him. 'But I'm *telling* you that I was in the French Foreign Legion,' he would wail. '*That's* why we don't believe you,' we would retort. And then, blow me down, he produces a magazine which has a photograph – with his name – of him in French Foreign Legion kit. So you never know with the Bad Man.

We were six this evening. The usual five plus Roger, a fellow-American Douglas met through work. I think Douglas's pitching to him. Douglas owns an advertising agency called The Kennedy Agency (as in Douglas Kennedy). I once berated him for this: 'I thought all ad agencies were named after their partners, not just one guy?'

'Well, so's mine,' drawled Douglas, 'but I bought out Mr The and Mr Agency a few years back.'

I don't mind Douglas inviting who he wants to his flat (big of me) but I immediately took a deep dislike to Roger.

For a start, he had a big bushy moustache and was wearing a lumberjack's shirt. Non-indictable crimes, I know, but coupled with his attitude, they set my teeth on edge. He was just so cocksure in that infuriating way that Americans overseas can be (see also Korea and Vietnam). I found everything about him loathsome, from the way he tucked his cards right into his chest (as though we're a bunch of cheats), to the way he called queens 'bitches', to the way he kept accusing Gerard of not having put in the right money. The fact that he was invariably correct was neither here nor there: Gerard may be a bit of a rogue but he's *our* rogue.

Having said that, I seemed to be the only one – even including the Bad Man – who didn't like him. When he went out the room to go to the loo, I hissed 'Creep' and the others all looked surprised.

The main thing that wound me up about him – and the others did at least concede this when he'd gone (he was the first to go) – was the way he crowed every time he won a pot. In our crowd, the form is to sympathise with the losers (up to a point: then we tell them that we have no interest in their lives and they should find someone who has). Roger not only took our money but he also told us – in ungracious terms – what we'd done wrong. When he did it to me, I chucked in a quid chip and told him I was grateful for the lesson. The cunt kept it and the others, damn them, laughed.

I lost £300 but Douglas 'I'm bleeding from every orifice' Kennedy lost nearly £500. What lovely guests we all were.

SATURDAY, FEBRUARY 6

I wish I could be like my sister, Sue. She pays every bill the day it arrives – even if the money's not due for a month. What's clever about Sue is that she's realised that if you do as I do and only pay on red (or worse), you only appreciate the benefits of it once: the rest of your life you're playing catch-up. Sue, meanwhile, has always got that safety net of a month in hand plus who knows how much goodwill.

So here I am juggling bills, deciding who is going to get paid. Gas can wait. Water – run by fucking-snouts-in-the-trough-fat-cats – can *really* wait. Telephone can't wait and nor, it seems, can electricity, and the credit-card companies will have to be sent the bare minimum which seems to be pure interest anyway.

I have actually got the money but I was earmarking it for my latest master plan: spread betting.

I think I've got a handle on this spread-betting lark. Basically, the s.b. firm gives its prediction, in the form of a spread, on a particular sporting (or, indeed, non-sporting) event. I, as a punter, can either 'buy' or 'sell'. So if, say, Man. Utd. are playing Arsenal, the s.b. firm might predict that the first goal will be scored between the 29th and the 32nd minute. If you think that the first goal will be scored *before* the 29th minute then you 'sell' and if you think that the first goal will be scored *after* the 32nd minute then you 'buy'. You nominate your stake – e.g. £10 a minute – and wait to see what happens. So if I 'bought' the first goal at £10 a minute and the first goal was scored in the 53rd minute, I'd make 21 times my £10 stake: £210. If, on the other hand, the first goal was scored in the 20th minute, I'd lose 12 times £10: £120. Presumably, the firm makes their profit on the spread (i.e. between 29 and 32 minutes).

What I like about spread betting is that, unlike 'traditional' betting, you have much more control. If I've bought the first goal

– i.e. predicted that it won't be scored till much later in the match – but there's suddenly a lot of goalmouth activity at the end of the first half, I can always 'close' my bet by accepting the 'sell' side of the current spread which will of course have moved upwards to, say, 68–71 – meaning that I would 'close' at 68 and win 36 times (i.e. 68–32) my £10 stake. It looked complicated at first – even for a mathematician – but actually it's piss simple. I've been doing it with myself ('fnarr fnarr') for the past few days and I've made some good 'profits'. I'm sending in £1,000 I've been saving for just such an occasion and I can't wait to get started – especially as I managed to blow the best part of four hundred quid this afternoon at Henry's.

MONDAY, FEBRUARY 8

I went to the races today. I had to see a client in Arundel at midday and another in Worthing at 4.30. With the best part of three hours to kill, I had intended to find a bookie's but when I looked at the racing pages, I noticed that there was a meeting at Fontwell.

I have to say I enjoyed myself. The weather was unseasonably mild, Fontwell's a fine course and there's something rather wonderful about a busy racecourse on a midweek day: it shows that there are a lot of people with the right priorities in life.

I lost the first three races but, during the third, I got talking to a bloke who advised me to back a horse in the next each-way, which I did at 16–1. It finished second and I was back to even money for the day. Then in the next race (my last as I had to get to Worthing), something extraordinary happened.

For the only race that day, I decided to stand by the finishing line (waiting till the steward wasn't watching as I didn't have the appropriate badge). I don't know what made me do it but I was glad I did because there was an incredibly close photo finish between Rosie's Pride and Kernel Tom (neither of which I'd backed). The thing is, as the only person actually *on* the line, I *knew* that Kernel Tom had won. I mean, I *knew* it in the same way that I know that Maggie's eyes are green. No, I'm not a zillion per cent certain that Maggie's eyes are green but I was that certain that Kernel Tom was the winner.

All the bookies were betting on the photo. Unfortunately, all of them were offering Rosie's Pride, which was utterly useless to me. All of them, that is, except this little old geezer who looked a lot like Albert Steptoe. He was calling 1–2 Kernel Tom.

It was the chance of a lifetime.

I didn't blow it by biting his hand off. I merely placed £440 (my total stash) in his mitt and waited to hear the result that I – and I alone – already *knew*. Kernel Tom was the winner and I'd made the easiest £220 of my life, giving me a total profit of £260 for the day.

TUESDAY, FEBRUARY 9

As usual, I was stuck in the office today because Tuesday is office day where they can check that you're not working for anyone else or whatever. I also wanted to find out whether there's any chance of switching over to the 'slow track' on the February bonus promotion as there's no way that I'm going to reach target (answer: no).

Trevor, who's spotted me down at the local bookie's on more than one occasion beckoned me over to the little alcove which he insists on calling an office.

'Listen, Steve, I've been given something fabulous for the Derby.'

'But that's not until June.'

'That's why we can get an incredibly good price. This horse is the donkey's bollocks. It did absolutely nothing as a two-year-old but my mate who knows the trainer says it's a fucking wonder-horse over the gallops. Reckons it's the next Shergar.'

'What, pet food?'

'Don't be a cunt, Steve, this is pay day.'

I hope it is. By the law of averages alone, I'm due a little luck. Trevor says that he backed the horse at fifties. I went straight down to the bookies and put on two hundred quid at

33–1 and I fully intend to keep on backing it all the way down to twenties.

WEDNESDAY, FEBRUARY 10

I never take a day off sick (unless I'm genuinely sick) as I'm superstitious enough to believe that if I do, I'll be genuinely ill the next day but I woke up feeling so can't-be-arsed that I phoned in sick.

I told Maggie (who wasn't working) that I was staying home and she was less than thrilled.

'I've got Julia coming over for lunch and we were planning to have a really good goss.'

'Oh, I'm so sorry to interrupt your dyke scene,' I said childishly.

'You're pathetic, Steve,' she said and walked out of the room, giving me no chance to start the row I really needed.

'This is my house too,' I shouted after her. Then, full of *l'esprit d'escalier,* I added, 'Who was it who was moaning at me just the other day that I ought to spend more time at home?' Silence: the sound of winning a one-person row.

Goaded by her offishness, I went out at midday. After a pint and a half, a pie and twenty quid in the one-armed bandits at the pub, I went to the bookie's.

I think I've only ever been to Henry's on a Saturday and it's always been pretty crowded. Now, at lunchtime on a wet Wednesday in winter, I saw the place in a new light. Racing had already started but there were only four people in the shop besides me, Henry and Maureen, his cashier.

I had a light bet of £20 on a horse I chose because it was the only one holding its opening price while all the others were going wildly in or out. I went up to the counter to place my bet to find myself in a queue behind my fellow punters and I was struck by how small their stakes were. Twenty pee each way, fifty pee win, and even, God help us, 'Two bob each way'. It's not exactly Vegas, is it?

I suggested to Henry he ought to get a grant for his care-in-the-community work.

'Tell me about it,' he sighed. 'If it wasn't for my account customers, I wouldn't bother opening during the week.' He turned to look at the door as though he could see right through the plastic tassles that are the bookie's equivalent of the barber's red-and-white pole or the pawnbroker's three balls. His voice went quieter and he sounded wistful. 'You know, Steve, it's not much more than ten years ago that Mecca offered me fifty thousand for this shop. Fifty thousand and I don't even own the freehold! Now, I couldn't even give it away. I tried last year. I asked the freeholder if I could surrender the lease but he told me that I'd have to find a new person to take it on *and* indemnify him if they didn't pay the rent. Well, I asked the local estate agent to help me sell the lease and he told me that not only couldn't I sell it, I wouldn't even be able to give it away!

'Reckoned that I'd have to *pay* someone to take it off my hands. Called a reverse premium or some such. I don't know, I really don't.' He shook his head in sorrow, perhaps pain.

'And I thought there was no such thing as a poor bookie.'

'Don't you believe it, my son. There are independents going bust every day of the week. It's the Lottery you see, we just can't compete. I wouldn't mind but we're not on a level playing field. And then there are the Switch-card betting services operated by the big boys. Yeah, I know that you use them too, Steve, and I don't blame you: so would I if I was you. Who needs to go to a bookmaker when they can bet without leaving the comfort of their armchair?

'And then there's spread betting,' he said looking at me with his head cocked to one side, causing me to go red. 'Fantastic idea: all the fun of betting and no fucking tax, pardon my French. Trouble is, it creams off all the wealthy punters and leaves me with this lot.' He gestured towards his loyal congregants. They don't have Switch cards and, even if they did, which firm's going to take their dollar trebles?'

'I've started spread betting,' I confessed. 'Well, I've opened an account and I'm going to start as soon as it's set up.'

'Take care,' he said avuncularly. 'Spread betting looks innocent enough but it can clean you out in no time. You're not stupid but you do go a bit over the top.'

'Don't I know. Remember Fireman Nick?'

'Of course I do, he won me a fortune.'

'What do you mean? Didn't you have money on him too?'

'No, Steve, I'm a bookie, not a punter. I don't make decisions, I just accept yours. Look,' he was warming to his subject, 'if I toss this coin up in the air and invite you to call, you'll call. Eventually, you'll get it wrong and that's why I win.'

'But surely having a bet is an important part of being a bookie?'

'No. Oh, I'm not saying I'm not tempted and sometimes I suppose I don't lay off quite as much as I should do if it's good money from a useful punter, but I shouldn't think that happens more than once or twice a year.'

'So you didn't reckon Tim's source then? I mean, Tim's a regular winner.'

He was about to say something but decided on silence.

'But, Henry, isn't gambling for a bookie as much of an occupational hazard as drinking is for a publican?'

'That's right, my son, that's why I don't do it.'

'That must take a lot of self-discipline.'

'No, I don't think so.' Then he added *sotto voce*, 'You see, my dad was a compulsive gambler: threw it all away at the bookie's. So I became one. I was determined that my kids were going to get the Christmas and birthday presents I never got.'

What sort of man does he think *I* am? What sort of man do *I* think I am?

THURSDAY, FEBRUARY 11

I wasn't ill today – at least not physically – but I'm feeling really down. I can't see the point of anything any more. I've put in so much, I've got so little. Sometimes the credit side of wife, kids, friends etc. looks just like one more burden. The bottle isn't just half-empty it's fucking disappeared.

I went back to work but only in person. Luckily, I was out of the office all day long so I was able to go through the motions.

Maggie and I made it up which was good and then we had sex, which was not so good.

It's nearly mid-February and I'm down. Went into a nondescript bookie's and ladled a couple of hundred quid on to a couple of no-hopers which, for all I know, are still running.

I'm fucked, I really am. I don't think I can hold on to December 31. Spread betting's the answer: in spread betting lies my salvation.

FRIDAY, FEBRUARY 12

7.00pm. It's poker tonight and I'm feeling so fucked off that I really don't know that I can make it. Bloody Roger. We should have a unanimous vote before someone's allowed to join as a regular.

I had another wretched day on the road – sold hardly anything. Worse than that, the sales manager at Beckley's, Stewart, the cunt with the yellow teeth, he *actually* asked for a fucking backhander. I mean, I've had people *suggesting* it before but I've never had anyone *asking* for it, just like that. I told him no way but I won't gain anything for my honesty.

Shit, I'm going to go for it. We're playing at Gerard's new place which'll be interesting to see. He's also got himself two female flatmates and there could be some intense betting activity on whether he's shagging one, two or none (my money's on none with him claiming two).

2.00am. I'm really glad I went. I felt a bit 'iffy' for the first hour but then I started to relax and enjoy myself. Gerard's place is fabulous: a bad man's dream. It's only a *five*-bed, three-bathroom house, for Christ's sake!

There were eight of us over the evening though the way it worked out, with comings and goings, there were only seven at most playing at any one time. Besides the usual five, we had bloody Roger, Nathan, a surprisingly decent bloke given that he's someone Gerard found in one of his gambling haunts, and young Toby who still insists on calling Gerard 'Marcel'.

It's quite funny watching Gerard with Toby. He acts as if he owns him which, for all I know, he does. 'No, you want to fold, Toby,' he tells him in the middle of a hand or else he'll send him into the kitchen for another catering-size pack of taco chips (purely for his own consumption: Gerard currently seems to be putting on a stone a week).

This idea of Gerard owning people became the running gag for the evening. He was winning so much that, pretty soon, he was holding markers for Douglas, Nik and, sorry to say, me. This, he seemed to believe, gave him the right to tell us what to do. 'Butt out of this one, boys,' he'd say to Nik, Douglas and me, 'it's too heavy for you.'

I don't mind losing, it's being patronised I can't stand. And yet there's a certain fascination to watching the Bad Man winning at poker. He starts to cackle like a Bond-film baddie. I kept on expecting him to say 'My sharks have not been fed for days' or 'I should like to take you on a tour of my private island.'

Ben took great pleasure in pointing out to me that Gerard not only owned me, he also owned my children and their children. Ben conjured up a nightmare vision of Gerard attending the birth of Melanie's child saying, 'I think you'll find the baby belongs to me.' Ben and I go back a long way: we were at school with each other (and with Jake) but sometimes he can go a little far.

Gerard's new flatmates – Françoise and Jeanne – provoked a lot of debate (along the lines of which would you have and how: disgusting stuff, although my vote was for Françoise and a blow job). Amazingly, Gerard said he wasn't having either of them which was pretty impressive by his standards until he 'explained' why. 'I'm not going to have either until I can have both together.'

Later, he insisted on bringing down this collage of photographs of beautiful girls he's put together. 'These are all ex-girlfriends of mine,' he boasted.

'But they're naked, Marcel,' gasped Toby, who's understandably a little more innocent than the rest of us.

'They certainly are,' beamed the Bad Man.

'Have you actually met any of these young women, Gerard?' asked Douglas.

'I've had each and every one of them,' said Gerard.

We responded with the usual catcalls and insults but the Bad Man stood his ground and insisted that intimacy had taken place and, no, he hadn't paid them but he had conned one or two of the less willing ones into stripping off after he'd had his wicked way with them. 'I told them that I loved them and that I wanted something to remember them by. I gave them my word of honour I'd never show anyone else.' (Leaving aside the fact that this was proof, if proof were needed, that Gerard's word of honour is worth nothing, it showed that we have every right to call him the Bad Man.)

Roger, meanwhile, insisted on telling us about *his* sexual feats. Apparently, in Tampax, Missouri or wherever he comes from, he's had three of the last four homecoming queens. Or it might have been that he's come over the homes of three or four queens. To be honest, by the time he'd told us, in depressingly graphic detail, how he'd 'fucked the butt' off some cheerleader he'd introduced to Tequila Slammers, I'd deliberately tuned out. Christ knows I'm no feminist but I do believe in consenting adults etc. and I was rapidly feeling the need to punch the creep's lights out.

Actually, that's what I don't like about the poker crowd. They'll take the piss out of me but they're far too polite to newcomers. I would have said something but, remembering last week, I decided to let it go.

I ended up slightly down but the good news was that Roger lost £400. With a bit of luck, he won't come again.

SATURDAY, FEBRUARY 13

Midday. Today is S.B.D. SPREAD BETTING DAY! I'm not absolutely sure of everything I've done. All I know is that I want there to be lots of goals in the Premiership, no favourites in the frame at Kempton, low-card numbers winning at Newbury and lots of tries in the two rugby internationals. I don't *think* my liabilities can be that huge though I'm really feeling my way in the dark here.

6.00pm. Amazingly, after all the bets I did, I ended up winning precisely £10! A glut of goals in the Premiership compensated for a day of favourites at Kempton, while the losses incurred by high-card numbers winning at Newbury were offset (and a little bit more) by three late tries at Lansdowne Road. However, I can't remember the last time I had so much fun.

SUNDAY, FEBRUARY 14

Maggie woke me up with a kiss which was as nice as it was unexpected. The next thing I know, she's climbing on board and riding me. It was great for the first five minutes, fine for the next five minutes and then increasingly boring, turgid and soulless. I tried to picture her as Cathy but that didn't work: it never does, she's not pretty enough. Then I shut my eyes and thought of Naomi, the children's extremely cute babysitter, but that didn't work either. Eventually, I pushed her off (intending to have a wank later), at which point, Maggie said, 'Happy Valentine's Day' and handed me a card.

Shitfuckpisscuntbuggerbuggerbuggerbugger.

'I thought we agreed we didn't believe in this sort of thing,' I said gingerly.

'I think *you* agreed *you* didn't believe in this sort of thing,' she replied tartly.

'It's the thought that counts, Maggie.'

'As you say, Steven.' She always calls me by my full name when she's annoyed. I thought of putting on my breakdown face but decided against it in case it didn't work (which would, of course, mean I could never ever use it again).

I went out and bought a card (I couldn't find any bloody flowers anywhere – they were all sold out) but when I gave it to her, she took it without thanking me and put it down without even opening it. An hour later, I saw it in the kitchen still unopened.

There was football on TV so I did a spread bet. I bought total corners at 12 for £50 a corner In the event, there were only seven corners, so I lost £250.

And Maggie's still giving me the frosty treatment.

MONDAY, FEBRUARY 15

Bought Maggie some flowers on my way home from work (first time since we've been married). She was (hurrah, hurrah) thrilled. Fucking right: cost me twenty quid.

Lost three hundred quid on horses, dogs and life.

The pile of (unpaid) bills is getting no lower.

There was televised football again on Sky so this time I decided to sell the total corners at 11. There were thirteen corners, so I lost £100. No more spread betting on corners for me – besides I find I'm not watching the footie. I'm not even interested in the goals, just the corners.

TUESDAY, FEBRUARY 16

It's hard to know who I hate more: people who say, 'I'll be honest with you' and then aren't, or people who say, 'I'll be honest with you' and then are.

Phil called me into his office this morning and told me that he was going to be honest with me. 'I'll be honest with you, Steve,' he said. 'You're a very fine salesman, one of the best. When you're on form, there's no one to touch you. Unfortunately, you're not doing too good at the moment.' I fought down the temptation to correct him: although Phil's my boss, he didn't have the benefit of a university 'edumacation'. 'In fact, you're doing worse than everyone else except Martin.' We smiled at each other at the mention of Martin's name. Martin couldn't sell ice-lollies in a heatwave but he's untouchable by dint of the fact that his papa owns the company. Being the worst salesman bar Martin means I'm the worst salesman bar none.

'Is there anything wrong?' he added, with what seemed like genuine concern.

Yes, I'm in the middle of the most important bet of my life. If I don't finish the year ahead of the game, I'm going to top myself. Any chance of ten months' compassionate leave on full pay? 'No, Phil, everything's fine.'

'Well, you've been warned. Get your act together, mate.'

'Is this a formal warning?'

'Shit no, Steve,' he said, placing a hand on my shoulder and guiding me out of his office, 'just an informal chat.'

I don't need this. I really don't need this. This wasn't what I set out to do. Originally, I wanted to be a vet – OK, so then I was nine years old – but then I really wanted to study philosophy. I remember telling Dad that I wanted to read PPE at Oxford and him pooh-poohing it and telling me to stick to Maths. 'Keep your feet on the ground, Steve. The world needs mathematicians' – this was the early 1970s when his *Daily Express* was telling him that it did – 'it doesn't need philosophers, politicians or, heaven help us, economists'.

Instead of becoming a failed teacher and a failed salesman, I could have been a solicitor, a journalist, a TV producer. I could have had class, I could have been a contender etc. etc. If by some miracle I manage to win 'the bet', I'm going to go back to university and study psychology or sociology or even social anthropology (so long as it is what I think it is). In fact, I'm tempted to jack in everything right now (including the bet) and go in October but it doesn't seem fair to Maggie and the kids to have the downside of me not being able to provide for them if they're not allowed (the possibility of) the upside of all that insurance money. So the bet is on and, unfortunately, I remain in gainful employment. So fuck you, Phil, and fuck your fucking job but not yet, 'mate', not yet.

THURSDAY, FEBRUARY 18

Get off my back, Maggie. You get on my tits, bitch, I don't need you on my fucking back as well. I'm sorry I haven't paid the insurance premiums on the house and, yes, if it had burnt down, I'd be sorry, wouldn't I? But it didn't burn down and, if you watch what you're fucking doing in the kitchen and stop your fucking friend Andrea from smoking in the lounge, it won't burn down in the future. Besides, I don't get any thanks for making sure that *your* car insurance is completely up to date, so why should I get the blame when *our* house insurance is a month or two out of date?

Does she think that I *can't* pay a measly £120? I dropped double that – *without thinking* – in just one hour this afternoon.

FRIDAY, FEBRUARY 19

Tonight's poker (after an absolute *pig* of a day – least said, soonest mended) was once again at Gerard's. His flatmates weren't there (Douglas reckoned Gerard had them out on the streets working for him) but, once again, he had the boy Toby along. Worse, Roger hadn't been put off by last week's hammering. I sat at the opposite end of the table and tried ignoring him, hoping that the other guys would pick him up on his pathetic attempts to impress us, but no one obliged.

Example: 'Does anyone know where I can get some poon tomorrow night?'

Example: 'Hey, Nik-Nak (his name for Nik), I don't know what you do for a living but if you work like you play poker, I sure as hell ain't investing in you.'

Example: 'I can't entertain in my flat when my daughter's staying over because she's always spilling pussy juice around the bathroom.' His daughter is *four* . . .

'Cunt,' I said under my breath, hoping that he couldn't hear, hoping that he could hear. If he did, he didn't let on but Douglas, on my right, did and frowned at me to 'cool it'. Ben, on my left, gripped my knee and gave me a supportive wink.

I've had enough. I'm going to tell the guys it's him or me.

The poker itself was fast and fun and I was the big winner with £450.

Toby, whose poker has improved remarkably in a couple of weeks, plucked up the courage to ask why we call Gerard 'the Bad Man'.

'Because he's a bad man,' we chorused.

'But who was the first person to call him the Bad Man?' asked Toby.

'I think it was me,' said Ben.

'No,' said Douglas decisively, 'it was his mother.'

To give Gerard his due, he laughed as loudly as anyone. He also does a nice line in self-deprecation. In particular, I like the story he told us last week about this girl he was once engaged to.

Apparently, Gerard had met her at a party and wowed her with a pretend French accent. By the time he'd got her into bed, he realised that it was too late to speak his usual perfect English, so he continued his courtship of her still using this ridiculous 'sank 'eavens for leetle girls' accent. He was introduced to her friends and family and they all went on holiday together and still he carried on like Sacha Distel. Eventually, Gerard – who was by now engaged to this girl – tired of the pretence and decided to come clean.

'Tell me, *chérie,*' he whispered to her one evening in bed, 'I 'ave sometheeng to – how you say? – tell you.'

'What's that, darling?'

'Would you steel lerve me if I told you I had murdered a man?'

'Of course, my darling.'

'Would you steel lerve me if I told you I was married to anuzzer woman.'

Apparently, she had to think a little longer before answering but it was still in the affirmative. And then, switching to a perfect English accent, Gerard said, 'Would you still love me if you found out that I really speak like this?'

The relationship ended on the spot. The girl could accept Gerard as a murderer but she couldn't – not unreasonably – bear the thought of telling her friends and family that their favourite cartoon Frenchman was really a lying, cheating Englishman.

SATURDAY, FEBRUARY 20

I would have slept in until twelve but Jonathan woke me up at ten. Bloody Maggie had gone out shopping and he'd cut his finger on a can-opener. What on earth does the woman think she's doing leaving a six-year-old boy cooking his own breakfast? She knew I was asleep; the least she could have done was superintend the children till I woke up. Especially as I brought home the bacon last night.

I went down to Henry's after lunch and won two hundred quid. As I said to Tim, I don't have a problem with gambling; just with losing. I also did a few spread bets and came out about evens, apart from a 'match' bet between two horses which lost me £300 just because my horse fell while the other one (in the match) finished sixth or seventh. I bet twenty quid a length, expecting there to be nothing in it but my nag fell (I hope it broke its bloody neck) and that means it makes up at the maximum: fifteen lengths. That's what I call a steep learning curve.

SUNDAY, FEBRUARY 21

Dad phoned: wants his ten grand back. Shit. I wish he'd be a bit more consistent. He tells me how proud he is of me but then asks for his money back. Not that he was aggressive – he couldn't have been more solicitous: 'You're OK, aren't you, Steve? You're not *using* the money at the moment, are you?'

Well, no, not exactly, I'm not *using* the money at the moment, Dad, because I've spent it all. 'No, Dad, I'm not but Neil and I are still costing our project' – the pretext on which I'd originally borrowed the money – 'and so I'd really like to hold on to it. But do say if *you* need it, Dad.'

'No, son,' he said hesitatingly. 'You hang on to it.' God, I hate myself sometimes.

Still had lots of dosh in my pocket and so I told Maggie to phone her mother so I could take her (Maggie, not her mother) out for 'a surprise'.

The surprise in question was the casino. My only fears were that staff there would acknowledge me as a regular (Maggie thinks I've only been the once) and that Maggie would throw a wobbly. In the event, the casino staff were discretion itself and I pre-empted Maggie's fears by pointing out that we could get a free dinner at the casino which was worth at least £60. So all we'd do is eat dinner and then gamble £60 (i.e. the casino's money). No downside and the possibility of upside. Sounds like a good idea: I even managed to convince myself.

So a mollified Maggie and I helped ourselves to pretty good oriental eats at the buffet (shame about the tiny plates which make you feel like a pig for going back three or four times) and then tried our luck at the tables.

I sent Maggie off with thirty quid (i.e. her half) to the roulette tables while I went off to try my luck at blackjack. Or at least I would have done but the tables were all full. They wouldn't have been if people had been restricted to playing one box each but, ridiculously, you had one or two punters playing anything up to five boxes while people bet behind them. Well, I'm just not prepared to do that. If some stupid cow won't draw at thirteen against the dealer's nine, why should I suffer too? It's absurd. Unfortunately, the casino staff, although sympathetic, could do nothing about it. 'But surely you could *ask* her to give up a box?' I asked, gesturing towards a geriatric mountain of lard in mauve chiffon.

'Leave her alone,' screeched a woman at the adjoining table who looked like Rosa Klebb in *From Russia With Love*, 'she's been here for twenty years.'

'Well, isn't it about time she had a break then?' The croupier smiled conspiratorially at my witticism but Rosa looked daggers so, rather than run the risk of her kicking a knife into my shin, I went to the roulette table – not the roulette table Maggie was playing at (though I did pat her bum as I passed by) but another one.

The reason was obvious. Maggie was betting just one £1 chip – I swear it – on every spin; my intention was to be a little more bold and so I changed five hundred quid into £5 chips and set about the table as though I was on piece-work.

Wish I had been because I managed to lose *all* of it in eight spins. Unbelievably, neither 26 nor any of the numbers surrounding it came up. Not one. But then, why should those numbers come up? I was backing nine numbers: is it so extraordinary that only the remaining twenty-eight numbers should come up over just eight spins.

I did all this *de facto* rationalising as I made the short way from my table to Maggie's. Obviously, I couldn't let her know what had happened.

'How's it going?' I asked her as cheerfully as I could.

'Look, darling,' she said excitedly, showing me a pile of

chips worth, oh, at least fifty quid. 'Haven't I done well? How about you?'

'Done my money.'

'What, all of it?'

'No, I've still got some left in my pocket.' I pulled out a much-depleted wad of twenties.

'So you've lost your thirty pounds. Never mind, I'll cash up now and we'll hardly have lost anything! You're quite right, Steve, this is exciting and, what with dinner being free, it's not expensive. We must come again.'

MONDAY, FEBRUARY 22

I bought the time of the last goal on the TV football. I try not to do more than one trade on the same match for that way lies madness but I couldn't resist also buying goalscorers' shirt numbers. In the event, the only goal was scored in the 90th minute winning me £240 but, by the same token, the goalscorers' shirt numbers made up at 9 and lost me £230. If only I'd stuck to my one-trade rule, I'd be quids in. If only, if only, if only . . .

TUESDAY, FEBRUARY 23

Phil tells me it's official: I 'have' to go to Reading next month. YES! I'm going to find Cathy's precise address and go and see her. Or maybe I'll just hang around and see what she looks like now. Better be careful, she's with a DC now: the last thing I need is a run in with the polizei. No, I'll be discreet.

I guess I went too far in '87 but there's no reason why I shouldn't be able to patch things up. Actually, there's every reason why I shouldn't be able to patch things up: I've still got the solicitor's letters and I'm sure she's still got the hump – though I don't see why a chap shouldn't be able to contact his ex-girlfriend if all he wants to do is be friends with her? This time I promise not to phone her thirty times a day.

* * *

Did a trade tonight: bought the bookings in the TV football and won £107. Thank goodness for hot-blooded foreign footballers!

WEDNESDAY, FEBRUARY 24

Four bets: four hundred quid lost. I can't even bear to think about it let alone write about it.

FRIDAY, FEBRUARY 26

Flash flash. Fuck fuck. I set off a fucking speeding camera on the A3 today. Nigel tells me that I'll know whether I'm going to get done in the next fourteen days. So that's two weeks of sleepless nights worrying about whether I'm going to get another three points. I can't afford any more points on my licence, I really can't.

God, I hate speed cameras – they're so fucking un-British. They really take the fun out of driving.

They also take the fun out of poker. I didn't enjoy tonight's session. I won a few quid as well (about £70) so it's not sour grapes. I just have this overwhelming feeling of impending doom. Everything seems stacked against me.

Roger wasn't there. I don't know what Douglas told him but apparently he got the message. Douglas accepts that I'm more important to the poker group (gee thanks, buddy) than Roger but is pissed at me for jeopardising a business relationship.

At first, the guys thought my bad mood was a reaction to the Roger situation but pretty soon they realised that it was something else. Eventually, I told them about the speeding camera. Douglas and Ben were sympathetic. Nik, whose work also depends on his car, was sympathetic and empathetic. Jake reassured me by telling me of all the speed cameras he's set off without ever getting done.

The Bad Man just couldn't see what I was worried about. 'You'll get cabs,' he counselled.

'Don't be an idiot, Gerard,' said Douglas, 'it would cost him more than he earns. Can't you see he has to drive?'

'So why not use a false licence,' tried the Bad Man. 'That's what I would do.'

It was the first – and only – time I laughed all evening.

I left at eleven o'clock. It's a sign of how wretched I must have looked that no one tried to persuade me to stay.

SATURDAY, FEBRUARY 27

Woke up feeling a lot better. So maybe I'll get three more points on my licence. It's not the end of the world. I'll just have to drive extra carefully for the next few years . . .

Took Jonathan to Woolworth's and bought him a couple of pocket-money toys. When we got back, he kissed me on the cheek and told me – *without being asked* – that I'm the best Dad in the world.

Returned to find Moaning Maggie holding a couple of ominous-looking bills. I thought I had dealt with today's post but there must have been another delivery while I was out.

'What are we going to do about these, Steve?'

What *are* we going to do about these, Maggie? I don't know, you stupid bitch, otherwise I'd be doing it. 'Wait a second, I'll go and get my cheque book.' Never complain; never explain. I want that on my tombstone.

Must phone Mr Watson on Monday.

Doesn't Maggie *realise* that her nagging makes me want to spend more, not less? Instead of sitting in front of the TV all afternoon, watching the rugby and having a few spread bets, I went down to Henry's looking for ACTION.

Tim was there – as ever – and the sight of his cheery face helped to cheer me up. We talked about horses, dogs, women and life and came to no firm conclusions about any of them. I lost about a hundred quid but it was an extremely agreeable way to spend a Saturday afternoon.

Meanwhile, the spread bets I did (on Premiership goals and on rugby hotshots) came off, winning me £280.

SUNDAY, FEBRUARY 28

I can't stand these mood dips. Why is it that one moment I'm feeling fine and the next (i.e. today) I'm feeling wretched.

I don't know what – if anything – I want. I *think* I want to win the bet but do I, do I *really*? Maybe I want to lose and let someone else – a jockey, a footballer, a poker player (no, *not* a poker player) – pull the trigger.

Currently, SNAFU. I'm (just over) £2,000 down on the month and the running total for the year is £3,700. Grim but there's plenty of time to go. Too much time to go. Not enough time to go. Depends on how I feel.

MONDAY, MARCH 1

11.00am. Woke up this morning feeling shit awful. I couldn't have gone to work if I'd tried. Told Maggie that I was feeling lousy and was going to stay in bed – bad throat, head, sinuses blah, blah, blah – but she was on her way out to work and I don't think it really registered.

Why couldn't I have just told her the truth? That I think I'm heading for another fucking breakdown?

Because what I told Maggie *was* the truth: I couldn't get out of bed if I tried. Shit, man, I'm low – lower than a snake's belly.

But it's not enough to feel low. No, that would be too easy, wouldn't it? I've also got to feel incredibly tense and anxious and frightened and scared. And very scared and very frightened. I can't face anything. Like Ol' Man River, I'm tired of living and scared of dying. And scared of just about everything else in between.

Funnily enough, I'm not scared of the BIG THINGS: my financial situation, my marriage, the kids, THE FUTURE etc., I'm just (huh!) scared of the minutiae. Maybe if I write down what I'm scared of, it might go away.

I'm frightened of – in no particular order – seeing anyone I know, seeing anyone I don't know, being on my own (who would look after me if I needed looking after?), throwing up, having a crap, eating anything (for fear of throwing up or of needing a crap), going absolutely anywhere, the telephone ringing, the doorbell going (if I answer it, I'd have to talk to someone; if I don't answer it, it might be a burglar checking to see if anyone's in and that would end up as a worse confrontation), going mad, becoming incontinent, not being able to look after myself, never being able to sleep again for feeling so tense, ever having to go back to work, driving, getting done for speeding, getting dressed (in case that made me think I was in fact well enough to go out), phoning up work (I can't face Jayne's sympathy or Phil's anger), falling behind with my work so that when I do go back to work I have even more work to do, never again being able to leave the house, the house being taken away because I owe so much money on it, Maggie throwing me out because she gets tired of how pathetic I am, not being able to breathe properly, having a heart attack and dying because there's no one here to look after me (even as I write this I'm struck by the fact that for someone who intends to top himself at the end of the year, I'm inordinately afraid of dying – and yet, if I'm honest, I'm more scared of living), going downstairs (in case I trip and break my leg and have to go to the hospital's emergency department), drinking alcohol (in case I lose what little control over myself I currently have). What control? I think I'm cracking up.

On the other side of the equation, the one thing I'm *not* frightened of is lying in bed with the covers on top of me. Unfortunately, as a mathematician, I know this equation doesn't balance.

I'm not feeling any better at all for writing this down . . . I'm beginning to hyperventilate . . . I think I'm starting a panic attack . . . I'm going to take some Valium and see if I can't get some precious sleep – not that I didn't sleep last night . . . but I don't think I can get too much sleep . . . at the moment . . . fuck me, it's times like this I really, really, REALLY wish I was back in the clinic.

6.00pm. When Maggie came home, I broke down in tears and told her how I was really feeling. No bullshit, just the full monty. Fortunately, she was genuinely sympathetic and concerned. She's made an appointment for me for tomorrow morning with the doctor (and promised to go with me as I don't think I could do it on my own). Good old Maggie: I couldn't live without her – I swear I'll never cheat on her again.

TUESDAY, MARCH 2

Midday. Still not gone to work. Couldn't go out if I tried. Maggie took me to the doctor's. She (the doctor) wasn't the most sympathetic person in the world but at least she made what seems like a decent diagnosis. Apparently, I'm suffering from anxiety and depression and mild agoraphobia (she wouldn't call it mild if she could have known how many Valium it took me to get to her surgery this morning). She told me that it's all to do with serotonin (which is what keeps us feeling happy) passing through my brain too quickly and she's prescribed me an SSRI (stands for something like Serotonin Slow Re-uptake Inhibitor) which will, she says, keep me happy for longer and get rid of the depression and the anxiety which in turn will stop me feeling scared to go out or do anything. She's also prescribed me some more Valium. I know nothing about SSRIs but I know Valium all right and it hits the spot every time.

As she was writing out the prescription, she asked me if everything was all right at home, at work and so on. I was going to tell her but then I could see that she didn't really want to know and, besides, there was nothing she could do for me apart from give me some drugs so I decided to keep shtum.

Typical of the fucking NHS, I guess. I'm having a fucking breakdown (or whatever) and I still don't get more than two minutes, thirty-eight seconds. That's doctors for you. I could have been one myself but they discovered that I had a heart.

Maggie took me home (we couldn't find a parking space which set me off into another panic attack) and then went out to get me my prescription. I took the pill and now, two hours later, nothing's changed. I'm still feeling as wretched as I was yesterday and this morning. Fuck, if this doesn't work, then I've really had it.

Meanwhile, I haven't yet had a gamble this month – can't think of anything I fancy less. I suppose this is saving me money. On the other hand, it's doing nothing to offset my negative gambling balance.

Truth is I'm fucked whatever I do.

WEDNESDAY, MARCH 3

In bed. Took three Valiums (five mgs). Feeling fucked but I don't give a fuck. In or out, I don't give a fuck. Maggie's fucked me off by going to her mother's to look after her because she's got flu or something. I'm more important than her mother or at least I fucking should be. Bitch. Fucking bitch (not Maggie, her mother).

I'd watch some telly if I could be fucking bothered.

I'd have a bet if I could be fucking bothered.

I'd have a wank if I could be fucking bothered.

THURSDAY, MARCH 4

I can finally see some light at the end of the tunnel. I just hope that it isn't the oncoming train.

I'm still in bed and I'm still a bit tranked up but I've stopped having those awful panic attacks and I'm not feeling so incredibly *low* all the time. I suppose I just feel moderately pissed off, a little apprehensive, a bit numb. On a depression scale of one to ten, if one is the feeling you get when you record the wrong channel on the video and ten is get-out-the-razor, then I'm about a five now. Yesterday, I was an eight, Tuesday I was a nine and Monday I was off the scale altogether.

As for my anxiety quotient. If one is the surprise you get when the alarm goes off in the morning and ten is the feeling you get when the Japs have discovered that the forbidden radio in the POW camp is in fact hidden in your bunk, then I'm now about a three or four. I think I did get as high as about eight on Tuesday morning. I don't know – maybe these things are unquantifiable.

FRIDAY, MARCH 5

11.00am. I'm feeling a *lot* better today – I wonder if the pills are kicking in now (they've taken bleeding long enough). I haven't been out of the house since I went to the quack's but I might try to get out to the park for a stroll. I wouldn't mind going to Patel's and getting the kids some sweets for being so lovely the past couple of days. Maggie explained to them that Daddy was feeling poorly in his head and needed lots of peace and quiet so that he could rest and get better. Jona, bless him, interpreted this to mean that I needed a new head and so he knocked on my door yesterday and offered me the head off his Action Man. Mellie, being older, is much more clued up than he is and insisted on quizzing me like a doctor would (or should). She ended up diagnosing me as 'sad' and said that I needed a kiss better. They really are wonderful kids.

4.00pm. I'm glad I bought them some sweets because each of them came home with presents for me. Mellie had made a card and Jonathan had gathered some acorns 'so that you can grow an oak tree if you want to'. When I'm better I'm going to find more time to spend with them.

I had no problems while I was out and half considered playing poker tonight but just the thought of what Maggie would say if I suggested it made me think twice. If she really loved me, she'd want me to be happy – but then it's not fair to expect her to look after me as a sicko only to go out and leave her on her own the first chance I get.

Maybe I'm as good a husband as I am a father.

SATURDAY, MARCH 6

10.00am. Feeling fine. Seems like this week was a temporary blip, thank God. Maggie comes into the bedroom with a cup of coffee and a newspaper – bless her – but then she starts to give me all sorts of grief.

'Steve, I'm so pleased, so relieved to see you're better.'

'No small thanks to you, sweetie.'

'We have to talk.'

Oh oh. 'OK.'

'What are we going to do about these?' she asks, taking out a sheaf of (horribly red-like) bills from beneath the newspaper.

'Bad timing, Maggie.'

'When isn't it bad timing, darling?'

'Look, give them to me and I'll deal with them next week. I was going to see Mr Watson last week but for obvious reasons I couldn't.' We shared a watery smile. 'But I'll see him this week, I promise.'

I know Maggie's genuinely concerned but I really don't need this. I'm off to Henry's.

5.00pm. Now I *know* I'm feeling better. I didn't feel panicky once. I wonder how much is due to me and how much is due to the pills? Better keep taking them, I guess.

I was betting like a mug and yet only ended up losing a hundred quid – and given that I haven't had a bet all week, that's hardly excessive. The so-called professional gambler bets on, top whack, one or two horses a week; on a good day, I reckon to have at least thirty bets across half a dozen meetings on horses I hadn't even heard of five minutes before the race. The 'professional' doesn't necessarily win – witness the number of beaten favourites and winning rank outsiders – and he certainly doesn't derive the entertainment that I do from gambling. So who's the mug?

I think at one stage this afternoon I was six or seven hundred quid up thanks to a horse (Cheyenne something or other) which I backed for £80 when it was 6–1. Luckily (for once) I didn't take a price and it drifted out to 14–1 before winning in a canter.

Maggie's cooking something special for tonight and I can hear her warning the kids that they've got to be in bed by seven. I think I'm on a promise tonight. Lucky me. Lucky her.

MONDAY, MARCH 8

Back to work. The one thing I like about my job is that I'm not stuck in an office all day long. Although I have to be at specific places at certain times, I do have a fair degree of autonomy: I'm not my own boss but at least I don't have the soul-destroying routine of nine-to-five and the daily commute.

Felt invigorated by my week off and got some good orders. Phil will no doubt hold them up to me as an example of what I should be achieving *every* day. The cunt.

As far as gambling's concerned, I feel as if I'm making up for lost time. I found myself in a bookie's in Kensal Green with half-an-hour to kill and I had four singles at £100 each. I lost the first three races – one in a photo-finish where mine was called first (usually a sign that it's going to win) – but struck lucky in the fourth with a horse named Arctic Gnome which won at 6–1. So I made £300 – or would have done if I'd bothered to pay the tax. Unfortunately, I didn't and so only made £237. Still pretty good but not as good.

Paying the tax or not is another one of those issues on which gamblers divide. As a mathematician, I *know* that paying the tax makes sense; as a gambler, I can't face it unless I really believe in what I'm backing (typically a football or cricket bet).

Take today. I had four single bets of £100 each and I didn't pay the tax. Now, if instead of doing that, I'd bet £91.75 plus tax each time, the total would still have come to £400 and the first three bets would still have come to nothing but, on the fourth, instead of getting back £637, I'd have got back £642.25. True, it's only (just over) a fiver but there's a mathematical principle at stake: why take less than you have to?

On an intellectual level, I have no problem seeing this. As a mathematician, I have no problem working out the net stake to achieve the desired gross stake and yet . . . and yet . . . Like so many gamblers, I'm a superstitious bastard and paying the tax first feels dangerously like cockiness. We gamblers need all the help we can get and we certainly don't want to piss off the gods. The odds are already stacked against us enough without adding hubris as well, thank you very much.

TUESDAY, MARCH 9

Sometimes, if I think about Cathy long enough I get soul screams. I mean that, there's no other way I can put it: my heart, my soul, every fibre of my being *yearns* for her. I had a – I don't know – 'crisis' last week and there were lots of things which were frightening me but there's *nothing* as truly terrifying as the thought that I'll never see or touch or talk to Cathy again. If I think about it too long, I just go. The thought completely overwhelms me. That's it, there's a kind of cut-off where I completely lose touch with reality. It's only happened three or four times but it never fails to frighten the life out of me. That's how much power one person can have over another – without even knowing.

I'm only thinking about her today because there's a 'y' in the day. Other times, I don't give her a second thought. No, the reason I'm thinking about her even more than I normally do is that I'm going to Reading tomorrow week and I don't think I can – fuck,

I *know* I can't – resist seeing where she lives and what she looks like now.

There was football on Sky so I had a few trades (bought goalscorers' shirt numbers, bought hotshots and sold bookings) and made a staggering £480.

WEDNESDAY, MARCH 10

Got down to the post before Maggie (as always). Along with the usual domestic bills and junk mail (same thing really: they all go into the same bin), there was a nasty looking buff-coloured envelope with a window for the address. Experience has taught me that there's never any good news in an envelope with a window for the address. Sure enough, it was a ticket from that fucking speed camera that went off a couple of weeks ago.

I don't believe it. I do not fucking believe it. If I plead guilty – as if I've got a choice – it means nine points on my licence. And that means at least three years of driving at 28mph and letting police cars out at junctions. I can't fucking *bear* it.

I've not been able to think about anything else all day. I had (or thought I had) a brainwave at lunchtime and phoned Maggie.

'Listen, sweetheart.'

'What do you want?'

'Now don't be like that.'

'Like what? I'm always wary when you call me sweetheart. It always means that you want something.'

When she's right, she's right. So I told her about the speeding ticket and then, holding my breath, put forward my suggestion.

'Listen, sweetheart, Maggie, you know I love you and would do anything for you. Well, I need you to do a favour for me. I need you to say you were driving my car when the speeding camera went off.'

'What do you mean?'

'Look, darling,' I said with more sarcasm than was good for

my cause, 'it's not exactly a difficult concept. I have six points on my licence. Another three will give me nine. Three more than that will see me banned from driving and I'll lose my job. You, on the other hand, have no points on your licence. So you say you were driving.'

'Sorry, Steve, I can't . . .'

I didn't let her finish but just screamed a torrent of abuse down the phone at her. The words 'bitch' and 'fucking' were used in conjunction on more than one occasion as I recall. In the end, she put the phone down on me, which was, I suppose, not unreasonable.

However, when I returned home (with a grudging apology), she explained to me the reason for her refusal to co-operate. She's got no objection to lying for me *per se* – although she had read of a case in the *Daily Mail* about a woman who, in similar circumstances, had said that she was driving and had gone to prison for perjury – but on the day and time in question, she was teaching in school and I was out in my car working. The assumption would be that I was liable unless we proved otherwise, which would be impossible to do.

She's right, of course. And I'm not only a total fucker but I'm also totally fucked.

FRIDAY, MARCH 12

3.00am. By rights I should be asleep. I'm tired enough but, after a night's hard poker playing, my mind's racing too fast.

We were playing at Gerard's. His flatmates were out but he had his latest doxy round. Her name's Sharon and although her boat's a little sharp and spotty, she's got a fabulous figure with great tits. Fortified by her presence, Gerard was even more full of it than usual.

The entire evening could be characterised by a single hand – at least as far as I'm concerned.

To set the scene: it's quarter to one. Gerard's at the top of the table (natch). With Sharon ministering to his every (non-sexual) need, he's absolutely lording it. He looks like Sid James playing Henry VIII – and the resemblance doesn't end there because the Bad Man seems to have put on an alarming amount of weight in the two weeks since I last saw him. He also looks tired – too much head, not enough bed? – whatever, he'll still be playing long after I've gone. Judging from the fact that he's not chivvying us to hurry up, Gerard is probably winning at the moment.

On Gerard's left – a great position because you've not committed yourself to staying in before the Bad Man launches one of his ludicrous raises – sits Nathan, possibly losing but he's so impassive it's hard to tell. The more I see of Nathan, the more I like him. Apart from (maybe) Jake, he's the only one of us to play poker properly: for example, at five-card stud he'll fold immediately if he doesn't like his first two cards – something I'd never do because I always want to be involved in the action, I hate sitting out. So Nathan plays the percentages, biding his time for the right cards. Occasionally, like good players do, he'll look at what the other players are showing and how they're betting, take a view on what he thinks that they think that he's holding and attempt to bluff. Unfortunately, this rarely does him much good because in our game there's always someone who'll go all the way, if only out of boredom.

Ben is sitting on Gerard's other side. Ben has had a couple of beers and he's gone. If ever a man shouldn't mix booze and cards it's Ben. It's not that he's drunk, it's just that he's so naturally ebullient that *any* drink takes him over the top and, in a poker game, that can be disastrous. In the last hand of seven-card stud (dooces and one-eyed jacks wild), he's holding (as it turned out) a natural flush. Very nice too and yeah what a shame that we were playing wild cards: the thing is to stack 'em and have a whinge afterwards while we sympathise by giving him ten pee to go and phone someone who gives a fuck etc. Only Ben has persuaded himself that he's got a great hand. Jake (sitting on Ben's right) – Judicious Jake, for fuck's sake – is showing three *natural* 10s. True, if that's all he's got, Ben's beaten him but Jake only needs *one* wild card out of the three in his hand and he's won. Jake's also betting cautiously, which probably means he's made it or else he's worried that Ben's got a running flush. It's only Ben who *knows* that he's got diddley squat. Jake trap checks. Ben bets twenty. Jake raises twenty. Ben's hooked now but instead of retiring gracefully, he tries to buy his way out of trouble and continues to re-raise Jake every time Jake raises him. Eventually, Jake, out of boredom/kindness/embarrassment, sees Ben and shows *two* wild cards – i.e. *five* 10s – and Ben has lost two hundred quid on one hand.

Next to Jake is Douglas who is, as he so graphically puts it, bleeding from his butt.

I've stayed in too many pots for too long. I'm 'only' a hundred quid down but unnecessarily so as I've had some pretty good cards. And now it's quarter to one and, unknown to us, we're about to play the defining hand of the evening.

Dealer's choice. Ben calls seven-card stud high-low (without the wheel of ace 5). Gerard, who else?, wants 9s to be wild, but luckily Ben isn't so far gone. Now I can't remember the precise cards but after five cards (two dark, three open), the situation is something like this: Nathan has folded after two open cards (one high, one low); Gerard is showing 2, 5, 6 and is betting as though there's no tomorrow (maybe there isn't and the Bad Man has some inside information?). Fortunately for those people going high (i.e. Gerard won't be able to milk us all), Jake is looking equally low with A, 3, 4; Ben has a pair of jacks and a 9; Douglas has A, 10, 9 all in hearts; I've got a pair of kings in the hole and I'm showing 9, 7, 5 so I look low even though I know differently.

The last open cards are dealt. Gerard gets a 10 which at least shuts him up, if only for a nano-second; Douglas draws a 4 of spades; I get a 2; Ben deals Jake an 8 and deals himself my bloody king. Everyone checks to Jake who puts in twenty. Douglas raises another twenty but there are a lot of hearts out and I, for one, don't believe his flush. Everyone calls.

The last, dark card is dealt. I've got a 4. It's not what I wanted. Least I don't think it was. Hard to tell. I've got a 9 low. Hmm. By the time I look up from my cards, the others have long since composed their poker faces (or what they think are their poker faces)

Final round of betting. Gerard's got – or persuaded himself he's got – a good hand and he's betting big following Ben's exploratory twenty quid. Douglas, with much groaning, folds. I'm in, trying desperately hard to conceal my uncertainty with bullish enthusiasm. Jake is calling without a moment's hesitation while Ben, curse him and curse Mr Budweiser, re-raises to set Gerard off again. By the time the merry-go-round stops, there's some £1400 in the pot, about three hundred quid of it mine.

Now we have to decide whether to go high or low. I don't know, I really don't. A 9-low *can* win, a 9-low *could* win, but will it? I've got to take Jake for at worst an 8-low – with A, 3, 4, 8 showing, he only has to have a 2, 5, 6 or 7 in his hand to cremate me. Gerard looks low but you can never tell with the Bad Man. As for Ben, well he could have anything and, after four Buds, it's lucky for him that the cards 'talk' because I'm not sure that he can – that's to say I don't know if he'll be able to call his best cards.

My heart's thudding as I take two chips under the table (none for low, one for high, two for high and low). 'Bad Man, you're going low,' I tell myself. 'Ben, you're full of shit!' I go high.

Predictably, Ben's gone high but, incredibly, Jake's gone high and Gerard's gone high and low. What the hell's going on?

Ben declares his pair of jacks: that's all he's got, the fool. So far so good. I put down my pair of kings. Jake shows trip 8s. I can't believe it and I'm still reeling from the shock when the Bad Man lays down his hand: he's got a 7-low and two pairs. However, he went high and low and therefore has to win both to win at all. Because Jake won high, Gerard gets absolutely nothing, a fact that he's not slow to bewail. Even Sharon, who rushes to his side on hearing her master's misery, can't console him.

And then it dawns on me. If I had gone low, I'd have split the pot with Jake who, as it is, scoops the lot. Although Gerard had a better low than me, by having gone high and low and losing high to Jake, he'd have forfeited his low hand, leaving me the low winner. I don't fucking believe it. I make the right call – any poker player would have done the same – and I get fucking shafted. Out of interest, I ask Jake what his low would have been. Jake's not a great one for revealing his cards after a hand but, buoyed up by a huge pot (as well he might be), he revealed that he'd have been queen low.

We carried on playing for another forty minutes or so but I don't think any of us had our hearts in it. Except Jake, that is, who won a record (for our group) £2,000. That's real money, that is. I contributed £330 of that but I wasn't the biggest loser: that was Ben who lost £600.

SATURDAY, MARCH 13

I made over twenty trades today. I did three match bets on horses at £5 a length; I sold the double card numbers across three meetings, again at £5 a point; I bought four 'mini-performances' (Villa, Manchester United, Arsenal and Leeds) at various amounts from £3 to £10; I bought the goals in the four other Premiership games playing today; I then bought bookings at all eight games – on the basis that a programme featuring important championship and relegation issues would yield an above-average number of bookings and, if I was lucky, sendings-off.

Here's how it panned out: I lost £110 on the racing match bets (they're not dumb bets as such but if a horse falls it loses the maximum fifteen lengths even if the other horse trails in last). I lost £80 on the double card numbers. As for the football mini-performances (fifteen points for a win, ten points per goal and five points for a clean sheet), I made a profit of £280, mainly because of a 4–0 victory by Leeds whose performance I'd bought for £5 a point. I broke even on the goals in the other Premiership matches and made a massive £460 on the bookings. I was right, there *were* a lot of bookings today – not to mention *four* sendings off. What a great result and, hey, didn't the 'experts' at the spread-betting firms get it wrong?

A profit of £550 on the day which not only wiped away last night's losses but also put me into profit for the weekend. Lush.

SUNDAY, MARCH 14

Dad popped over this evening. I think Maggie must have told him about the way I was two weeks ago because he asked me very pointedly how I was feeling 'within myself' (whatever that means) and I caught him glancing at me worriedly a couple of times. More significantly, he told me that he'd had a little bit of luck with one of his investments so he wouldn't be needing the ten thousand I borrowed for a while. 'Little bit of luck' indeed! Dad doesn't get involved in things which carry luck – good or bad. No, he's decided to write off the debt for however long he can. I (sort of) love him; I (sort of) hate him. I (certainly) hate myself.

TUESDAY, MARCH 16

In the office today. It's Reading tomorrow so I kept out of the way as much as possible in case Phil caught me and changed my calls – something he's entirely capable of doing.

Maggie reminded me – again – to go to the travel agent's across the road from the office to pay the deposit for the holiday. We're due to go to Cyprus – her choice, not mine – and I have to say that I'm *not* looking forward to it. She knows I hate greasy food and that's the staple diet out there, if the local Greek restaurant's anything to go by. She also knows that, with our colouring, Mellie and I can't stay out in the sun and there's not going to be too much shade in July. I don't know why I let have her own way. Yes I do, she effectively made the decision earlier in the month when I was going through my crisis and I couldn't really talk her out of it.

As I popped out in the afternoon to book the holiday, a beautiful thought occurred. I could hop in a cab to the casino and gamble the deposit. If I won, I'd upgrade us to a five-star hotel; if I lost, well I didn't want to go to bloody Cyprus anyway. The other thing is, it would keep me out of Phil's reach.

The casino was almost empty. I went to the blackjack table

where, because I was the only player, I was obliged to play two boxes. With no fellow gamblers to talk to, and only a dozy, uncommunicative flat-chested croupier in a cheap crimplene frock to look at, I found my mind wandering while I was playing. I always have this fear that the pit boss will think I'm counting the cards and will – I don't know – take me out back and have me duffed up or something. So I always try to look like I'm not counting, which is a very hard thing to do since one inevitably looks as guilty as hell.

But not only don't I count, I don't think counting's fair to the casino. If you play blackjack properly, the casino's edge is only one or two percent and, what with the fact that it's the punter and not the casino who decides when to start and stop, I reckon that's pretty fair. On that basis, the casino would be entitled – as they do with casino poker – to shuffle the pack(s) after every hand (which they don't do because it's too time-consuming) or, in this day and age, to generate the cards via a computer (which they don't do because the punters, quite properly, wouldn't trust them). The fact that the casino uses several packs of cards and puts them in a shoe is a perfectly reasonable solution. To count is, therefore in my opinion, against the spirit of the game and the relationship between the casino and its clients. As Percy Paranoid, I find myself explaining all this to the croupier/pit boss.

After all that, I played blackjack mechanically for a whole shoe and ended up exactly where I started, having been up and down as much as £200 either side.

I then went to the roulette table. Forgetting that the wheel has no memory, I looked at the electronic board to see what had been going on. There had been some twenty spins of the wheel so far today, of which all but three had been black. Did this influence me? I honestly don't know but I placed £1,000 holiday deposit on red and the ball landed on 26 black.

I felt (and still feel a little) sick. To land on black was bad enough but to land on 26, the number I *always* back, was a real kick in the teeth.

Suddenly, from out of nowhere, came an image of little Jona crying because he couldn't go swimming in the sea. The image stayed with me for all of two seconds but it was long enough to bring tears to my eyes. Then I rationalised it by deciding that I wouldn't tell Maggie. That's to say, I'll tell her I've booked it and I'll sort it out when the time comes in July. Hopefully then, I'll have won so much money from spread betting that I'll be able to buy her a whole bloody Greek island.

Cheery postscript. Did just two trades on the televised soccer. I sold the 'multi-corners' (corners in the first half multiplied by the corners in the second half) and won £190 and I sold the time of the second goal to make a further £170: a profit on the night of £360. Not bad for sitting on my arse, watching footie and drinking beer!

WEDNESDAY, MARCH 17

Cathy's still got it. I can't quantify what 'it' is: Claudette Colbert had 'it', Grace Kelly had 'it'; Cameron Diaz and Greta Scacchi have 'it'; Maggie, alas, doesn't have 'it'. Maybe it's subjective but I think most guys would agree with me that Cathy had 'it' and the good news is she's still got 'it'.

I found this out by tracking her down to a semi-detached house in the backstreets of Reading.

Having spent ten minutes – and resented every second – on my sales call, I went to the library. I had a desultory look through the telephone directory even though I know by having phoned directory inquiries (fucking bastards) that she's not listed. Presumably, the phone is registered in the name of her boyfriend, DC Plod.

Unfortunately, I don't know Plod's real name, nor, indeed, anything else about him, except for the fact that he left a wife and three kids for Cathy which sounds about right. Linda, a mutual acquaintance, also told me that they don't have any kids – well they didn't two years ago when I met Linda – which also sounds right knowing Cathy who's not the sort to give up a night's sleep for a child, let alone her figure.

So, in the hope that a) she's still in Reading and b) she hadn't got married or, if she had, retained her maiden name, I went through the electoral rolls.

Fortunately, Cathy's surname, Kandrick, is an unusual one but, even so, it took me three hours (by which time my eyes were dizzy) before I found a Catherine A. Kandrick living at 49 Carlton Close Reading. Cathy's middle name is Anne, so it had to be her. Bingo! I missed my vocation in life, I should have been a private detective.

At the cost of only nine 'Scusemes' (i.e. the number of times I had to stop the car, wind down the window and say, 'Scuseme, do you know the way to . . .'), I was in Carlton Close outside her house.

There was no sign of activity in the house and no car in the drive. It was four o'clock, so I decided to wait until she returned home or, in the unlikely event that she was at home, went out. I made a few work calls on my mobile and listened to the radio but I didn't, as I'd have liked, read my book in case I missed her.

In the event, she didn't appear until 6.30pm, obviously on her way home from work. I knew it was her as soon as I saw her walking up the road. My heart didn't so much skip a beat as miss out a whole drum solo. She had aged an imperceptible amount but she was still breathtakingly gorgeous: her hair thicker and darker, her eyes – even at thirty yards – a vivid bright green and her figure as stunning as ever. Thank God for the street lighting in Reading.

She didn't notice me as I took good care to slink as low as possible into the seat. In fact I was probably unnecessarily cautious. As the observer, I was probably too self-conscious: I found myself wanting to be like the little child who puts his hands over his eyes and says 'Now you can't see me'. The fact is she wasn't expecting anyone to be watching her and so she wasn't looking out for anyone. There's also the fact that Cathy has always been supremely wrapped up in herself.

Once she'd gone inside, I was somewhat poleaxed. I had three options: knock on the door and risk – no, dammit, guarantee – a confrontation; stay and hope to see her come out later or leave. Having already rejected the first, I decided to leave on the basis that she might not return and, anyway, I didn't much fancy seeing lovaboy returning to their lovenest.

So I drove home in a daze. I must still have been pretty far gone when I came in because Maggie asked if I was all right.

'I'm fine, thank you, darling, I'm just tired. I've been stuck in the car most of the day just waiting for things to happen.'

'You poor thing,' cooed Maggie, ushering me into my armchair, 'what you need is some tender loving care.'

How right you are, my dear, sweet Maggie. If only I wanted it from *you*.

THURSDAY, MARCH 18

Dreamt about *her* last night. Of course. Cathy, Cathy, Cathy. Sometimes I find myself doodling her name like a twelve-year-old girl with a crush on the geography teacher. Steve loves Cathy. Cathy hates Steve. There's an unusual, if ghastly, symmetry to it all.

Had a spare five minutes so I stopped off at a bookie's with the intention of putting £100 – or, a oner, as betting-shop-big-dicks would have it – on the trap-four dog in the next greyhound race. However, when I saw the card, I couldn't help backing trap one, Mellie's Wish – well, it was fate, wasn't it?

Amazingly enough . . . trap three won. So no cause for complaint there.

I've noticed it before about myself but although I gamble on a lot of horse races, I'm not a horse-racing fan *per se*. This year, for a whole host of reasons, Cheltenham's completely passed me by.

I honestly couldn't care less what won the Champion Hurdle or the Gold Cup or which lad won the prize for the best-turned-out nag or whatever: I leave all that sort of thing to civilians. To me, horses are just a medium for gambling and I'm no more interested in them than I would be in the grooves on a roulette wheel.

FRIDAY, MARCH 19

Yet again we played poker at Gerard's. He doesn't mind and we certainly don't as it's the perfect venue for poker: no wives, no kids, a fridge containing nothing but poker food and any number of loos. Although you don't have to be fastidious before using one of Gerard's loos; you just have to have eyes or, indeed, a sense of smell.

'Where's Sharon, Gerard?'

'Who?' grinned the Bad Man.

'Your girlfriend.'

'Oh, her,' said the Bad Man dismissively, 'I gave her to one of my friends.'

'You *what*?' The Bad Man is differently moralled, but this seemed to be extraordinary even by his standards.

Ben came to his senses first. 'What do you mean 'gave' her? Shouldn't that be 'sold' her?'

Gerard cackled.

Douglas, as usual, trumped Ben. 'What do you mean by "friends", Gerard?'

There were seven of us tonight. Gerard, Douglas, Jake, Ben, Nik, Toby and me. The crack was good but the poker was scrappy. There were too many variations, too much dragging from the pot and, consequently, too much post-pot talk. The poker *hands* were fine but the settling up after each hand was interminable. I can't see why everyone can't make sure they have adequate chips before each hand but it seems I'm a lone voice in the wilderness. Meanwhile, I have to endure endless 'I-owe-you-twenty-but-you-dragged-thirty-and-the-pot's-light-by-forty' conversations. Like the old whore said when she retired, 'It's not the sex, it's the stairs.' That's my favourite quote: I think I want it on my tombstone when I die.

Nik, who's not the world's greatest poker player has become addicted to baseball – the absurd game in which we're each dealt seven cards which we place face down on the table. We then go round the table turning over sufficient cards to beat the previous player whereupon the next player has to turn over his cards until he can beat the last player etc. etc. All 3s and 9s are wild and 4s are also wild if you pay for them (fifty pee or half the pot depending on the whim of the dealer before the game). The reason Nik likes baseball so much is that it's entirely luck . . . and balls – and, to be fair to Nik, he's got plenty of balls (or, as they're known at our poker table, *cojones*). Consequently, he does well at it because the percentage players (Jake and, increasingly, Toby) and the 'proper' poker players (Douglas, Jake and a sober Ben) don't have the appetite to go all the way. I tend to go for it until the Bad Man starts bringing out the real folding stuff but then I too back out of it. I'm not a poker snob and I don't really mind how much I lose but I don't like the others to think I'm a cunt or, worse, a loser, so I mind how much they *see* me lose. And baseball is a real bitch of a losing game: there's always a real grandstand finish. So I'll just stick to omaha, stud and hold 'em, thank you very much.

What with all the drawing and dragging and loaning, it was impossible to work out who won or lost what – even if any of us were prepared to tell the truth. I *think* I lost about two hundred but there's a margin of error of plus or minus two hundred.

SUNDAY, MARCH 21

Sometimes with gambling it's not how big the stakes are quantitatively but how important they are qualitatively. Jonathan (especially) and Melanie have been nagging me to play Frustration with them for ages. I've always procrastinated – hell, I've got better things to do – but today I finally got caught.

The game itself is just ludo with a fancy dice which you pop instead of roll and, I got to say, it's addictive. The point is, it's almost pure chance. The only decision you ever get to make is which piece to move – and that's only if there's a choice. Consequently, it's just about the only game the kids can play with me on level terms.

We played three games. Mellie won two and Jonathan one. So I thought, 'Right, let's spice this up a little' and went off to get some Opal Fruits or whatever it is they're called these days (I still think of everything in 'old money' terms).

'OK, children,' I told them. 'We've each got a packet of sweets. What we have to do is each put down three sweets and whoever wins the game wins the sweets.'

We played four games and I swear the tension was, if anything, even greater than it was at poker on Friday and, one thing's for certain, there was no bloody dragging. It was phenomenal fun. Jonathan lost the first two games and I could see his bottom lip tremble. I love the kid and I hate to see him upset but, hell, there's no point in playing unless you do it properly. So I told him to stop whingeing and put in his three sweets. Fortunately, he won a game and was soon merrily chomping on his tuck (though if truth be told, I'd have given him my sweets – but only *after* the game: he's got to learn). One thing made me laugh: in the same way that the Victorians believed that men had only so much semen in their bodies and that every wank depleted them, so the kids think that there are only so many sixes and therefore complain bitterly if they throw a six when they're 'practising'.

More spread bets; more profits. Bought the first goal in today's televised football. It was a goalless draw and so it made up at the maximum. That's another £300 – less the £180 I lost on bookings (bought) and multi-corners (sold). I must learn to have just one trade.

MONDAY, MARCH 22

Did some spread betting on the Liverpool match. I bought their performance (won £140) and, oh-I-know-I-said-I-would-only-do-one-trade-but-what-the-hell, I bought the goalscorers' shirt numbers (made £90) and sold the multi-corners (won £30).

Seems like the only place I'm in credit is my spread-betting account! I'm tempted to start tapping into it just to improve the cash flow. Everywhere else I'm surrounded by overdrawn statements, red bills and threatening letters. I've finally made an appointment to see Mr Watson for next week, so that's something positive I'm doing.

WEDNESDAY, MARCH 24

Had to go to Reading today. Truth is I could have done my work on the phone but I used the pretext of 'keeping the customer satisfied' to go there in person.

Once again, I went to Carlton Close but this time with a carefully-thought-out plan. Nervously, I rang the doorbell of number 49 but, as I expected, there was no one there. Good. I went next door to number 47 but that too was empty, so I tried number 51 and, as luck would have it, struck gold, in the shape of a kindly elderly woman who promptly invited me in when I said I was an old friend of Cathy's who happened to be in the neighbourhood etc. etc.

It didn't take much for the neighbour to open up. 'Oh, she's so lovely, isn't she, Cathy? And so pretty.'

No argument from me on that one.

'And she and Mike are so happy.'

Grrr. 'Mike? Oh, you mean her boyfriend, or should I say "partner" in these politically correct days?' Do I know how to speak to old ladies?

'Yes, that's right, dear. He's a policeman, you know, a detective constable.' She put inverted commas around his rank. 'Oh he is lovely – and so handsome: he looks like Cliff Richard.'

Bizarre thought.

'Mike, Mike? What's his surname again?'

'Littleton, I think, yes, Littleton. Yes, he's so nice. Do you know he cleaned out my gutter when it was blocked?' Yeah, that's why they call them the filth.

'That was nice of him,' I said through gritted teeth.

'I always think it's a shame that they didn't have any children although I do believe he's got children from his er, first . . .' she allowed her words to trail away.

Just for the sake of mischief, I was really tempted to spin her a line that Cathy had had an illegitimate child as a teenager and put it up for adoption, but she was a nice old lady and I didn't want to upset her, so, with a lot of smiles and profuse thanks for all her help, I took my leave.

'Excuse me, young man,' she called out to me as I went back to the car (it's a long time since anyone called me young man), 'you didn't tell me your name so that I can tell Cathy you popped in.'

'I'm sorry,' I said, thinking on my feet, 'it's Douglas, Douglas Kennedy.' Cheers, mate.

There was no point in hanging around for a few hours just to see Cathy come home (now where have I heard that before?), so I drove to Bagshot for my next call, pausing only to phone directory inquiries to ask for Littleton, Michael at 49 Carlton Close. There was no one of that name for that address. Shit. Eventually, after three calls, I found a listing for a C. Lyttleton at 49 Carlton Close – I guess as a copper he's got to be careful, perhaps it's easier to put the number in a combination of both their names.

I'm not a fucking perv or anything, just a weak-willed sad sack, so it pains me to confess what I did this evening. I waited until 6.30, the time I'd seen her get home last week, and then phoned. I got the answering machine with a message recorded by him, by 'Mike', unfortunately. Quite a high voice – Cathy's probably got him by the balls – and trying hard, like most of us do, to sound posher than he actually is.

Every minute, on the minute, I hit the redial button until, hallelujah, I heard *her* voice, breathless from having just got to the phone before the answering machine cut in.

'Hello.' Hello. One word but it swept over me like a wave of pure joy.

'Hello.' Again, bliss, true bliss.

'Hello, who's that?' It's me, honey, it's me. I'm back.

She tutted and put the phone down.

I mustn't phone her again. I promise I won't phone her again. Well, not after seven, just in case *he's* home.

THURSDAY, MARCH 25

Had a row with Maggie today. Not about Cathy – at least not ostensibly – but about poker tomorrow night.

'I'm *not* having it here, Steve, and that's final.'

'What do you mean *you're* not having it here. That's right, *you're* not having it here: *I'm* having it here. This is my house, too, you know and if I want to invite my friends over to play cards, then I bloody will.'

'It's bad enough that you play poker without having to rub my nose in it. There are also the children to think of. I don't want them to grow up watching their daddy gambling at home.'

'Better they should see me gambling with friends and enjoying it than . . . besides, they'll be asleep before the guys arrive.'

'That's not the point.'

'But you like my friends, don't you?'

'I do, but I don't like the idea of you taking money off each other.'

'I don't mind; they don't mind.'

'But I do and I'm your wife. And I'd say that none of their wives like it much, except most of them seem to be unmarried or divorced.'

Ah, so that's what it's about then, you feel threatened by . . .

what? Poker? Gambling? Single men leading me into temptation. Poor Maggie. Truth be told, I'd much rather play at Gerard's. I was just trying to establish a point and maybe provoke an argument with Maggie. For not really approving of my poker; for not respecting my rights as an individual; for not being Cathy.

SATURDAY, MARCH 27

Didn't write up last night's poker last night or, rather, this morning, because I didn't get in till this morning. I'm confused. I can't work out yesterday and today, this morning before I went to sleep and this morning after waking up. It's like I can never work out how I'm affected by the clock going forward or back an hour.

The poker was great. The usual crowd was present: Gerard, Jake, Douglas, Ben, Nik plus Nathan and a guy called Warren who stayed for two hours which was just long enough for him to be cleaned out. Warren, an habitué of Gerard's *demi-monde,* was introduced by our host as 'a friend of mine'.

'Don't be silly,' said Ben, 'you don't have any friends, Gerard.'

'No,' I added, 'just marks.'

'They're only kidding,' Gerard said to Warren, glaring at me. Gerard isn't bothered by my jibe – water off a bad man's back – he's just worried that Warren will believe me.

Like I say, it was a bloody good night – not least because I finally got to 'read' Jake. That's Jake as in Judicious Jake, aka Inscrutable Jake. Not that I told him, of course, as I wouldn't want him to change. Nor, indeed, did I tell any of the others, for why should they benefit from my perception? What I actually noticed was that on the three occasions when Jake successfully bluffed the pot, he bit the fingernail of the little finger of his left hand. Nothing significant about that in itself – Jake bites his nails almost as badly as I do which is maybe what made me notice – but, before bluffing, Jake *cradles* the little finger of his left hand and then bites the nail. It's the cradling that gives away the bluff. I spotted it the first time and then acted on it the next two times when I called him holding very little to discover he was holding even less.

Inevitably, that dented his profits (they were both big pots) and boosted mine. In fact, I finished the night about £300 up and was the big winner on the night/morning.

This afternoon saw (a now customary) frenzy of spread betting. By the time I actually got going, it was too late for the horse racing so I stuck to the football. I decided to put all my eggs in one basket and bought total Premiership goals for £40 at 21.5. There were 32 goals, so I made a profit of £420.

MONDAY, MARCH 29

Saw Mr Watson today. From the name, I expected him to be Dad's age or older. In fact, he's about thirty. Christ, you know you're getting old when bank managers start looking young.

He took me through all my outgoings – the mortgage, finance-company loan, the credit cards, little luxuries like gas, water, telephone etc. – before raising an eyebrow. 'I notice you take out a lot of cash, Mr Ross.' He cleared his throat. 'Can I ask why that it is?'

Yeah, because I'm gambling for my life.

'Oh, just all the things that cost so much – you know, food and . . .' – *don't* say entertainment, Steve – '. . . things like . . . you know, general household expenditure. You know what it's like with a wife and kids.' I looked at him for a sympathetic reaction but got none. Shit, the bastard's single or, worse, gay.

'We're going to have to do something about this, Mr Ross.'

I tried to look like the sort of man who reads *Money Mail*.

'Consequently, what I propose is that we restructure all your debts and consolidate them into a single mortgage. How much is your house currently worth?'

'I don't know, about a hundred and eighty thousand.' (I *do* know, it's worth £160,000. There aren't many weeks when Maggie hasn't got a bloody estate agent round to do a valuation.)

'Fine. Then subject to our own valuation, we could let you have a mortgage for . . .' he looked down at his notes '. . . a hundred and forty thousand.'

Ah, yes, um. That's all very well but Maggie doesn't actually know about the loan from the finance company: I got her to sign the document when she was half asleep and not really on the ball. Hmm. 'Mr Watson, is there any chance that we could do this without involving my wife? I mean, she has lots on at the moment . . . under stress . . . wouldn't want to worry her . . . know what I mean?'

He fixed me with a look that said, 'I know *exactly* what you mean' and said, 'I'm very sorry, Mr Ross, if the house is in joint names then your wife must be involved.'

We discussed a few more details and I left. As I went out I saw his name in letraset on the staff board: Mr N. Watson, Assistant Manager. Great, I'm not even worth a local bank manager.

Douglas phoned with a great Gerard story. Apparently – and this is all according to the Bad Man himself and so must be taken with *several* grains of salt – Gerard was playing in a private poker game in Luton (of all places). Gerard says that he was fucking the host's girlfriend and, while he was in mid-hump, the door was blown open by police staging a drugs raid. The cops manage to separate Gerard from his inamorata and tell him he's under arrest.

Gerard is carrying fake I.D. (like you do) and so gives them a false name. He's then taken out and put in the paddy wagon along with all the other players.

So he's riding along with two other bad men when the wagon stops to load up some even worse men, one of whom waits till the door's nearly shut before kicking it open again and flattening the copper who was closing it. All the bad men, including our own dear pseudonymous Bad Man, make their escape – in Gerard's case to a cafe whence he made his way home to Chiswick.

It's a hell of a story and one wonders how much of it's true. Douglas reckons all of it except Gerard having sex, the police raiding the joint, Gerard being arrested and his subsequent escape.

TUESDAY, MARCH 30

I know I'm desperate when I start betting on European football where there isn't even a Scottish team involved, let alone an English one. We are talking two flies going up a wall – particularly when it comes to bookings (bought – they're all temperamental foreigners) and goals (sold – Eyetie defences give nothing away). Still, the bank's thrown me a lifeline and £310 also says it was the right thing to do.

I phoned Cathy again this evening. She sounded even more annoyed than last time but it was so sweet to hear her voice that it didn't matter.

I really mustn't phone her again. Besides, if I do it too often, she'll only go and change her number.

WEDNESDAY, MARCH 31

It's that time of the month again and for once it's good news! As a result of my brilliant spread-betting, I'm a massive £1,700 up on the month (even taking into account the thousand quid holiday-deposit money I dropped in the casino) – that's to say, just £2,000 down on the year. Looking back, it seems like I'm now not bothering to record wins or losses of under a hundred and so it's possible that that figure of £1,700 could be anything up to three or four hundred out either way but, even so, I'd say I'm 6–4 to win the bet and, the way I'm going, I wouldn't mind having a monkey on me. So to speak.

THURSDAY, APRIL 1

I phoned Cathy at the 'usual' time, once again savouring that wonderful voice with its trace of huskiness (it's amazing what Gitanes will do).

'Hello.'

Hello, my darling.

'Hello.'

Have I told you how much I love you?

'Hello.' Anger, persistence.

And miss you?

Suddenly. 'Steve, is that you?'

Shitfuckcuntbollockstits. I rang off without saying anything.

Instinctively, I hit the redial button,

'Hello.'

'Cathy, listen, it's me.'

'You bastard!'

'I'm sorry.'

'You fucking sod!'

'Cathy, I'm sorry . . .'

'How dare you? Don't you remember what happened last time?'

'Yes, I do . . .'

'Then how dare you phone me again? Was that you the other times and did you go round to my next-door neighbour?'

'Yes, no, yes. Cathy, I'm sorry, I wasn't thinking, I need you, please . . .'

'You creep!'

'Cathy, please . . .'

'Listen, and listen good, if you ever phone me again, I will tell my boyfriend, who is a serving policeman, and he will make sure that your life is made hell. Do I make myself clear?'

'Yes, Cathy, but . . .'

She put the phone down on me. What a bitch. What a beautiful bitch.

FRIDAY, APRIL 2

Today, I didn't phone Cathy. I sound like a fucking alcoholic ('today I am sober') but that's how I feel about her.

Poker at the Bad Man's once again. He's got yet another new flatmate: a Spanish girl named Maria (which got one of us – I'm ashamed to admit it was me – doing the 'I've just met a girl named Maria' routine from *West Side Story*).

Just the core crowd present – Gerard, Douglas, Ben, Jake and Nik and me – which suited me fine as it meant that a) the money will stay within the group, b) we all know what we're doing (except, of course, for Nik) and so no explanations are necessary, c) we all know each other so we can talk in a kind of shorthand without worrying about alienating outsiders and d) with only six players and the prospect of many high-low hands, I might actually win a few pots.

In the event, I won more than just a few pots although, with my luck, they were *all* tiny pots. Can't complain about the cards I got but I just couldn't get anyone to stay in with me. I don't know, maybe it's the way I am when I get good cards that encourages everyone else to stack but I don't think so. I did everything by the book: sometimes checking, sometimes double-bluffing by making it look like I was trying to buy the pot but each time I had good – great – cards, it just seemed to coincide with everyone else getting dross.

Meanwhile, in all the games of seven-card stud using wild cards, *all* the wild cards I received were open. The one time I got anything wild in the hole was in Follow-the-Queen when the queen got followed by a 3 and I ended up with five 7s showing nothing more than a pair of 7s. Unfortunately, no one else had anything more than trips and so I made like maybe twenty quid on the whole hand. I'd earn more money sweeping the streets.

The thing with poker is that it's a relative game. Cards don't exist in a vacuum: it's how they measure up to other players' cards (allowing, of course, for bluffing). It's better to have a flush if your opponent's got a straight than to have a running flush over a pair.

I think, on balance, over an evening I'd rather have honest-to-goodness bad cards – with the hope that next week the pendulum of luck would swing the other way – than adrenalin-pumping good cards which earn me nothing. It's what the bubbles call hubris: those whom the poker gods seek to destroy, they first deal great hands to.

Unfortunately, out of frustration, I ended up staying in big pots when, ordinarily, I would have stacked and, consequently, finished the evening three hundred quid down. Worse, I felt like every sort of cunt: I didn't just lose, I played badly – and everyone else knew.

SATURDAY, APRIL 3

Today's the one Saturday of the year when gamblers and civilians come face to face to bet on the Grand National.

I've loved the race ever since I won a sweepstake on Anglo in 1966 when I was just nine years old. Critics say that it's just a lottery – it's not, but even if it were, it would still be a lot more fun than the bloody National Lottery. A four-and-a-half-mile race offers a damn sight more entertainment than the 'spectacle' of six – sorry, seven – balls dropping, no matter how much whooping the TV people do. Incidentally, if the National Lottery is so fucking wonderful, how come there's never a winner (of any significant prize) in the 'live' TV audience?

Henry's was absolutely choc-a-bloc with once-a-year punters, all trying to outdo each other in helplessness, gormlessness and general moronism. How can a grown man not know how to fill out a betting-slip? Or, for that matter, a teenager? What's the point of having a core curriculum?

We regulars greeted each other extravagantly, our sense of unity heightened by the presence of so many strangers.

I found myself looking indulgently at these pinstickers with their lit-up faces and bulging eyes, like kids in a chocolate factory. All that excitement, all that anticipation. If I could bottle that feeling and sell it back to them, I'd be a billionaire.

Actually, how dare I accuse others of being pinstickers when I've backed horses using the most absurd criteria? The only difference between them and me is that they don't seek to disguise their ignorance, their superstition, whereas I have trouble confessing it to myself.

Tim, who will happily blow a couple of hundred on a complete whim and is therefore no mean pinsticker himself, had decided that, this year at least, he would approach the race a little bit more scientifically.

'Right, mate,' he said – for some reason, Tim never calls me Steve – 'let's start whittling through all the losers and find ourselves a winner by the process of elimination. OK, give me that copy of the *Post*.' I handed over my copy of the *Racing Post*, my proof of professionalism. In the kingdom of the blind, the one-eyed man is king; in the world of the pinsticker, the *Racing Post* reader is an expert.

We then proceeded to eliminate all horses out of the handicap – that's to say, all horses carrying ten stones. We also took out all of the following: any horse wearing blinkers (with a large field, the winning horse will be one which has got good all-round vision), any horse that hasn't finished in the first three in a steeplechase with a field of sixteen or more (i.e. it has to be used to doing well in big fields), any horse that hasn't won a single race this season, any horse that hasn't won at a distance of over three miles, any horse that was still running in novice chases in the past year or two (the winning horse will invariably have more experience than that) and, finally, any horse that's fallen this year.

Amazingly, we were still left with three horses: at ante-post odds of 12–1, 14–1 and 20–1. Confident of our methodology, we backed all three. I personally did three singles for £50 each, a £10 forecast combination (six bets = £60) and a £10 tricast combination (six bets = £60). Having taken prices on the singles (and paid the tax!), I worked out that if I got the first three in descending betting order and the odds stayed the same for the forecast and tricast bets, I would get a minimum return of £650 + £1820 + £33,600 = £36,070.

Like the family man I am, I went home to watch the race (I wonder if Tim has a family – he never mentions anything about children or anything). I'd done some bets for Maggie (at her request) and for the kids (at my initiative) – just fifty pee bets on horses with apposite names – and so I felt like Santa Claus as I walked in.

'How much am I going to win, Daddy?' asked Melanie.

'What toy will I buy, Dad?' asked Jonathan.

'Whoa, kids, you haven't won yet!' I told them I'd hang on to their betting slips until (and unless) they did but gave Maggie hers.

'How much did you spend, Steve?'

None of your fucking business. 'Oh, just a few bob on three different horses.'

'How much?'

Fuck you and the horse you rode in on. 'Fifty quid.' Which wasn't entirely a mistruth.

Maggie whistled. 'That's a huge amount, don't you think?' Ever the schoolma'am.

'No I don't or I wouldn't have done it.'

She should only know. She shouldn't only know.

Maggie's attitude set up an atmosphere for the race itself which almost spoilt it for me. Some of my happiest memories of my childhood revolve around the Grand National, which we always watched together as a family. Jay Trump, Anglo, Red Alligator, poor old Crisp, Red Rum (of course) – these are all names which spring to mind whenever I think of the National and I remember them a damn sight better than some distant aunt or cousin.

The children loved every minute of it. 'Look, Dad, my horse is winning!' shouted Jonathan after they'd travelled all of five furlongs. Melanie, meanwhile, watched with utter intensity, her hands drawn into fists which turned her knuckles white. She's her father's daughter all right.

My selections weren't really mentioned for the first circuit which is how I like it best in the National. Then, after they'd jumped Becher's Brook for the second time, all three of mine started to come into contention.

I tried to ignore Jonathan's cries about his horses falling and Maggie's inanities about 'cruelty' (as if . . .). 'Come on, my son. Go on. Gawan, my son,' I said louder and louder as I slowly rose from my armchair to 'ride' them home.

With three fences to go, there were only four horses in it and three of them belonged to me!

'Gawan,' I called as I rhythmically pretended to whip my own leg, 'Gawan!' My voice built up to a frenzy until I could see that the outsider of the four – i.e. the one horse I hadn't backed – was going to get it on the run-in.

I slumped back into my armchair feeling sicker than a pregnant woman with food poisoning. Just one word escaped my lips, 'Cunt.'

The children learned a new word which earned me a lecture from Maggie later. Fair dos but I have to say that, at the time, I couldn't have cared less. If the fucking winner had fallen at the last, I'd have been £36,000 up, instead of £280-odd down (aye, and add to that another hundred I dropped in the shop betting on dog races whilst waiting to make my Grand National selections).

MONDAY, APRIL 5

Letter arrived today from the bank confirming the new mortgage. It was addressed to Mr and Mrs Ross and, unfortunately, came in the second post so Maggie opened it.

When I got home she was waiting for me.

'What's this about, Steve?'

We waltzed through the 'What's what?', 'You know what it is' and 'So why are you asking?' routines.

'Look, I thought I told you.' I took the attack to her. 'I

did, I told you I was going to see Mr Watson at the bank, didn't I?'

'Yes, but he's written to say that he's arranging a mortgage for £140,000.'

'Yeah right.'

'Why so much?'

'It's cheap to borrow at the moment, so I'm borrowing.'

'But why do we need so much, Steven.' Steven, eh? Oh-oh . . .

'We don't need so much, Margaret,' I said obstreperously, trying to reroute/provoke her into a more conventional, comfortable row from which I'd easily be able to extract myself.

She wasn't going to be riled. 'Then why?'

'Oh, I don't know, it's useful to have money available – who knows what business opportunity might come our way?'

'Don't try kidding me, Steve, I'm not your father.' Ouch.

I considered bluster but one look at her face convinced me that it would have been futile. God, I hate her. If it weren't for the kids . . . As I struggled to come up with something – anything – I found myself wondering why it is that men divorce their wives when it costs them so much: you lose your home, your kids, your money. How much simpler to arrange an accident? Then there's the insurance. It's win, win, win.

These bizarre thoughts did nothing to help me as I stood there trying to outstare her whilst simultaneously avoiding her piercing eyes (not an easy task) but I found the thoughts curiously comforting – like that feeling of passive power I used to get when Mum would tell me off for doing something naughty when I knew that I had done far worse things that she didn't know about.

Eventually, I came to a simple decision: I can't win, so I won't compete. 'Look, Maggie, if you want us to keep the house, we need to take out this mortgage, which means that you're going to have to agree to it. It really is as simple as that.'

Before she could say anything else, I walked out of the room and out of the house.

* * *

I went to the pub to watch the televised football, stopping only at a telephone box to place a huge spread-bet – huger than I would ordinarily place just to spite Maggie (just in the same way that I would find a way to spite my mother after *she'd* told me off). The trade I did was to buy corners at 11.5 for £100 a corner. That's right, £100 a corner. That would serve her right if I lost. That would serve me right if I won.

Even though the crowd they had in watching the game were a bit younger (and a bit flasher) than me, I enjoyed the atmosphere. One or two of them noticed me triumphantly making a fist and whispering, 'Yes!' every time there was a corner and correctly guessed that I'd bought corners for a spread bet. After that, they were cheering with me all the way.

In the event, there were five corners in the first half and six in the second, so I lost a grand total of £50! Still, it was fun while it lasted and now I'm sitting here writing, trying to put off the moment when I have to go to bed and see *her*, the bitch.

She knows why we have to have such a huge mortgage. I know she knows. She knows I know she knows. I know she knows I know she knows.

I give up. I'd rather spend a frosty night with Maggie than do my brain in.

TUESDAY, APRIL 6

The night wasn't just frosty: it was icy. There's nothing lonelier than being with someone who doesn't want to be with you.

I thought of appealing to her by telling her how 'broken' I was feeling but decided not to because it wouldn't work. Also, I actually feel fine at the moment: whether it's the pills or whether it's because now at least Maggie knows (one way or the other) about the finance company loan and the extent of our indebtedness, I don't know, but I feel far too good to dissemble successfully.

Pity all this serotonin coursing through my brain doesn't translate itself into better sales figures but I have to say, I really couldn't give a toss about work at the moment: I'm just going through the motions. Fortunately for me, there's a level on which I can operate and achieve (just) enough sales without unduly taxing myself. Phil knows I'm coasting but I think he's biding his time until I fail to make target. He's got his own problems with key guys quitting so I have a fair amount of latitude.

Having not troubled the scorers much in the past few days, I had a real result this evening on the televised football.

Usually, if I bet on the multi-corners, I sell. The reason for this is that you only need one half to yield fewer than five corners to be quids in. But, for some reason, tonight I decided to buy, £20 per corner at 37.

After twenty minutes, there hadn't been a single corner and I was dead worried. Then, suddenly, in the space of fifteen minutes, there were no fewer than *eight* corners! In the final ten minutes of the first half, there were two more, making a total of ten.

The second half was not quite so productive but there were still seven corners – meaning that the market made up at 70 and I made £660.

WEDNESDAY, APRIL 7

Maggie's still colder than a witch's tit. Snap out of it, bitch, or I'll give you a *real* reason to be miserable. Hell, we're not homeless or anything. All that's happened is that we're having to increase our borrowing: shit, it happens to third-world countries all the time.

I wish I could tell her all this but, at the moment, discretion – or, rather, silence – is the better part of not having my balls cut off.

FRIDAY, APRIL 9

Fabulous poker session – all the boys were on top form.

Douglas's got a wonderful new expression. He described

someone – I think it was Gerard and the way he was gambling – as being 'All over the place like a mad woman's shit.' We all loved it and it became the catchphrase of the evening.

Ben and Gerard have been swapping their respective party tricks. Gerard can hypnotise people (so *that's* how he gets laid) and Ben is a surprisingly good magician. Although they've always refused to divulge their secrets to the rest of us, they were prepared to do so to each other in exchange for the other's speciality. Now *there's* principle for you.

Ben, who is married, is just curious to extend his range. Gerard, on the other hand, is quite upfront about why it is he wants to do magic: he thinks that this too will help him to get laid. Mind you, Gerard needs all the help he can get at the moment. He has started to balloon alarmingly. He must have put on four stones this year and he wasn't exactly skinny to start with.

The funny thing with Gerard is that he's inordinately proud of his biceps. He thinks that they ripple and, whatever the weather, he'll wear these sleeveless t-shirts to show them off – especially when he goes to wine bars in search of prey.

His biceps may have been muscular in the past but now they're just fat and, unfortunately, his stomach has caught them up. The trouble is that Gerard's self-image is still that of a lean and muscular man. He doesn't realise he's got this enormous gut and an arse described by Douglas as being 'the size of Kansas' and so he still goes into wine bars unveiling his fat arms at every opportunity.

So there are Gerard and Ben down in this seedy wine bar – full of typists and shop girls just itching to have their snatches filled – and they're showing off their newfound skills. Ben is trying to hypnotise people and Gerard is showing off his magical prowess to girls for whom Paul Daniels is a mystic.

All is going well until Gerard gets pissed and decides to do Ben's favourite trick: the scarf-and-fake-thumb routine which, I have to say, is jolly good. Unfortunately, Gerard drops both the scarf and the fake thumb, leaving his 'audience' in fits of giggles and Ben, whose party piece is now ruined (at least in The Slag and Legless), in a state of rage. Or, anyway, as close as Ben ever gets to a state of rage, which is what the rest of us would call mildly annoyed.

As ever, with Gerard, it wasn't so much what happened that killed us as much as his interpretation of what happened. This time was no exception. 'It would have been fine if you had diverted their attention,' he said reproachfully to Ben.

'Me?' asked Ben incredulously. 'I showed you how it was done. You got pissed and fucked it up.'

'That's as maybe,' replied the Bad Man, showing all the ability of a politician but less of the charm, 'but once the shit hit the fan, it was up to you to help put it right.'

'Listen, Gerard, I told you before we started that you had to be very careful to make sure that you didn't drop anything. Now what part of that did you find hard to understand?'

Gerard decided unilaterally to end this particular conversation. 'Never mind. OK, boys, let's play cards.'

Which we did for hour after fun-packed hour. Nik is emigrating to New Zealand at the end of the month so there was something of an end-of-term feel to his playing – even more than there usually is. Jake's got himself a new girlfriend which always cheers him up and Douglas's advertising agency has just won some award so he was even jollier than usual.

We played lots of wild games – Baseball, Funday Times, Southern Cross, Follow The Queen and (what we know as) Willy-Wanky-Woo. The funny thing with poker-game variations and their names is that one doesn't know how universal they are. Follow The Queen and Baseball are, I know, played by men like us all over the country and I'm pretty sure that Willy-Wanky-Woo is unique to us, but what about, say, Funday Times? To suggest that to a room full of strangers could be as embarrassing as it was when, as a kid, one would use a family word for penis or urinating to a teacher in front of the whole class.

Ben surprised everyone – and, I dare say, himself – by being the big winner on the night with £500. I won £280. Gerard was the big loser with £620. Douglas couldn't resist a parting shot at Gerard: 'Hey, Gerard, that was a bit like a winning poker session without the increased bank balance bit at the end.' Gerard, to his enormous credit, grinned. Good man, Bad Man.

SATURDAY, APRIL 10

Went to Henry's only intending to stay for a few races but he's got this gorgeous new cashier and so I found myself lingering for the whole afternoon. Her name's Samantha and she's quite unlike any of Henry's previous cashiers. For a start, she's not common; secondly, she hasn't got big tits and, lastly, she's got this wonderful fresh-faced, Irish-colleen look to her. Not my usual sort at all but I found her enormously attractive – not least, I suspect, because she looked at me with (what looked like) wide-eyed approval.

I have to say that she had an effect on my gambling. Because I wanted to impress her, I found myself betting big; at the same time, because I didn't want her to think I was a loser, I was trying my hardest not to lose. Now I know that I always try my hardest not to lose – or should do anyway – but I was *particularly* careful with my selections (except for the football bets which would be settled one way or the other after she'd left the shop).

Tim was there but acting . . . I don't know . . . *oddly*. He's never been the most jovial of men – his style is too laid back for that – but today he was abrupt, even with me, almost to the point of terseness. I tried, more than once, to get him out of his shell but eventually gave up.

As a result of my careful gambling, I 'only' lost a hundred quid – and that was including the football bets which, of course, all lost. I have to say that does it for me with football accumulators: they always look so tempting but it only takes a late equaliser here or a disallowed goal there to fuck up the whole bet.

Evening in with Maggie. Boring. We watched telly. She complained that I always have the remote control but what does she expect? I am the man of the house, after all. Show me a house where the woman is routinely in charge of the remote control and I'll show you a woman living on her own.

There was silence as we watched the lousy programmes – why is telly so useless on Saturday evenings? – but it wasn't a companionable silence. The few times I tried to make conversation, I found myself rebuffed: not obviously but enough for me to get the message. 'Shh, this is interesting.'

No it's not, it's *Casualty* and it's as predictable as diarrhoea after a vindaloo.

I went to bed first and, surprisingly, she came up soon afterwards. I thought we had a tacit arrangement to avoid potential nocturnal conflict by waiting until the first to go upstairs fell asleep. God, I hope she doesn't want sex: even with Samantha dancing around in my mind, I really couldn't face it.

I couldn't bear lying next to her, listening to her biting her nails and turning pages, a moment longer, so I came downstairs to write this.

I'm sorry, Maggie. I'm sorry I didn't tell you about the finance-company loan. I'm sorry I didn't tell you about all the other debts. I'm sorry I didn't tell you about my gambling. I'm sorry I don't fancy you any more. I'm sorry that I'm not the man you want me to be. But, more than anything, I'm sorry for myself that I married such a humourless, dreary, colourless *drudge*.

SUNDAY, APRIL 11

It was Melanie's birthday today. She's ten – I can't believe it! – where have all the years gone? it seems like only yesterday that I was changing her nappy (OK, so it was just the once, but even so).

I left Maggie to organise her present and party – well, that's what mums are for – and, I have to say, Maggie does that sort of thing really well. I could see the other mums – the ones who stayed and helped as well as the ones who came to pick up their kids – watching approvingly. Notwithstanding her other shortcomings, I suppose I have got reason to be grateful and she also seemed to appreciate my presence and help (with the party games etc.) – especially as her friends kept on reminding her of how *their* husbands invariably absented themselves from these sort of occasions.

There was one mum present – Denise – whom I fancy quite a bit. Apparently, she's one of the mums at the school and although she's not a natural beauty, she's got a lazy eye.

Did some trades on the football – sneaking away from the party every few minutes to see how the match was progressing. I had intended to sell the time of the first goal – that's to say, I thought there would be an early goal – but I got confused and ended up buying it. Easily done. Unfortunately, the first goal was scored in the ninth minute and I lost £550. Bad call.

MONDAY, APRIL 12

Just because I don't write about Cathy doesn't mean I don't think about her morning, noon and night. Everything in me yearns to phone her, to hear her, to speak to her, but I know that she would only rebuff me. And that's something I don't need and can't take.

WEDNESDAY, APRIL 14

I won £260 – thanks to a 4–1 shot which I backed because the only winners across the cards had either been favourites or rank outsiders and I thought it was time a (clear) second favourite came in.

THURSDAY, APRIL 15

Driving along . . . making calls . . . going through the motions . . . thinking of Cathy . . . wanting her . . . . . . NEEDING HER . . . accept no substitutes . . .

Listening to an oldies station and every song is about her, me, her and me.

If I have to die at the end of the year, she's the one person I'll tell about it. And I know precisely the reason why. Even if I lose my bet and am about to kill myself, Cathy is the one person who could stop me by agreeing to live with me again. But since the odds against that are currently considerably greater than the odds against me winning the National Lottery, it doesn't figure in my plans.

FRIDAY, APRIL 16

Gerard's just returned from California – where he's been on (what he calls with due solemnity) a 'trading mission' but which we assume to be something extremely nefarious – with an extraordinary tale of how he found himself in a poker game at the racetrack playing with this (in his words) 'really hard man'. They're playing seven-card stud with no wild cards. The 'hard man' is showing three kings. Gerard looks like he's got a low straight but, in reality, he's got a running flush.

They get to the final round of betting and they're both all in. The hard man says he wants to bet again. The dealer says that's impossible whereupon the hard man tells him to shut up 'or I'll gut you like a fish.' Now this is, as I seem to recall, a line from a movie. The pertinent question is: who got the line from the movie – the hard man or the Bad Man?

Gerard agrees to carry on betting. His opponent puts up a gold Rolex watch with diamonds and some other gaudy jewellery of the type that only poker players wear; Gerard puts in all the money he's got: $200.

The hard man reveals four kings; Gerard shows his running flush. Exit the former, kicking over a chair. According to Gerard, he also said to the dealer, 'Deal him a flush, would you? I'll be waiting for you outside.'

Gerard claims to still have these baubles although, strangely enough, not with him tonight.

'Why don't you say what really happened,' asks Douglas.

'I did,' says Gerard.

'No, Gerard, what really happened,' says Douglas, 'is that some skinny black man in an alley fleeced you out of hundreds of bucks for a fake Rolex and you've spent the past forty-eight hours concocting a story that will make you sound like a hero instead of a zero.'

Gerard protested his veracity, which only made the whole thing even funnier. The sight of the Bad Man in a state of righteous indignation is something to behold.

'Be fair, Douglas,' said Jake, 'how do you *know* he was lying?'

'Because his lips were moving.'

At that very moment – I swear it, that very moment – the phone rang. Gerard, his mouth full to bursting with taco chips, asked Ben to get it.

'Gerard, it's someone asking for Philippe. Who's that?'

'That's me,' smiled the Bad Man as he bounded for the phone to conduct a 'business' conversation with (what he later described as) an 'associate'.

'So why are you now "Philippe", Gerard?'

'That's my middle name.'

'I thought your middle name was Marcel?'

'That's my other middle name.' Then Gerard looked peevish which never fails to crack us all up. 'Since when has it been a crime to have more than one middle name?' Before adding triumphantly, 'Prince Charles has more than one middle name.' QED.

Ben stopped laughing first. 'Prince Charles doesn't use different names to talk to different "associates" and, also, he's not differently moralled.'

Exit Gerard (to fetch more snacks) crestfallen. But he wasn't down for long – he never is – and soon, fortified by 4,000 calories worth of prime poker food, he was playing and gambling (but never folding) with his usual gusto.

In fact, he was the big winner on the night – thanks mainly to this game he learned in the States called Spit In The Ocean. Unusually for a Bad Man-approved game, this doesn't involve wild cards. On the other hand, there's nothing the Bad Man – or, indeed, any poker player – likes better than an edge and what greater edge can there be than to be the only person round the table to have played a game before and to have undergone its learning curve?

Spit In The Ocean – or 'Spit' as Gerard called it with frightening familiarity (did he do *anything* other than play poker while he was in the States? Yes, he probably also played blackjack) – is a cross between draw poker and Hold 'Em. Each player is dealt *four* cards and then there is the all-important communal card which is the fifth card of each hand. There is just one change of as many cards as you want. There are only two rounds of betting (after the deal and after the draw) and the scope for bluffing is immense – hence the Bad Man's interest.

Well, it sure as hell burnt my arse. I'd say that I finished ahead on all the other games (especially four-card Omaha which is 'my' game) but, thanks to Spit (which, needless to say, led to much clearing of the throat and pretend gobbing), I finished about £10 down – that's to say, I declared afterwards that I was £10 up. The £20 discrepancy was put down to Gerard exaggerating his win.

In fact, we all lost – except Nik! At last the man is coming out (nearly) on top just before he heads down under.

SATURDAY, APRIL 17

Went to Henry's. Nothing unusual in that on a Saturday but I'd be a liar if I didn't admit to sprucing myself up. I shaved, splashed on some after-shave and put on fresh clothes – including my tight black jeans which emphasise my tackle but not my gut.

The reason for all this care is, of course, Samantha. I was

expecting to be disappointed – often happens after you build up a person in your mind – but she was looking even fresher-faced and prettier today than she did last Saturday.

There were a few times in the intervening days when I was tempted to have a wank 'over' her (so to speak) but I resisted the urge. My experience – mainly based on my bachelor days – is that once I've wanked over a girl I've not yet fucked, I'll never get to fuck her. The corollary – that if I *don't* wank with her in mind – that I *will* fuck her doesn't always hold true but, even if there's no cause and effect (which there might be) and my theory's just pure superstition and therefore a self-fulfilling prophecy, I decided that Samantha's too gorgeous to risk losing for the sake of a five-finger shuffle.

Unlike last Saturday and emboldened by her evident encouragement, I chatted to her as much as I could. She really is lovely. She's twenty-one and studying history at London University with a view to becoming a teacher so I told her about my experiences as a teacher (omitting all references to breakdowns) and how rewarding/fulfilling/draining/undervalued the profession is and felt that we really struck up a rapport.

I filled in the time between chatting to/up Samantha gambling. Tim was there, as usual, but he's distant, almost offish – as though he's got something to hide. I tried to get him to do some gambling with me but he didn't want to know.

It was a shame really because I was testing two new systems. The first was one Jim from work gave me. He reckons that backing second favourites each-way in fields of eight to twelve runners yields a profit. Sounds a bit simplistic to me but he works in accounts and has a good brain so it seemed worth trying.

The other system I was testing is one I got from my neighbour Gerry who, touching the side of his nose in insider-information-mode (which is frankly absurd behaviour for an advertising account executive), told me that betting on three-year-olds who won their first race as two-year-olds but none of their others is a fine idea because a) it 'proves' they run best when fresh and b) they'll be a big price. He says that this only works now, for the first month of the flat season. Sounds tonto to me but any system is better than none (i.e. mine) and I decided to run it in parallel with Jim's.

Amazingly enough, on the races that the systems covered, I made a profit of precisely £21.06 (on an outlay of £300 plus tax). OK, it's not *that* exciting but a profit's a profit and it did allow me to spend time with darling little Samantha. Unfortunately, the other races – the ones not covered by the systems – lost me in excess of £100, so it's stick to the systems (and, if truth be known, die of boredom) or carry on as I am (and die at the end of the year). Nice choice.

Knowing that I was going to be at Henry's for most of the afternoon, I placed my spread-betting trades before I left home. I didn't really trouble the scorers, except in the Liverpool game where my hunch that it would be a rough game paid dividends to the tune of £140. So I finished sixty quid up on the day. Pretty good, especially considering all the pleasure I derived. I also enjoyed the gambling.

MONDAY, APRIL 19

I dreamed about Cathy last night. It was such a powerful dream that I awoke in a muck sweat convinced that it had all really happened. I dreamed that I went to Cathy's house in Reading (which had turned into a municipal swimming-pool) only to find her mother (whom I always liked) blocking the entrance. 'You can't come in, Steve, she's life-saving Mike.' 'He doesn't need her, I do!' I shrieked but Cathy's mum said, 'Cathy can only save one life at a time, Steve, and it's Mike's!'

Most dreams evaporate within seconds of waking up but this one stayed with me through my shit, shower, shave and breakfast. It sounds paranoid but it was almost as though Cathy was punishing me for thinking of Samantha. As though, if she, Cathy, doesn't want me, then she'll make sure that I can't have anyone else. I don't know. I'm as sceptical as the next man (provided the next man isn't Uri Geller) but it was such a powerful dream that I found myself wondering whether it wasn't a 'sign' or something.

Crap, of course, and fortunately, it was only a fleeting thought. Nevertheless, on the strength of it, I rearranged my schedule so that at five o'clock I found myself driving west on the M4 towards Reading.

I was sitting outside Cathy's house when she got back from work. I got out of the car.

'Cathy!'

'What? Steve, what the hell are you doing here?' Surprise turning to anger.

God she's beautiful. Intoxicating, that's what she is. 'Cathy, please . . .'

'I have nothing to say to you.' She ran to her front door, fishing her house keys out of her bag as she did so.

'Cathy, please . . .'

'Look,' she screamed angrily not even looking at me, 'Get out of my life!' The contents of her bag flew over her garden path.

'Cathy . . .'

'I'm going to scream "Rape" if you don't leave this minute.'

I paused and then said, softly and deliberately, 'Go on then.'

She looked at me piercingly over her shoulder and then, turning towards me, she cocked her head to one side and said in a (slightly) more conciliatory tone. 'OK, Steve, what is it you want?'

I was speechless.

'You see,' she said, more in exasperation than in anger, 'you don't even know.'

'You,' I said weakly, 'I want you.'

'No, you don't, Steve.' She sounded almost tender. 'You want the me of fifteen years ago.' She hushed my protest. 'And if I wanted you at all – which I most definitely don't – I'd want the Steve of those days too. I'm with Mike now, we're happy. You're married, aren't you? You've got children, haven't you? Aren't you happy?'

'Yes . . . no, I don't know. I just want to know I can *talk* to you. Is that unreasonable?'

'No, it's not "unreasonable", Steve,' even in the pain, it was great to hear her using my name: of course I was concentrating on what she was saying but there was a part of me trying to memorise the way she said 'Steve'. 'But you know what happens. It starts with an occasional phone call – which is fine – and it ends up with you phoning every day. That's why I had to get my solicitor to write to you.' I looked embarrassed. 'So it's best for both of us, for all of us, if we just don't have any contact at all.'

As she was talking, I was aware of someone behind me but I was too intent on listening to her to turn round. In the event, it was Cathy who acknowledged the third party's presence by saying, 'Don't worry, Mike, I'm handling this.'

Mike, taller than me, younger than me and, if it came to it, stronger than me, stood there glowering at me. I returned the stare, determined not to be the first to look away. 'Honestly, Mike,' said Cathy coming between us but putting her arm around his waist, 'it's OK.'

Without taking his eyes off me, he said, 'Uh huh.'

I looked over to Cathy – damn, I was the first to look away – and then back to him, 'This is between Cathy and me, it's nothing to do with you.'

'If it concerns Cathy, it concerns me.'

Fuck off, plod. 'Listen, Cathy and I were together before she even knew you existed . . .'

'I don't care what you was . . .' jerk can't even speak proper English '. . . but she's with me now and you've been bothering her.'

'Mike, please . . .'

'Shut it!' Who the fuck does he think he is, Jack Regan of The Sweeney? But, amazingly, she demurred. She wasn't so submissive in my day: she must like being told what to do by her piece of rough. 'If I see you round here again or if you phone just one more time then I'm going to have you! Do I make myself clear?'

If I'm honest, I found him physically intimidating, so I tried to back off without losing face with Cathy. I sort of nodded while walking backwards to my car. Out of the corner of my eye, I could see Cathy going into the house, dabbing her eyes with a tissue.

Was she crying for me? Or for herself, forced to live with this Neanderthal creep?

He was still eyeballing me as I climbed into my car and drove off as quickly as I could. Then I slowed down. The cunt's probably friends with the traffic cops.

I was all right on the journey home. I was angry with him and shocked with her so I boosted my self-esteem by telling myself that two against one were impossible odds and that he was attacking me against her wishes. But by the time I got home, the encounter itself had receded leaving me only with the result, with the cold, desperate truth: that there is no future for Cathy and me – not in any shape, size or form.

Later, as I lay in the bath pondering the events of the day, I suddenly understood one thing with absolute clarity. I want to die. I want to kill myself. I want to end it all right now. Not because I can't have Cathy (well, not just because of that) but because I can't keep making compromises with myself.

I'll carry on with 'the bet' but I really don't care if I win or lose. No, that's not true, I *do* care: I hope I lose.

TUESDAY, APRIL 20

Bloody Cathy. To think I'll never see her again. Bloody Maggie. To think I'm stuck with her.

Betted mechanically and soullessly in a bookie's and won three hundred quid. Did likewise on the televised football and won another four hundred and sixty quid. Perhaps that's how to win money: not to care one way or the other. No, that's not true: I *want* to lose now – *that's* how to win.

WEDNESDAY, APRIL 21

It's odd but I'm experiencing something akin to relief vis-à-vis Cathy at the moment. It's possible that it's only temporary relief but it's also entirely possible that a cloud has lifted.

I didn't lose Cathy on Monday: I lost her years ago – not even in 1987 but before that. I'd come to terms with that by 1990. What's happened in the past couple of months is a sort of vestigial lunacy caused, I suspect, by the bet, exacerbated by my 'crisis' and prompted by Phil sending me to Reading. All of these factors conspired to send me over the edge reason-wise and Cathy-wise and turn me into some sort of stalker. But I've done that now and (I think) I can honestly say that it's out of my system.

It took Gerard, of all people, to put my little local difficulty into perspective. If I thought I had problems, they're nothing compared to his, as I discovered when I phoned him to check the arrangements for Friday. I thought he sounded a little less chipper than he usually does and asked him if everything was OK. He insisted – too emphatically – that he was fine, so I pressed him.

'Well, I have had a little hassle.'

Gerard's idea of 'a little hassle' would be enough to totally freak out a normal human being.

It turns out that the Bad Man has been betting with someone called John he met at a backgammon club. When I say 'betting', I don't mean one-on-one card or dice games, I mean betting in the sense of using this John as a bookmaker. The way Gerard tells it, it's a perfectly common – and legitimate – arrangement to avoid having to pay betting tax.

'You know, Gerard, you should use a legitimate spread-betting firm, there's no tax to pay on spread bets anyway.'

'Yes, I know, but I've been using him for ordinary bets which are tax deductible.'

'But didn't you worry that he wouldn't pay up if you won?' I asked, unable to hide my incredulity.

'I realise that now but I didn't think of it then – particularly as John also gives me tips.'

'Hang on, Gerard, let me get up to speed. This guy John sells you tips and then you *bet* with him?'

'Almost. He *gives* me tips and then I bet with him.'

For all his swagger, Gerard can be incredibly naive. Sometimes I wonder whether he shouldn't give someone power of attorney over his affairs.

The facts – in so far as one can believe *anything* the Bad Man says – are as follows.

The Bad Man takes John's football tip and does a spread bet with him based upon it. At the same time, he places a golf accumulator (despite knowing nothing about golf – 'It was a tip in the *Racing Post*') also with John.

Gerard loses £2,900 on the football spread-bet but wins £4,000 on the golf accumulator. In a well-ordered world, John would hand over £1,100. Ah, but any world boasting Gerard as one of its citizens is, by definition, not well-ordered. John has a record of the losing spread bet but not – 'Even though he admits that he remembers me placing it' – of the winning accumulator.

Shades of a Mexican stand-off; I am intrigued to find out what happened next.

'My view is that if he pays me what he owes me then I'd happily pay him what I owe him.' Er, yes, Gerard. 'It's the third time it's happened with this man.'

'What is?'

'That he's tried to knock me.'

My jaw drops with amazement. 'So why do you bother with him?'

Gerard shrugs and continues with his narrative. 'John turns up at the door of my house because he knows I have a backgammon game at home every Wednesday.' I didn't know that: they must be absolute scuzzballs if Gerard hasn't invited me to come over – I know he thinks of me as one of his more 'respectable' friends. 'I leave the front door open on Wednesdays so I'm not disturbed when I'm playing.' I bet he does. 'And John walks straight in and demands I pay him for the spread bet.'

'So what did you do, Bad Man?'

'I grabbed him by the arm, twisted it and marched him out. I told him if he pestered me again, he'd regret it. I think he was really worried that I'd kick the crap out of him.

'The next day I got a call from a bloke saying "I'm John's backer and you'd better pay up or else." I just put the phone down on him.

'Then, a couple of days later, I'm playing poker in this casino'

– does the Bad Man ever *not* gamble? – 'when this big black bloke comes up to me and whispers in my ear that he's John's backer and that he wants me to go outside. I tell him to get lost or I'll tell the management and he eventually disappears. When he does go, I ask the casino for his name and address. They tell me that they can't divulge that sort of thing so I tell them that this man threatened me on their premises and that if they don't give me his details, I'll call in the police. So they told me everything I wanted to know. But anyway he was just small potatoes, so I wasn't bothered.

'A few days later, another bloke came round to my place. He looked a lot more serious than the first bloke. I told him that not only did I not owe John anything but that he owed *me* eleven hundred pounds. He said, "If I find out you're lying, you're dead" and then left.

'The next day, I'm awoken at six in the morning by the sound of my windows being smashed in. Then the phone goes. It's John telling me that next time it'll be more serious. So I phoned the police. A Detective Constable came round but his attitude was pretty crappy – he recommended I move home, so I said, "Right, I want to speak to the Chief Constable".' Bless. Only Gerard can bet illegally and then threaten a DC with the Chief Constable.

Nevertheless, it must have worked – although I only have Gerard's word for any of this – as a Detective Inspector came round and took some details. 'I told him everything but I changed the facts – I told him that it was a private bet and John had threatened to petrol bomb me.'

Apparently, the CID sent four officers round to John's place and took him off to the cells for twenty-four hours where he was told in no uncertain terms not to bother Gerard again.

The coda to this story is that Gerard met a friend of John's in the course of a gamblingfest and told him that he went to school with a CID bloke and that, if John winds him up again, the CID will break into his place at five a.m. and find some drugs there and he'll go to prison for twenty years.

'Hee hee,' says the Bad Man with glee, obviously feeling relieved for having shared his story (*le mot juste*?) with me.

I was left with the conclusion that, impossible as it may sound, the Bad Man has found an even worse man than him and that the moral low ground is extremely crowded.

THURSDAY, APRIL 22

Maggie has, at last, agreed to sign the new mortgage forms. She did it with as little grace as possible but at least she did it.

'I'll never forgive you for this,' she said with hatred.

I retreated into platitude. 'I'm sorry, Maggie, it's just one of those things. There are many men who are worse than me; there are many women who are worse off than you.'

'Don't try to justify it, Steven, don't ever try to justify it.'

She went out the door and then out the house. Fuck her, I've had enough. Yeah, I'm sorry that I've lost money – believe me, bitch, I'm more sorry than you are – but that's life, that's me. Whatever Maggie loves about me (if anything) is only the other side of the coin which has gambling as its flip side. Love me, darling, love my faults. I'm not asking you to love me because of them but, if I'm going to stay with you (and, boy, is that a big if), then you're at least going to have to love me in spite of them. Like I love you in spite of the fact that you're quite possibly the most *boring* woman in the world. No, that's wrong: you're not the most boring woman in the world as the most boring woman in the world would be, by dint of her title, an interesting person to meet. You're the *second* most boring woman in the world, Maggie, that's what you are and I'll give up gambling the day that you give up boring for England.

As always when I've had a row with Maggie or, worse, needed a row and not had one, I spent more money gambling than I would otherwise have done.

Five hundred quid I got through in half-an-hour in a Purley bookie's. That's what happens when bookies take Switch bets. That's what happens when you bet on four favourites and *none* of them come in. That's what happens when you're on tilt.

FRIDAY, APRIL 23

Poker at Gerard's. It's become our Friday night ritual – not just playing poker but playing poker at the Bad Man's. And it always starts in exactly the same way. I arrive first and make derogatory comments about the state of cleanliness in Gerard's house. Gerard and I consume a one-kilo bag of nacho chips (he eats 800 grams to my 200) while we play backgammon. By the time the next person arrives, I have lost about fifty quid. It would be less but Gerard has bored me into submission with tales of his derring-do in the bedroom, the boardroom and, inevitably, the casino. By the time I can get my mind back on to the game, he has doubled, I have beavered and he is taking off pieces: sometimes as few as four at a time. Not that he needs to cheat for there is no question – especially in his mind – that he is a better backgammon player than me.

There were eight of us tonight – too many for my liking – because besides the six regulars and Nathan, Douglas had brought along a fellow named Roy who glories in the nickname 'Rowdy' because he is incapable (as we later discover for ourselves) of hearing the words 'Hold 'Em' without singing the theme tune to *Rawhide* (in which Clint Eastwood played Rowdy Yates – hence the nickname). As Ben pointed out when he heard the reason for Rowdy Roy's nomenclature, 'There's nothing like a great poker nickname and this is nothing like a great poker nickname'.

Douglas has a neat line on poker nicknames. He reckons you should never sit down at the poker table with a guy named after a city (e.g. Dallas Pete) or a man named Doc.

Douglas also provided the (non-poker) surprise of the evening. The conversation at the table turned to polygamy and thence to Mormonism. Quite how we got from 'You dragged twenty-four pounds, so you have to give me that much before we can split the pot' to 'Poor bastards, fancy putting up with all those mothers-in-law,' I don't know, although such conversational flights are not uncommon at the poker table: women, being more mature than men are perfectly capable of just talking for an evening – men have to have a displacement activity (e.g. poker) before we can do the same.

Anyway, I was just putting in my two penn'orth of considered conversation, when Douglas, quietly but firmly, brought me up short.

'You don't know what you're talking about, Steve.'

'Hang on, Douglas, I think I know more than you do about Mormonism, I once saw a film about Joseph Smith.'

'Well, that's dandy, Steve, but I used to be a Mormon missionary.'

Talk about a conversation stopper, this even stopped the poker.

We pumped Douglas for more information and he told us that it all started with his mother in California. His father was in jail (something else I didn't know) and his mother was looking after Douglas, his elder brother (now a fire chief) and their baby sister. Tragically, the baby died and his mother, a Catholic, turned to the priest for comfort. However, he told her that because the baby hadn't been baptised, it would stay in limbo for ever. Not exactly the comfort Douglas's mother was looking for.

Living next door to them at the time was a Mormon and he did offer them comfort and spiritual solace and so the family embraced his religion, Douglas particularly. When he was twenty-one, he was sent abroad for a year to China to spread the word as a missionary.

Understandably, this led to (more than) a few jibes along the lines of 'missionary' and 'position' and someone dragged out that girl (Joyce McKinney, I think her name was) who kidnapped a Mormon missionary and asked Douglas whether that ever happened to him etc. It was all very good natured and Douglas took it in the same spirit. He reckons that he's still a Mormon although he doesn't exactly live the lifestyle. Nevertheless, he is adamant (and who are we to gainsay him?) that polygamy no longer plays a part in (official) Mormonism.

This epic distraction served to put me off my game and make me lose – although it could have been equally caused by my stubborn refusal to fold. Indeed, the only time I did fold – holding a pair of kings in a game of seven-card stud (nothing wild) – Jake scooped the pot with a pair of 3s. Like one of Pavlov's dogs, this helped to further condition me to see anyone who couldn't actually beat me on the table.

By the end of the evening, I was £360 down having given markers to Douglas and to Gerard who were the only winners.

I know I treat poker as a bit of light relief from the rest of my life but the amount I lose playing it is no laughing matter and it could, if it continues, actually jeopardise my life. Given how much poker means to me, it would be fucking ironic if I lost the bet by less than I lost at poker during the year.

SATURDAY, APRIL 24

Went to Henry's and stuck around long enough to ask Samantha if, in principle, she'd come out for a drink with me. She said yes, next Saturday, after work. Result!

I placed a few bets at Henry's which, thanks to a 100–30 winner, showed me a profit of £200 but I saved most of my betting energy for spread betting on the horses.

I bought the favourites at Sandown and sold the double card numbers at Leicester. This, together with two successful match bets on individual races which made up at the fifteen-length maximum, helped me win a further £325. That's a profit of £525 on the day which will more than pay for drinks next Saturday. Not to mention a hotel room.

SUNDAY, APRIL 25

Did a few sundry trades on the televised football – it really does 'heighten your viewing pleasure' like the ad claims. I bought corners at 12 for £50 a corner, sold bookings at 44 for £20, bought the time of the last goal at 63 for £30 and bought the total goals at 2.7 for £10 a 'tick' (i.e. £100 a whole goal).

There were sixteen corners (plus £200), the booking index made up at 80 (plus £720), the last goal was scored in the eightieth minute (plus £510) and there were two goals (minus £70) making a winning total of £1,360 – my biggest win ever!

TUESDAY, APRIL 27

Didn't have time to go to the bookie's yesterday or today so I went home via the casino. Place was deserted, as if every foreign scuzzbucket were out of town at a symposium on scowling, stinking of garlic, leering at waitresses and blowing cigarette smoke in strangers' faces. Not that any of them seem to need any help.

As a mathematician, I have no time for superstition; as a gambler, I have little time for reason. So I watched the first three spins just to see how the wheel was behaving: 4, 8 and 9. Figuring that there wouldn't be four spins in a row in the first third, I split all my chips (£600 worth) on the second and third thirds and was mightily relieved when the ball stopped on 17.

For the next six spins, I split my chips (just the original £600) on two of the three thirds, pocketing all the winnings. By the time I eventually lost (on the sixth turn), I had made a profit of £1,800 (that's to say £300 per spin).

That was the point when I should have left.

I know this now because I know what happened to me. Unfortunately, I didn't know it then. As the French say, 'If the young only knew; if the old only could' and a couple of hours in a casino counts as an age.

Because I had enjoyed some success, I took it into my head that I was on some sort of lucky streak. This is, of course, nonsense. There isn't the lucky streak invented or experienced which didn't eventually come to an end: the only question is how long it lasts. The answer in my case is the six spins it took me to treble my money followed by the eight spins it took me to lose it.

The really annoying thing was that, unlike other times when I've over-ridden my luck, I was actually playing *more* conservatively after I was ahead than before by only betting on even money chances but nothing (and I mean *nothing*) came off for me. If I bet on low, red and odd, it came up high, black and even. And vice-versa. Even the croupier was clucking sympathetically.

Ordinarily, when I lose, I feel sick but there was no way I was going to leave that casino without getting something for my money. So I crammed huge amounts of free food – hummus, spicy lamb, halva etc. – down my gob and left. True, I now felt *genuinely* sick but at least I'd got myself a free (only £600) meal.

THURSDAY, APRIL 29

This is just what I don't need at the moment. Maggie's mother's just been diagnosed as having cancer. Apparently, it's inoperable which means that she is going to die – some time within the next six months.

Maggie is devastated. She and her mother have had their ups and downs over the years but they are extremely close.

Naturally, I've been doing all I can to cheer her up and I suppose I'll have to be extra nice/attentive/supportive for as long as it takes.

The only good thing is that it's completely taken Maggie's mind off such trivial matters as unpaid bills and the second mortgage. It's at times like this that one gets a proper sense of perspective about what *really* matters. It's an ill wind . . .

FRIDAY, APRIL 30

Gerard is in jail. I can hardly believe it but, it's true, he's been sentenced to nine months for housing-benefit fraud.

I didn't even know he'd been charged – none of us did. The first that any of us knew about the whole thing was when Jake got a call from Gerard asking him to go to court with him this morning. I don't know why he asked Jake rather than someone else – perhaps because he knows that Jake is self-employed and can take time off whenever he likes.

I'm shocked, I really am. I can't believe I didn't know or guess that something was up: it shows how furtive Gerard can be. And now he's in Wormwood Scrubs, sharing a cell with who knows how many other men – *really* bad men – and with who knows what sort of toilet arrangements. Poor Gerard.

Stupid Gerard. At least that's what Jake says. The facts, as far as he can make out, are as follows: Gerard's house belongs to his brother. Gerard claimed housing benefit while renting out rooms. Gerard got caught several weeks ago and was bailed until his trial today. It's not the crime of the century and there's every chance that, given his previous good form, Gerard would have escaped with a bit of community service and/or a 'bender' (i.e. a suspended sentence).

Except that, in his infinite wisdom, Gerard decided to conduct his own defence.

They say that a lawyer who represents himself has a fool for a client but that's nothing compared to the folly of Gerard defending himself.

The way Jake tells it – and there's no reason to doubt *his* accuracy or veracity – Gerard pleaded not guilty on the basis that the whole thing was purely a bureaucratic mistake in that he only claimed the housing benefit that was due to him in his *last* home that he hadn't bothered to collect. As a plea in mitigation it would be pathetic but, as a defence, it was a complete joke. Even after he was found guilty, Gerard refused to bow the knee and was busy shouting the odds to the (one has to say) poor judge.

So Gerard was sent down for nine months.

Sitting in the wine bar with Jake, Douglas and Ben, we mulled over Gerard's fate. Obviously, we all feel desperately sorry for him but we're also bloody annoyed with him for being such a total fuckwit. Only Gerard . . .

One of us (I'm ashamed to say it was me) suggested a game of poker as it's Friday night and it's what Gerard would have wanted etc. etc. but I got voted down – not on the grounds of bad timing or taste – but because the poker chips are at Gerard's place.

* * *

Not that it matters (by comparison with what Gerard's going through) but I finished the month £900 up which means that I'm only £1,100 down on the year which, given the tens of thousands I've spent gambling, is quite extraordinary.

Yesterday, Maggie's mother, today it's Gerard. Given that bad news comes in threes, I'm frightened to go to sleep tonight for fear of what tomorrow might bring.

SATURDAY, MAY 1

10.00am. Poor old Gerard.

I didn't sleep well last night. He's not my best friend but I couldn't help thinking about Gerard all alone in his jail cell. Or worse, *not* alone in his jail cell ('Come here. Frenchie, you're *my* baby now.'). Jake says he'll be transferred to an open prison very soon but it won't come soon enough for the Bad Man.

It's certainly got me thinking about my own miscellaneous dodgy deeds which are, I suppose, limited to fiddling my expenses. Just as well, as I don't think I'd have what it takes to survive in prison: I'm not physically strong, financially strong or sexually ambiguous and, from what I've heard, you've got to be one out of three to survive. Perhaps that's why I *don't* commit serious crimes. Also, there's a class thing here: barring the odd bent lawyer or accountant, middle-class guys don't do porridge. I've known one or two blokes who've been inside – a board man in a bookie's I used to frequent, a barman from my local – but they're acquaintances and not friends. And notwithstanding his 'different morals' and his scams, Gerard is indisputably middle-class. We're the people in whose interests criminals are caught and punished.

Poor old Gerard.

He likes to think of himself as a 'made man' but he rarely fools anyone who's known him longer than a minute. He's so obvious, he might as well wear a t-shirt saying 'COUNT YOUR FINGERS'. He's the light relief masquerading as the heavy masquerading as the hero; Peter Lorre trying to be Sydney Greenstreet trying to be Humphrey Bogart. He belongs in a suburban theme bar not in a maximum-security institution. The only person who needs protecting from Gerard is Gerard. If he's committed a crime at all – and there's enough proof to suggest that his only offence is to have got up the nose of the judge – then it's pretty victimless.

Poor old Gerard.

Still, everyone goes to hell in his own way and I've got my own furrow to plough. I have to say I'm feeling pretty good and not a little optimistic about 'the bet'. Brecht defined an optimist as someone who hasn't heard the bad news but it's possible – and it's not just the Prozac coursing around my veins talking – to be buoyant without being fucking Pollyanna. There are gamblers who win; there are bookies who lose. There's sun after rain and rain after sun – it's a cycle – and, at the moment I'm near the top of the revolution. Yes, it will go down but it will take me back up again.

Nevertheless, my *joie de vivre* was enough to defy even old Bertolt. A good night's sleep, a cuddle with the kids, the prospect of an afternoon's gambling topped off by a date with Samantha: life doesn't get much better. If only I could tell Maggie about how (and why) I feel so good. Trouble is I want her as a mother (which is how so many of my friends treat their wives, coming home from work to eat their supper and go straight out again to indulge in adolescent pursuits) and she wants me as a husband. Tough tit, darling, you should have married a man rather than a boy while I should have married a girl instead of a woman, which is what Maggie, to be fair to her, has always been. We got together when I needed her and that served as the template for our whole relationship. I *need* her but I don't particularly *want* her. As far as I'm concerned, I only want Maggie when I need her and when I don't need her, I don't want her. I'm not especially proud of it but it's the way that it is. And if it means that we don't go the distance then so be it: one in three marriages ends in divorce – what makes our marriage so special?

* * *

10.00pm. It's twelve hours later and I'm feeling fucking elated. I'm more elated than Mr Elated on a particularly good . . . shit, I can't do that *Blackadder* stuff but I can say it doesn't get much better than this.

Spent the afternoon watching the racing on TV. I was going to go down to Henry's but, given that I was going to be meeting Samantha at six, I thought it best not to – don't want to fuck up in any way. So instead I did several trades on all three televised meetings. At the end of a fabulous afternoon's racing, I was richer to the tune of £974.50!

Consequently, I had a huge spring in my step when I slipped out – on the pretext of meeting Douglas for a drink (hope he doesn't phone while I'm out!) – to pick up Samantha.

My timing was excellent. She was just leaving the shop as I arrived. I caught Henry's eye behind the counter and I swear there was a glint in it but he said nothing and neither did I.

Samantha – 'Please don't call me Sam' – looked gorgeous, even after a day at work. We then had to decide where to go as, incredibly, I hadn't given it any thought – as if to pre-plan anything would jeopardise everything. Knowing I was going to drink, I didn't want to drive (although with nine points on my fucking licence I've hardly got anything to lose) but I didn't think it was a good idea to go anywhere local in case we were spotted by a neighbour or someone and they told Maggie.

So we took a cab into town to a really good upmarket pub I know in the West End. The conversation in the cab was light, even impersonal, but our eyes belied our words. Even the most anodyne sentence was transformed into something magical and precious as her eyes sparkled with excitement and pleasure.

In the pub we drank (she was on lagers, I was on gin and tonics) and laughed and chatted and laughed and looked at each other and laughed and held hands in a non-corny, unselfconscious approximation of two teenagers on a first date. Then we laughed some more. It's not that she's got such a great sense of humour (and, for all that I can be witty, I don't – unlike, say, Douglas – have 'funny bones'), it's just that she makes everything seem so . . . I don't know . . . *light*. She's the human equivalent of the froth on a cappuccino. Not that she's thick or anything – she's actually extremely intelligent – there's just nothing subterranean, no darkness of the soul.

In fact she's *so* damn lovely that I found myself loath to (try to) get her into bed. So I didn't. I'd told her that I was married with children, albeit that my relationship with Maggie was a non-sexual one (which it more or less is) and after we'd been in the pub a couple of hours, I told her I had to go home which she accepted without explanation. I offered her a cab ride home but she said that she wanted to stay in town and perhaps visit a friend. Oh to be single again.

As we parted, I kissed her on the lips. It wasn't quite as wonderful as (in the five minutes leading up to it) I'd hoped it would be because although her lips parted slightly, she didn't offer her tongue and so it didn't turn into the French kiss I was expecting. On the other hand, because I didn't (as, once upon a time I would have done) try to ram my tongue down her throat there was no embarrassment attached to it.

'Can I see you again?' I asked her as I climbed into the taxi.

'Next Saturday,' she replied, tilting her head deliciously.

'In the bookie's or afterwards?'

'Both, if you like.'

I am on cloud fucking nine.

MONDAY, MAY 3

Maybe I'm still lightheaded, maybe I just had to give something back: I don't know but I popped into a bookie's and in just twenty minutes I lost £600 – over half of what I won on Saturday.

I was doing my progressive losing system. I started with £40 on the favourite in a dog race. It lost so I put £80 on the favourite in a horse race. When this too lost I put £160 on the favourite in another horse race and when *that* lost I put £300 on the favourite in a dog race. Once again I lost and so I managed to get through £600.

The thinking wasn't stupid: in any four races (horse or dog) the favourite *usually* comes in at least once: in fact, the odds are one in three and the great thing about backing favourites like this rather than even-money casino chances is that a favourite can come in at much more lucrative odds like 2–1 or 11–4. Indeed, if I'd continued long enough, eventually a favourite would have come in somewhere. Unfortunately, I didn't have enough time, enough money and, above all, enough balls to wait long enough. One of these days though . . .

TUESDAY, MAY 4

Samantha, Samantha, Samantha. Once again, I find myself doodling her name at every (safe) opportunity. Am I a complete kid or what?

FRIDAY, MAY 7

Our first poker session (at Ben's, which stopped Ben turning up late) since Gerard was sent down. To start with, we were all a little edgy, a bit strained, as though we were at – if not a funeral – then a memorial service. 'Good old Gerard, wish he could be here,' that sort of thing.

The news from the penal front is excellent: Gerard is being moved to Ford Open next week (or Club Bad Man, as Ben puts it). Apparently, the Scrubs wasn't *too* terrible although Gerard was obliged to point out to one yobbo that he (Gerard) has a black belt in karate. It's the first I've ever heard of it but the funny thing is, knowing Gerard, he probably has.

The poker was terrific – much better than I anticipated – though all of us agreed that four (Ben, Douglas, Jake and I) is two too few. Douglas was on absolute top form. The fact that he had a huge pile of (our) chips in front of him could have had something to do with it. This, of course, meant that every time one of us needed more of the smaller denomination chips we were obliged to get them off him.

'Change me please, Douglas,' one of us would say tossing him a £20 chip.

'OK,' he would respond before counting out £20-worth of £1 and £5 chips, 'you're a nice guy.' It was funny for, gosh, maybe the first four or five times and then, it has to be said, it began to pall.

Nevertheless, this was not the extent of Douglas's repertoire this evening. Someone (it might have been me) was complaining about his wife to which Douglas, with more than a little feeling, commented, 'Women, huh? Can't live without them; can't shoot them.'

He's also got this unbelievable-but-I-have-to-say-effective trick of asking an opponent 'Do you have a good hand?' when he's deciding whether or not to call. He fixes you with his eyes and you find yourself trying to look like someone who has a) got a lousy hand (when you've got a good hand) or b) got a good hand (when you're bluffing). Either way, you end up completely wrong-footed so it is extremely effective.

Ben, evidently the self-appointed keeper of Gerard's flame, was guzzling poker food and betting recklessly, even before he started on the beers. I was going to point out to him the causation link between him drinking and going on tilt but then thought better of it: if we were playing tennis instead of poker (especially if we were playing for money) I wouldn't give him tips on how to improve his serve, would I?

Jake was his usual, infuriating steady self. It really, really, *really* pisses me off to see him fold his first two cards in five-card stud when I'm sitting there with a (concealed) pair. It's not even as if he knows that I've got a pair, he's just playing his fucking steady percentage game and folding two low(ish) non-suited cards. It beats me how he can be so controlled. He must be the most extraordinary lover. Or maybe that self-control makes him a bad lover. I don't know. Hell, perhaps that trait has nothing to do with his sex life. I don't really know that much about Jake's sex life. I've met a few of his girlfriends and they've all looked pretty fit but he's not what you might call a talker. As far as I know, there's never been anyone serious which is extraordinary for a forty-year-old but then living at home with your parents – as Jake still does – isn't necessarily conducive to long-term relationships. I don't know. Jake's not at all religious or anything but he's a Hindu and maybe when it comes to things like marriage, it has an atavistic pull on him.

Meanwhile, I don't give a fuck about the man's lovelife: I just wish he'd stop being so bloody cautious. Except, of course, when I'm bluffing and he calls me as he so often does. Having said that, I caught him out once or twice, cradling the little finger of his left hand before biting the nail, his tell-tale sign that he's bluffing. Unfortunately, it didn't do me any good as he took fright at my too-large counter-bluff. Still, it was good to nail his foray into *my* territory.

The Gerard Memorial Game ended before midnight because Ben decided he'd lost enough and, even though he said we could stay, Jake refused to play three-handed.

Douglas won £350 (actually £460), Jake won £100, I lost £200 (actually £240) and Ben lost £250 (actually £320). Doing the maths does even my head in. If schools genuinely wanted to prepare their pupils for life, they would offer Poker Maths alongside Pure and Applied Maths as A-Level choices.

SATURDAY, MAY 8

11.00am. Today's the FA Cup final and I intend to cover almost every angle in spread-betting trades.

Ordinarily, I'd have gone to Henry's as well – especially as my Derby horse is racing in a trial today – but I *think* I want to avoid Samantha today.

I know I sort of arranged to meet her after work but the truth is I'm still feeling a bit unsure about her – not because of adultery or anything like that (what Maggie doesn't know about can't bother her) but because what I like most about Samantha is her freshness and the one thing that a relationship with her would, by its very happening, destroy (not for her but for *me*) is her freshness. It reminds me of that thing that Quentin Crisp (or

John Hurt) says in *The Naked Civil Servant* about his ideal man being a rugged heterosexual who couldn't possibly *be* his ideal man because the moment he responded to Crisp, he would *ipso facto* not be a heterosexual. So maybe I'll let the Samantha thing wither away on the vine: remember it for what it was, a wonderful interlude, a magical promise. Maybe in a parallel universe, we'd have ridden off into the sunset together. And then there's Melanie and Jonathan to think of. Although, for the life of me, I can't see what Samantha and I have got to do with them: if Maggie were to find out about Samantha and me that should be *her* problem, not theirs. However, there's an eternity of suffering between the words *should* and *would*.

So I backed my Derby tip at 15–2 for £100 on the nose using my Switch card and, incredibly, wonderfully, fabulously, deliciously, astoundingly, it WON! And I paid the tax! That's £741 pure profit. Wish I'd been in Henry's – I could have shared it with someone like Tim (except he's being so offish at the moment) or Henry (except it would have been his money I'd have won) or Samantha (except that I would have immediately suggested celebrating with her). Oh well, perhaps I don't wish I'd been at Henry's (except that it's so damn lonely betting – or, at least, *winning* – on my own).

Then it was time for the Cup Final. As a match, it was pretty boring – to be honest, I'm no longer that much of a footie fan: now they pay players so much as a basic wage, they no longer have that much incentive to play for their win bonuses – but as a betting vehicle/medium it was superb. I bought the corners at 12 for £50 (Wembley's a big ground), sold the bookings at 43 for £20 (for the referee this is the pinnacle of his career: he doesn't want to mar it by making lots of bookings and he certainly doesn't want to send anyone off – viz the fact that Gazza wasn't sent off when he made that horrendous challenge just before he broke his leg) and sold the hotshots at 33 for £20 (it's usually the unexpected players who score in F.A. Cup finals).

There were fifteen corners (plus £150), three bookings (plus £260) and *no* hotshots scored (plus £660). That makes a total of £1,070 and, of course, there's no fucking tax.

That's a grand total of £1,811 on the day. At the risk of upsetting the gambling gods, EASY! EASY! EASY!

SUNDAY, MAY 9

4.00pm. Maggie's friend Pauline is round again. God I hate her and her pained, pinched face with its disdainful, scornful eyes. Worse still, *she* thinks she looks like Michelle Pfeiffer. She doesn't but she's one of those women who *could* be attractive – even beautiful – if they weren't so full of . . . I don't know . . . nastiness. I've met many women who are uglier than her but who are a damn sight more attractive and appealing because they *want* to be. But it's not only her appearance, it's also her knee-jerk liberal-but-there-is-no-non-fascist-alternative views and the vibes she puts out that make her so incredibly loathsome. She's the living embodiment of the saying that 'beauty is skin deep but ugliness goes right to the bone'. She also sits in *my* chair.

Maggie adores her for the same reason I can't stand her. It reminds me of that scene in *Annie Hall* where Woody Allen and Diane Keaton are each asked by their psychiatrist how often they have sex ('Three times a week – hardly ever'; 'three times a week – all the time'): Maggie would say that Pauline knows her own mind and is wonderful; I would say that Pauline knows her own mind and is loathsome.

I hate her for her right-on predictable views – many of which I happen to share – and her slavish obedience to humourless PC orthodoxy. Example: she's forty and unmarried and so decided to have a baby by artificial insemination. Example: she gave up smoking and drinking during pregnancy but was still working twelve hours a day and doing advanced aerobics during what the Americans call the third trimester of her pregnancy. Example: I know she's not but she does satisfy more than enough *prima facie* criteria to be a dyke. Consider the following evidence:

Never wears make-up
Never wears skirts or frocks
Lives without a man
Has a job

Has own opinions
Doesn't fancy me (mind you, that makes Maggie a dyke too)

OK, so she isn't a lesbian – I know this because she's always going on about wanting to 'fuck guys' (her words), as though her stridency wouldn't defy even Viagra – but I wouldn't mind who (or what) she fucked, except I think she's making Maggie more – yawn – *assertive*. Tell-tale signs of this include:

Reading *Bridget Jones's Diary*
Taking charge of the remote control
Making me fetch my own tea
Expecting me to stay in and look after the kids
Contradicting me – especially in public
Nagging me about extremely tedious matters, like mortgage payments, rates and bills

Doesn't the woman know that I'm seriously planning to *kill myself*? Well, no, in fact, she doesn't. But the point is that *I* do and her Pauline-inspired attitude is pissing me off bigtime.

Midnight. Couldn't stand any more dykery so I slipped out after supper and went to the casino.

I started off playing this new (to me at any rate) casino poker game. It's like the casino stud-poker game I've played before except that this one has some aspects of draw poker.

It works like this. From a single deck of cards, freshly shuffled before each deal, the dealer deals each player five cards and herself five cards. All cards are dealt dark. As with the other casino stud-poker game, you have to put down an ante before the deal. Now comes the first decision: to play or fold. If you play, you can change up to two cards. However, if you play, you also have to place double your ante in the bet box.

The dealer qualifies with a pair of 8s or better but also has an obligation to improve her hand by changing up to two cards (she'll change just one if, for example, she's got four diamonds). If the dealer doesn't qualify, then the players win (even if they're holding less than the dealer) but are only paid out on the ante part of the bet. If the dealer qualifies and wins then, obviously, the player loses *all* his bet. Unlike the other casino poker game, two pairs only pay even money but everything over that pays two, three or more times the bet (not the ante).

It's no less dumb than ordinary casino stud-poker – in fact, if anything the odds are even worse – but it's more fun as there are more decisions to make and more twists and turns.

Over two hours, I had trips twice: once the dealer's hand qualified, the other time it didn't. Fair enough: according to the pit boss, you can expect the dealer to qualify one hand in three. But much (much) worse than the dealer not qualifying was the dealer qualifying and beating me. I was dealt a pair of 3s, 7, 8 and 10. I changed 7 and 8 and was overjoyed to get another 3 and another 10 to give me a full house of 3s over 10s. Seven to one that pays if the dealer qualifies and that would mean seven times my back bet of £40 – £280. The dealer turned over her cards. A king, a jack, 4 and a pair of 9s. Hurrah, I thought, the dealer's qualified! But, wait, she's discarding the jack and the 4 and – I couldn't believe it (still can't) – drawing two more kings!

The rest of the table forgot their own cards in amazement. Even the dealer called over the pit boss to have a look. One full house beating another full house. Neither of them had ever seen anything like that before and were decent enough to express sympathy. Indeed, everyone was so damn pleasant about it all that, somewhat surprisingly, I found myself not being too bothered. Something along the lines of it is better to have loved and lost etc.

Notwithstanding that (extraordinary) setback, I finished about £300 up which I took straight to the £20 minimum blackjack table where I played long enough to lose all of it, together with another £300. The problem was my old enemy, the twelve. I hate twelve in blackjack more than I hate any other number. At least if you have sixteen and you have to draw and then bust, you accept it as just one of those things. But when you're holding twelve against a dealer's 2, 3, 7, 8, 9, 10, jack, queen, king or ace and are therefore

– at least according to 'the book' – obliged to draw, why do I always hit a fucking 10 to make twenty-two? Why can't I hit a 5, 6, 7, 8 or 9? After all, there are *more* of those cards than there are 10s and court cards in the packs.

Even worse (as if . . .) is doubling down on eleven and getting an ace to make twelve. Yet another thing I'll make illegal when I'm supreme head of the universe.

MONDAY, MAY 10

Shit, shit, shit.

Phil phoned to say he wants me in the office tomorrow because he wants to discuss my expenses. He told me that I'm entitled to have a witness present which means, of course, that I've been rumbled. Only question: is it my petrol expenses (can't remember the last time I paid for my own chocolate, or indeed, jazz mags), that dodgy Guildford invoice or those three private dinners I claimed?

Shit, shit, shit.

TUESDAY, MAY 11

Got to the office early wearing my best bib and tucker. Hung around – feeling as though I was waiting to go into the headmaster's study – for a couple of hours before Jayne came to fetch me. She smiled sympathetically which only served to a) worry me even more and b) highlight her moustache which has, if anything, got even worse: it can't be long before a lookalike agency asks her to do Charles Bronson for them. Except that old Charlie hasn't got such a terrific pair of charlies.

Phil started by asking me if I had a witness with me but I told him it wasn't necessary.

'OK, Steve, here's the problem. You've claimed for two restaurant dinners when I know for a fact that the customer was away at the time. What do you have to say?'

Only two? Before I could say anything in my defence, he decided to launch a second broadside.

'Steve, I've got to tell you that I'm not overly impressed with you or your figures at the moment. This is the thin end of the wedge. I'm going to have to give you an official written warning.'

I was going to (try to) 'explain' the dinners (I hadn't claimed for larger, genuine dinners the month before); I was going to do the same with my sales figures (I've had family problems which I can't talk about): I had had, after all, long enough to come up with a convincing explanation. But then I thought why bother: never complain, never explain. I hate Phil and I hate the job, what do I care? And so I just shrugged my shoulders and grunted. And vowed to work even less hard.

Did my old trick of going into a bookie's just before the last race of the day. Wading through a sea of discarded (losing) betting-slips, I went through the *Racing Post*'s guide to the newspaper tipsters' selections. With two favourites and two second favourites having won, there was only one tipster who hadn't picked a single winner. His selection for the last race was Butler's Salver. I put a £150 on it at 7–1 (paid the tax) and walked out with over £1,000 profit!

The last race of the day is usually strictly for the *real* losers, the punters who can't bear the thought of leaving without winning something back. These people are in need of redemption as surely as any Catholic and they will stake everything they've got – and more – to get it.

Or maybe it is more existential than that. Tomorrow is another day for the rest of the world but it isn't for them. They've got no proof of tomorrow: the only day that exists is *today*. And if they carry on betting as though today is the last day of their life, the end of the world, then surely one day they'll be right.

THURSDAY, MAY 13

Latest news from the prison front. Gerard duly arrived at Ford and, as is his wont, wanted to find some gamblers with whom he could gamble. So what does he do? Well, according to Jake (to whom the Bad Man boasted of his ingenuity), he goes along to Gamblers Anonymous to find his gamblers. Bad or what?

FRIDAY, MAY 14

Black letter day.

We were due to be playing poker at Douglas's. He was going to try to get some fresh blood (did I say 'meat'?) to come along. He also promised to ring up some of the 'peripheral' players – like Moulinex, Rain Man and Pinocchio (so called because his nose twitches when he's bluffing) – but either he didn't or they couldn't make it.

Ben, meanwhile, cried off for the pathetic reason that he's in Germany on business which left just Jake, Douglas and me. Jake put his foot down when I suggested three-handed, damn him. And, no, he doesn't have Nathan or Toby's phone numbers.

This left me at four in the afternoon phoning round like a fucking madman inviting, cajoling, pleading anyone I could think of to take part. No one, *personne*, *nada*. Kerry the Rat's just had a major heart attack (pretty good excuse); Trevor and Larry from work are going out with their wives this evening (just about plausible).

Trouble is I'm not a great one for friends – I suppose I'm a bit of a loner – and those friends that I do have just aren't gamblers. Maggie and I have plenty of what-she-calls-friends-but-I-call-acquaintances – dinner-party people – but I wouldn't want to risk phoning any of the men: chances are anyway that none of them would have the bottle to leave the wife on a Friday night and, even if one did, I wouldn't want him to see the stakes we play for. He'd only tell his wife who would consider it her 'duty' to tell Maggie.

The truth is we're lost without the Bad Man's address book.

One of us is going to have to go down to Ford and charm him into releasing it or, more likely, offer to buy it off him. The alternative – and, I'm glad to say, it is unthinkable – is to 'do a Gerard' and go to Gamblers Anonymous to find some spielers.

SATURDAY, MAY 15

TIM IS DEAD. I can't believe it but he's killed himself: he's fucking hanged himself. Given his youth, his apparent good health and 'the bet', I'd have put a lot of money on me dying before him (much in the same way that I'd have put a fortune on the Queen Mother dying before Princess Di) but I'd have been wrong. Goes to show there's no such thing as a certainty.

I'm being flippant. I don't know, maybe it's a defence mechanism to stop myself being plunged into sorrow (I don't think so, we weren't that close) or depression (more likely but, thanks to the pills, not really a possibility). Maybe that's just the sort of heartless bastard I am although I honestly don't think so: it's just the way I react to bad news – I get embarrassed. I remember Dad walloping me when I laughed when he told me that his brother had died.

It was Henry who broke the news and, as I remember, I was too bloody stunned to laugh, smile, cry or anything else. It was so unexpected. I don't know, maybe it wasn't, but what I mean is that *any* bad news was unexpected for *me*, for me *today*. I had gone to Henry's to see Samantha. I'd found myself yearning for her again. I was feeling kind of light-headed, jolly even and then this . . . whoosh.

I looked across at Samantha. She smiled sympathetically and shook her head as if to say 'What a waste.' I'm ashamed to confess that even as I stood there, reeling from the shock, I found myself wondering what sort of impression I was making on her.

So there I was, experiencing shock, lust (however I try to disguise my feelings for her that's what it amounts to) and disgust with myself. It was some time – a few minutes even – before I started thinking about poor old Tim. And then I couldn't think about anything *but* Tim. I'd always wondered about Tim and now there was no containing my curiosity.

'When did it happen? How did it happen? Who discovered his body?'

Tuesday; he hanged himself in the bathroom; he was discovered by his mother. Sounds like a game of Cluedo when I write it down but this is a man's *life. Tim's* life. My *friend's* life. What could have possessed him to do it?

For a second, it crossed my mind that maybe he too had a 'bet' of his own but that's obviously absurd: I must get out of this habit of universalising my own personal experiences. So what did make him do it?

I asked Henry but he seemed, I don't know, reluctant to talk to me about it. Maybe I'm being overly-sensitive but I got the impression that he thinks that where Tim has led, I'll follow. In which case, he doesn't know how right he is.

However, from what he said – and from what he *didn't* say – I was able to piece together quite a lot. It turns out that Tim lived at home with his widowed mother. Incredibly, he'd *never* left home, not even when he went to college. Anyway, at the age of thirty-nine, it seems like he decided to cash in his chips. Not that he had many chips left. Big gambling debts from what I could gather. I mean BIG gambling debts.

'But he always seemed to do so well in here,' I said to Henry, genuinely puzzled.

'Maybe. Say you don't know, Steve, say you don't know.'

'You'd never put pressure on him to pay up. Besides, you don't give credit, or at least not very much.'

By putting him on the defensive, I got him to open up a little. 'It wasn't me, mate. There are worse people than me, you know, people who . . . you don't want to know. Thing is, they came on to his mum.'

'What and he couldn't stand the pressure, the shame?'

'Something like that.'

'Henry, one last thing. What did Tim actually do for a living. I always wanted to know.'

'Are you kidding me? You don't know? You didn't know?'

I assured him I didn't.

'He was an undertaker.'

I couldn't have been more surprised if he'd told me he was an armed robber: in fact, I'd have been less surprised. And yet, and yet, now I think about it, certain things *do* fall into place. The aloofness – stand-offishness – the neatness, the reluctance ever to talk about work or, indeed, to use Christian names. As for living with his mother, it's not so extraordinary now I come to think about it. He never mentioned women (or men come to that) except in a very desultory, unconvincing 'Cor, birds' sort of way and the one time he was obliged to refer to a co-habitee, he called her 'the woman I live with' which I seem to remember at the time thinking was a little odd.

Damn it, I never even knew his surname. And now I don't want to know. Let it die with him.

Samantha was really kind and supportive, asking me if I was all right and everything. I have to confess that I had been tempted to have a bet – after all it is a bookie's – but I somehow thought that it might be bad taste to do so in the light of Tim's death. Even if it wasn't, she might think it was.

So I made my excuses and left having arranged to meet her after work for a drink.

Watched the racing on telly and did a few trades. I don't know whether God (as if) was punishing me for my callousness, but I lost about £300. Great. See you soon, Tim. Thinking about it, I wish I'd told him about 'the bet'.

Picked up Samantha at six and we got into a taxi to go to town. This time I took her to a hotel bar. Thought I'd at least give myself the chance.

The conversation was at once deeper, less flirtatious and more sombre. Understandable, I guess, in the light of Tim's death. We talked about death and dreams and how hard it is to accept one's limitations. I mocked her: 'What do you know about having to come to terms with your own ordinariness?'

'When I was fifteen,' she told me in all seriousness, 'I could have been a champion show-jumper. By the time I was nineteen, I knew for sure I was never going to make it. That's a very young age to accept the end of your dream.'

We talked more about her and then we talked about me and I found myself telling her everything. About Maggie (the truth), Mum, the children, Dad, even my breakdown. The only thing I didn't tell her about was 'the bet' or, for that matter, this diary.

She did something that no one – not even Maggie – has ever done for me before: she listened. I felt her empathy without her needing to articulate it. I could have held her hand(s) during this time but it would have felt too much like a defendant's plea in mitigation: as though I couldn't trust her to give me a fair hearing without the bribe of affection. It would have been otiose: my words and her understanding of them were enough.

When I'd finished, she simply kissed her finger and touched my cheek with it. I don't know what she intended but, in the climate of honesty we'd created, it had a powerful effect. Without touching her, I said simply but directly, 'Samantha, I love you and I want to make love to you.'

'I think I love you too but you're a married man and I don't sleep with married men.'

'I don't want you to sleep with me as a married man. I want you to sleep with that part of me – that larger part of me – that is *me,* that isn't married. Look, this sounds corny, but at home I'm married; here I'm not.

'I told you: I love Maggie but as a co-parent, not as a wife. Loving you has everything to do with you and with me but absolutely nothing to do with her. There's what lawyers call a privity of relationship between Maggie and me that no other relationship breaches. What she and I have isn't particularly strong – and I honestly don't know that it will last much longer – but it's ours and is as personal and unique to us as our fingerprints are. You don't jeopardise Maggie and me; she doesn't jeopardise you and me. Not until you and I have children and perhaps not even then.'

She smiled. 'I believe you. I don't know if you're right but I think that you're telling the truth. So here's what we'll do. We'll go our separate ways tonight' – she anticipated my protest and hushed me – 'but I'll give you my telephone number and if you still feel the same way in a few days, then we'll . . .' She let her words trail away but there was no misunderstanding her meaning.

Every word I said to her was the truth. Now here's another truth. I am counting the seconds before I can phone her.

MONDAY, MAY 17

I know I've been here before – hell, I only have to look back through my diary – but that was Cathy and vestigial and manic and obsessive. This is fresh, decent, wonderful.

Samantha is loveliness personified. There is nothing about her that I don't love. If it weren't for the children, I'd be out of here so quickly it would make Maggie's eyes spin. And that's *before* Samantha and I have been the beast with two backs.

There is nothing – not a smelly pussy, nor bushy underarm hair, nor even hairy nipples (yuk) – that could put me off her. Not unless she revealed that she was in fact a bloke which, fortunately, I'm a hundred per cent certain that she isn't.

Key test: would I love her if she had to have her tits removed and her pussy were permanently out of order? Answer: yes, undoubtedly. And that's what matters. Traditional romantics blather on about the full moon and roses and all that monty but that's bollocks: I could fancy almost anyone given enough romantic stimuli. What matters is, do I love someone *without* those stimuli? *That's* romance. Those people who write love songs rhyming 'June', 'moon' and 'croon', they ought to write a song with the title 'I'd Love You Even If Your Pussy Was Bunged Up'. Now *that's* romantic.

TUESDAY, MAY 18

I find I've got a new zest for work. Don't know why – it certainly has nothing to do with Phil's fucking pep talk – but I'm running around like a blue-arse fly. Maybe it's a displacement activity to use up my excess adrenalin until I can see Samantha. Alternatively, now that I'm at last ahead on 'the bet' (I must be by now), I have the future to think of and even if I don't intend to work in this job for ever, I still want to make as much money as possible while I do.

This new work ethic didn't stop me popping out to the bookie's at lunchtime. A race was about to start at Pontefract so I had a quick look at the form and saw something which made my nose twitch: the favourite had never been in a race before. Now how can people bet on such an unknown quantity? I wondered. Even if its breeding is immaculate and its work at home is fabulous, there's no telling what might happen during an actual race.

So without going into the form of the other horses properly – which was a pity but there just wasn't the time as, these days in flat races, if you're not on before the off, you're not on at all – I backed the shortest priced horse with *any* form.

As it happened, it lost but so did the favourite and the horse that won – at 12–1 – *had* raced before. So the tactic of eliminating favourites which are new to the racecourse isn't altogether stupid.

I had three or four more bets in the time available to me but didn't trouble the scorers. All in all, I suppose I lost about £300 but, hey, I'm still up. Up, up and away!

Phoned Samantha at home. Another girl answered the phone and I thought I had the wrong number (why are wrong numbers never engaged?) but it turned out to be Samantha's flatmate. Samantha herself was 'washing her hair' and could she phone me back? Er, no, not exactly, not with Maggie liable to answer the phone. I'd phone back in fifteen minutes.

I waited until Maggie had settled down to watch *EastEnders* (can't stand it myself because it's so gloomy, yeah and unrealistic – why is it that in Albert Square, only heterosexuals contract AIDS, no one eats McDonald's, no one watches *Coronation Street* and no one ever fucking swears? – but Maggie, poor dear, can't live without it) and then slipped upstairs to phone Samantha again.

This time she must have been waiting just by the telephone as she picked it up as soon as we were connected.

'Listen, Samantha, I can't talk for long. With reference to what we were talking about, I *do* need to see you. Can you make Friday?'

She said she could and we arranged that I would go to her flat (in Crouch End) at eight o'clock.

As far as Maggie's concerned, Friday night's poker night. I don't even know if we've got enough players together for a game but, shit, if Ben can cancel to go to *Germany*, surely I can drop out to go on a date?

I'll have to phone the lads and delicately explain that I won't be playing poker on Friday but that Maggie thinks I am, if they get my drift . . .

WEDNESDAY, MAY 19

Made sure I stayed in tonight and I'll do the same tomorrow night. I don't want Maggie getting suspicious. Actually, I really *don't* want Maggie to find out. Apart from anything, I wouldn't want to hurt her. I'm surprising myself writing this because very often she gets up my nose but I do have a deep and abiding affection for her and I also feel gratitude towards her for always sticking by me, so there's no need to upset her. I have no intention – as things stand at the moment – of leaving her. Irrespective of how I feel about her, she is the mother of my children and I wouldn't want my children to have the sort of father who treats their mother badly. Besides, Samantha has nothing to do with Maggie and everything to do with *me*. Maggie expects me to be out on a Friday evening: what difference *should* it make to her whether I'm gambling or screwing? If anything, the latter's better as at least I'm not losing any money. There's also an argument that this is Maggie's fault anyway for not allowing me to hold poker sessions at home. There *is* an argument but I don't think I would be able to sustain it for very long – least of all with Maggie.

In fact, it was no great hardship to stay in because there was soccer on the telly (whatever happened to the close season?). England were playing some meaningless friendly. I did what I always do with these sorts of games: bet against England. It might not be very patriotic but since so many other punters are patriotic, the odds favour us traitors. As Nurse Edith Cavell *meant* to say: 'Patriotism isn't enough, I must get down to Ladbroke's and have a fiver on the Krauts.'

I didn't think England would actually lose, I just didn't see us getting the easy victory the papers were anticipating (they always do that as it gives them extra ammunition when it all goes pear-shaped). So I bought England's first goal at 40 for £10 and sold the England performance at 83 for another £10. I was going to buy the corners and sell the total goals but thought better as I've now got some winnings to defend (in the event, what I'd have lost on the corners, I'd have won on the goals – or vice-versa).

It was – yawn yawn (at least for the rest of the viewers, tee hee) – a goalless draw. I won £500 as the first goal made up at 90 and, as the England performance made up at 27, another £560 on that. Once again I've made a profit in excess of a thousand.

FRIDAY, MAY 21

4.00am. It's late, late, late and I'm sleepy (times three) but I have to do something between leaving *her* bed and getting into *our* bed. I know it's Saturday – at least I think it is – but *I'm* still in Friday and I never want to leave it. If nothing else ever happens with S. – and I pray that it does, does, does – I'll never forget tonight, this morning. It wasn't the sex that was fabulous (though it was) but her, her and me, me and her. She's a peach, a babe (no, not a pig) and a ten all wrapped into one. I love her more than I can say and a lot more than I can write. I'm no great respecter of time in relationships: I think you know whether you want to be with someone within hours, days, weeks. The rest is just details, a matter of filling in the *curricula vitae*.

SATURDAY, MAY 22

This is the morning after – correction, the afternoon after – the night before. Re-reading what I wrote last night (something I don't usually do), I'm just a teensy bit embarrassed.

Yes, what happened between Samantha and me was wonderful/magical/fabulous but it wasn't like my first time and the way I told it, I sounded like a lovesick fifteen-year-old who imbues the girl who's made the ultimate sacrifice with qualities she can't possibly possess just to satisfy his *amour propre*. Samantha is lovely, a delightful girl, and yes, I think I love her but there's nothing like actually having sex with someone to have the scales fall (ever so) slightly from the eyes.

I don't know, maybe it's me. For me (and I suspect for most other men too), sex is the end of a relationship: our curiosity is satisfied and we're off. For women, I think sex is just the beginning. Men and women have different biological and socio-anthropological drives. The man is genetically programmed to spread his seed whereas a woman needs a provider for her and her children. That's not to say that men can't fall in love and women can't enjoy one-night stands but, when it comes down to it, the first time we – damn it, *I* – have sex with a woman is by far the most exciting, even if, from the point of view of technique and performance, it isn't the 'best'.

Went to Henry's to say 'Hi' to Samantha. Well, it's the decent thing to do, like giving them a cuddle afterwards.

I have to say, she was looking lovely – especially for someone who had very little sleep last night – and there was something rather wonderful about looking at this girl working, knowing that a few hours ago she was writhing around on my dick.

I didn't stay to have a bet – somehow it didn't seem appropriate – but I managed to tell her that I'd give her a ring during the week. I think Henry caught me whispering to her – strikes me that whispering in public places only serves to attract attention: I'd have been better off talking in a normal voice – but he doesn't know Maggie and I *think* he'd be too embarrassed, too reserved, to say anything to Samantha.

There was another soccer international on TV. Once again we were playing against inferior opposition and I was going to bet along the same lines as the other night and then, after giving it some thought, I decided to follow the money. Two reasons: it doesn't do to follow any theory or system too slavishly for, if it always worked, there wouldn't be any bookies left in business. Secondly, and more conclusively, whenever England play badly (as they most decidedly did on Wednesday) they almost always make up for it next time out.

I bought the England superiority at 2.8 for £20 a tick which is, by far, the biggest bet I've ever done. In the unlikely (but not impossible) event that England got beaten 2–0, it would have cost me £960! I was also going to sell the first England goal at 17 but that's no value whatsoever, so I waited until they'd been playing for ten minutes and *then* sold the first goal at 27 for £50. England scored nine minutes later and I'd made £400. I must get more into the habit of doing trades *during* the play and, indeed, closing bets too. I'm still too hidebound by traditional betting where the die is cast and that's it.

Fortunately, that wasn't the only goal England scored but they only managed two more which meant that my big, big bet netted a profit of just £40!

I'd forgotten that Maggie and I were due to be going out tonight but, luckily, Maggie had a migraine and so we had to cancel. I'm sorry for Maggie and I don't mean to be callous but I was mightily relieved. I am absolutely cream-crackered and I don't think that *she* would have accepted me crying off tonight.

MONDAY, MAY 24

Just to remind myself of my fallibility during this wonderful winning sequence, I dropped six hundred quid in the bookie's. Just like that. Three races, two hundred on each (to win), two seconds and a third. Actually, the way I'm feeling at the moment, I refuse even to think of it as a loss: call it a (small) sacrifice to the gambling gods.

Phoned Samantha and arranged to go round to her place on Friday. After – not instead of – poker. I thought she might object to being treated like the pudding instead of the main course but she was fine. I like her.

WEDNESDAY, MAY 26

Today's Maggie's wedding anniversary. I'd call it *our* wedding anniversary but there's precious little sense in which it is even partly *mine* at all: it's Maggie who chose the wedding date in the first place, it's Maggie who remembers the anniversary and it's Maggie who gives me absolute hell when I forget it (as I invariably do). Sometimes I think that marriage is like a pinball game: you accumulate years like points but, along the way, you lose your balls.

I decided to celebrate it by a) going to the bookie's (on my own, natch) where I ended up about even (i.e. sixty quid down) and b) by taking Maggie out for dinner to her favourite restaurant.

I was surprised by how well we got on. In fact, it was a really enjoyable evening. By tacit consent, we didn't discuss my gambling, her mother's (very much declining) health or our children but talked instead about friends and fun times from 'the early days'. She complimented me on how handsome I am ('so much more handsome than any of our friends') and I told her how lovely she is and praised her for all her (genuinely) wonderful qualities. I can't remember the last time we had so much fun together. Maybe it's got something to do with the fact that, with all my recent winnings I've been drawing out of my spread-betting account (it's been hell always making sure that I get down to pick up the post before Maggie does), we're really quite flush with dosh at the moment. Alternatively – and it's a happier thought – maybe Maggie has reconciled herself to life with me, for better or worse, and is merely trying to make the best of a not-so-bad job.

The bottom line is that as I write this, Maggie is upstairs 'getting herself ready' and, for the first time in ages (at least with her), I'm really in the mood. There's life in the old dog yet – that's to say, her, me and our marriage.

FRIDAY, MAY 28

2.00am (Saturday). Had a much-needed poker session tonight. God, I've been suffering from withdrawal symptoms for the past couple of weeks.

The game was at Ben's house which meant that we had to play in a haze of smoke. No complaints from me though, I was only too happy to play. Douglas, Ben, Jake and I were joined by Nick (an associate of Douglas's from the advertising world) and Hugh (a doctor who Ben was at university with). I don't know how much it had to do with my need for a poker fix but I liked both guys. Nick, who, fortunately, *hasn't* got a pony-tail, slotted in as if he'd been playing poker with us and our arcane rules for years while Hugh, despite needing to refer to the sequence of winning hands which was extremely unsettling, seemed like a good bloke – for a doctor. Not once did he look bored or superior and he certainly gave us more than one and three-quarter minutes of his time.

The other good thing about new players is that they make sure that they have enough money to play. Not for them the perennial drag.

When I look back on any poker session, one variation, one type of poker game always emerges. Tonight it was four-card Omaha which is, after five-card stud, my favourite game and which I called every time it was my turn.

There was no one hand that stands out in my memory (particularly as I am not entirely sure that I can even remember my own name at this precise moment) but I got into a wonderful groove. I felt like a world-class batsman must do when he suddenly sees the ball as big as a melon: every hand worked, every bet clicked, everything gelled and I guess I won half the games of Omaha we played. There's a kind of snowball effect when you start winning: the other players become wary, fearful even, and it just helps contribute to success. Confidence is the antithesis of fear and, just as stronger players close in on a frightened player, so too do weaker players cower in the presence of a strong man. It's a virtuous circle – or whatever the opposite of a vicious circle is.

I left the game at 11.30 to good-natured catcalls – which, I suspect, had something to do with the Cheshire grin on my face – with £420 of their money in my pocket. I had, of course, given them all three hours' notice, which is fair enough.

I got to Samantha's by midnight and stayed for two wonderful hours.

I can honestly say I've never had such a great time in the sack. Suffice it to say, every stroke was a vinegar stroke.

The sex itself only lasted about half-an-hour but was followed by a full hour's intimate pillow talk. She's such a lovely girl, she really is. There's just no side to her: she takes me for what I am, not what she'd like me to be. That's rare in a woman. My experience is that men want women to be exactly the same as the day they met them whereas women want men to change as much as possible. It's too early to tell but I know that Samantha accepts me for myself. Oh I'm sure that she'd like me to be single, younger, more handsome (as if) but she understands that I'm not and she doesn't waste her time moaning about it.

As proof of the fact that Samantha and Steve has nothing to do with Maggie and Steve, I didn't feel at all guilty tonight (as I half thought

I would) now that Maggie and I are getting on so well. If anything, I think my marriage is *stronger* for my relationship with Samantha as it makes me value Maggie's qualities more and mind her bad points less. It sounds like typical errant husband bullshit – and if any other bloke were saying this I'd be giving him the raspberry – but I swear it's true.

SATURDAY, MAY 29

Dad was over this morning, playing with the kids (he dotes on them – makes me feel guilty) as usual. Suddenly, out of nowhere, he asked me for that ten grand back.

'What?'

'Yes, son,' he looked down as though he was too ashamed to look me in the eyes. How on earth could *he* feel shame when *all* the shame belongs to me for putting him in this position in the first place.

He continued. 'I should have drawn down all of my pension when I was sixty-five when annuity rates were higher. Instead, being prudent, I thought I'd hang on as long as I could, letting the rest of my pension accumulate interest and grow in my fund, and then draw it down when I had to. Well, when I spoke to my financial consultant' – he used the absurdly pompous name for a pension salesman as though it required quotation marks – 'he explained to me how annuity rates have gone right down. Said something about low interest rates and gilts. I didn't really understand, but the long and the short of it is that I really need to call in that loan.'

How typical of my Dad that he ends up getting screwed by the system for doing the *right* thing.

'That wouldn't cause you any trouble would it, Steve?' I couldn't be sure whether he meant financially or mentally but just as I was trying to figure it out, I had a brainwave.

'Look, Dad, you need this money for income, right?' He looked confused but nodded. 'I have plenty of income' (well I do at the moment) 'but no capital. I tell you what I'll do: I'll pay you a thousand a year for ten years and then five per cent – which is about what you'd get from a building society – on whatever's left.

'So, for example, I'll give you a thousand now. That leaves nine thousand. Five per cent of nine thousand is four-fifty. That's thirty-seven pounds fifty per month. Call it forty quid. That's what I'll pay you every month. Until next year when I'll reduce the capital amount owing to eight thousand and the monthly payments will go down accordingly. Unless, of course, interest rates go up, in which case I'll pay you more. Is that OK with you, Dad?'

He looked mightily relieved. I couldn't tell whether it was because he knew he'd be getting at least some money back or because he had discharged a particularly unpleasant (for him) duty but the important thing is that now we're both happy. I have to admit I've felt really terrible messing him around like this.

If I end up killing myself at the end of the year, I'll leave instructions that Dad is to get paid off in full. It's the very least I can do.

There was a one-day cricket international on Sky. Although I love cricket, I've never thought of it as a sport that lends itself to gambling. And so it isn't but it *is* a great game for trading.

The wonderful thing about trading on cricket is that you can dip in and out. So you can buy, say, Mark Ramprakash, at 35 for £10 a run and then close the trade (i.e. sell Ramprakash) after he's made twenty runs at 52, taking a profit of £170. Ramprakash doesn't actually have to make 52 runs, that's just the selling price of his revised spread after he's made twenty.

Now although I can see the fallacy in my logic – Ramprakash could have been bowled the very next ball after I put my money on and, by the same token, he could go on to a century after I've closed the bet – the former is very unlikely while the latter is just one of those things and I'm happy with my profit.

After an afternoon of ducking in and out of individual batsmen's scores, I'd made a profit of £860.

SUNDAY, MAY 30

Went down to Ford today. Jake, Douglas and Ben had all indicated that they might come along too but, in the event, I went on my own. Doesn't bother me: I'm used to driving around the country on my own – I enjoy it – and, to be fair to Jake, he's already visited him twice.

I've never been to a prison before and, I have to say, I was pleasantly surprised by Ford. For a start it's buried deep in the West Sussex countryside. Surroundings more inappropriate for a prison would be impossible to imagine: damn it, it's almost walking distance from Climping where we used to go for our holidays when we were children. Secondly, and even more amazingly, it's so *open*.

Now I'm not stupid, I know it's an open prison and therefore I shouldn't be surprised that it's, er, open but I wasn't prepared for the sight of prisoners – criminals for Christ's sake – wandering in and out of the prison and across the road to the car park. I even saw a sign for a car boot sale. I don't know if that's actually anything to do with the prison but, given the lack of (visible) security, I wouldn't be at all surprised.

Inside, it's no less unlike a prison – or at least what I'd expected a prison to be. The look and the feel of the place was like that of a 1960s campus university (Kent or Reading maybe) while the waiting-room, grotty though it undoubtedly was, was a lot more salubrious than the one in our local health centre.

I was sent through to see the prisoner. The reception/meeting room was, if not lush, then much lighter, cleaner and more informal than I'd expected. Not unlike the school hall in my old (teaching) school – without the smell of boiled greens. In the corner was a shop – a bloody shop, open to the cons – selling stamps, confectionery, odds and sods. I couldn't believe it. On my way over to Gerard's table, I said to a warder, 'Strewth, it's not bad here, is it?'

'Don't tell anyone,' he replied laconically, 'or they'll all want to come.'

Gerard stood up to greet me. Dressed in regular prison issue of striped blue-and-white shirt and blue chinos, he looked like a lawyer on a day off. He's also lost some weight. He offered me his hand which I took after a split second's hesitation out of a foolish but atavistic fear of catching prison. 'Thanks for coming to see me, Steve.'

'My pleasure, Bad Man, my pleasure. Well, you've certainly landed on your feet haven't you, Gerard?'

He hushed me. 'In here, I'm known as Philip.'

'What, Philip as in your middle name?'

'Yes, but this is an English version.'

'But why, Bad Man?'

'Why what?'

'Why are you not calling yourself Gerard and why are you Philip instead of Marcel?'

'I don't want to be Gerard because when I get out of here and go back into business, I don't want any of this lot' – he gestured towards other prisoners talking to their visitors – 'tracking me down.'

'OK. Why Philip and not Marcel?'

'In here, you have to work or study. I've chosen to study.' I looked puzzled. The Bad Man grinned. 'I'm studying French.'

'But you *are* French!'

Gerard leaned forward conspiratorially. I leant back as a reflex: I didn't want the watching warders to think I was passing him drugs or anything; just because I'm paranoid didn't mean I wasn't in a prison. 'That's why I'm calling myself Philip and not Marcel so that no one knows.' QED. I suppose there's a certain logic to it but I was staggered that anyone could be that cynical. Maybe it's the teacher or the auto-didact in me, but I'd have really relished the opportunity to take advantage of this appalling situation, to learn something. But not Gerard: he'd rather 'study' his native tongue as a foreign language and spend as much time as possible gambling. Is that place a finishing school for the Bad Man or what?

He interrupted my thoughts. 'Listen, Steve, I need a backgammon set and a Monopoly set so I can play people for money and I also need a couple of smutty magazines, which I can hire out. The fellows in here are desperate.'

'Perhaps you'd like me to get you a blow-up doll while I'm at it?'

I forgot that sarcasm is wasted on the Bad Man but he quickly reminded me. 'Great idea, I could rent it out and . . .'

I cut him short and told him that I would send him a backgammon set *or* a Monopoly set and give it to the next person to go down there and I would put a smutty mag in the post.

Gerard looked sulky. 'Well, if that's the *best* you can do.'

'You're fucking right it is.' God, he reminds me so much of Billy Bunter cadging off the other 'chaps' and then complaining when things don't meet his high standards. I don't believe Gerard. I drive sixty miles to see the bastard and he complains when I 'only' promise to buy him one game and send him one smutty mag (before I send that I'll phone the prison and check that I won't get into trouble for doing so: Gerard says it's OK but then he would, wouldn't he?).

Meanwhile, his shopping list reminded me that I did in fact have some things for him. I handed over some chocolate and soap and things like that (for some reason I had him confused with a World War II POW since those are the staple contents of a Red Cross parcel). I apologised as I did so because, of course, I didn't know that the Bad Man could buy himself most things he wanted in the shop or, as he later vouchsafed, pretty well anything else from the other prisoners.

He then went on to tell me how the system works at Ford. I must say, it doesn't seem too onerous. Great food, no work (at least not for 'Philip'), superb recreation facilities, four different TV lounges ('so there are no arguments about which channel to watch') and, of course, no shortage of bad men to gamble with. It's almost worth committing a nice white-collar crime to pass a relaxing few months – it certainly doesn't look like much of a deterrent to me.

For all that, Gerard/Marcel/Philip was bemoaning his fate. 'I miss my children,' he wailed.

'But you haven't seen your children for weeks, Gerard. You told me just before you went inside that your ex-wife won't give you access because you don't pay for their maintenance.'

He wasn't mollified but he did change tack. 'Well, I phone them all the time.' And, with that, he pulled out from his pocket a huge handful of telephone cards. 'I won them,' he said in response to the question I would have asked when I'd got my breath back. 'Telephone cards are currency in here. I'd ask you for some but these are special ones. That's what we use for stakes when we play cards or dice. That's why I want my own backgammon set. I can make a fortune.'

'But wait a second, Gerard, what happens to the men who lose? How do *they* phone *their* families?'

He shrugged his shoulders and grinned. 'They don't.'

I winced. 'Bad Man, I'm not sure that you're not too bad even for this place.'

Once again, he grinned and I found myself grinning back. The fact is that no matter how awful the Bad Man is, he is still extremely charming. When they were giving out charm he got a double helping, even if it meant that he never got the chance to pick up any scruples.

I left soon after, having made sure that I got the phone numbers of some potential poker players. Gerard also gave me the telephone number and address of the backgammon club he goes to. 'Tell them you're a friend of mine and they'll look after you.'

He is but I wouldn't dream of boasting about it.

MONDAY, MAY 31

Incredibly, once again, I'm up on the month – £4,200 to be precise (or, rather, not to be precise but to round it up/down to the nearest hundred). This means that I'm now £3,100 up on the year. This is the first time I've been up on the year and it feels GREAT.

The more chance I have of staying alive, the more I actually want to stay alive.

TUESDAY, JUNE 1

Took some more money out of my spread-betting account and now, for the first time in my life, I'm on top of all my debts. In fact, what with the new mortgage, I'd even say that I was ahead of the game. It won't last, of course, but I intend to enjoy it while it does.

Actually, that's a thought: if I *know* it won't last – and I do – why don't I stop gambling now and live a quiet, reasonable existence from now on? In many ways I wish I could but it's too late for that: I've lost too much, been down too long, to call it quits now. If I did, I'd always wonder what would have happened, how 'the bet' would have turned out and consequently, I'd only try it again. This way, the only way open to *me*, I'll find out.

Maggie's mum took a turn for the worst last night. Poor old her; poor old Maggie; poor old me as I had to take the children to school.

It doesn't look like Maggie's mum is long for this world and while I'm naturally sad about it there is a silver cloud. I'd forgotten about the holiday for which I was meant to pay the deposit (but didn't because the casino got its hands on my money before the travel agent could). Maggie's mentioned it a couple of times recently and I've made encouraging noises ('Yes, it's great, I can't wait' etc.) and assured her that we'll get the tickets in a couple of weeks.

Now, I don't mean to be callous or anything, but given that Maggie's mum's going to die soon, it wouldn't half be helpful if she could croak when we're due to be going on holiday because I could then, er, 'cancel' the holiday which I haven't booked in the first place. Then with all my winnings I could book something else, somewhere better.

WEDNESDAY, JUNE 2

Fucking tough day at work today. I hate writing up things that happen at work: I have to spend enough time as it is thinking about it during *their* time without having to do it in *my* time. But I'm having to deal with this client (well, he's something that starts with a 'c' and ends with a 't') who just won't return my calls or answer my faxes. I wouldn't mind if he simply didn't want to do business but, apparently, he does. Ordinarily, I'd ignore him and move on to another, easier client but the office knows about him and want me to pursue him – though how I'm supposed to do business with a man who ignores me, I have no idea. Apart from anything else, it's so fucking discourteous, so counter-productive, so time-consuming. I don't really know the bloke but I really hate him: I wouldn't piss on him if he were on fire.

Partly because of him and partly out of boredom, I decided to pay a visit to the Bad Man's backgammon club.

It was located in (what was essentially) a flat above a shop in Paddington and was hot, crowded, smoky and smelly but otherwise not uncongenial. I'd maligned Gerard in that the other people – all men apart from one seriously chunky female who, from the way she was standing with arms akimbo, obviously thought she was a babe (well, she was but only in the sense of *Babe*) – were, to use Maggie's favourite phrase 'PLU' (people like us).

I was offered the chance to join in a 'chouette' where a few players play against one person but I didn't fancy it: for me, backgammon is about one against one, *mano a mano*. To turn it into a team sport or, worse, to set up a committee to decide what to do defeats the object of a game which is fast, individualistic, spontaneous.

So instead I waited for a few minutes which gave me the opportunity to watch the other players. Although I didn't know any of them, I recognised several 'types'. There was the 'flash man' (shouting the odds the whole time, throwing the dice extravagantly), the 'businessman' (wearing a suit, brisk, serious), the 'wide boy' (like the 'flash man' but with more jewellery), the 'nerd' (spotty, under-dressed, pebble-dash glasses, sitting hunched over the board) and 'the smug man' (not paying attention – or at least pretending not to – above it all, condescending to his opponent). I was glad not to be playing one of them.

In fact my first opponent was a good bloke named David who works in the City as an analyst. We agreed to play for two pounds a point which seemed friendly enough but he was obviously as much of a *spieler* as I am because the doubling cube always reached at least sixteen and once even got to sixty-four. Consequently, by the time we finished, one of us had won £250. Unfortunately, it was him which meant that for my next three matches I was playing catch-up.

In those circumstances, it's to my credit that I didn't go on tilt and even managed to claw back almost fifty quid to end the evening only two hundred down. Not a bad result for what was an entertaining evening – although I'm not sure I'll go back there in a hurry.

FRIDAY, JUNE 4

Poker at Douglas's. Although it really is a tiny apartment, it is at least all *his*: he doesn't have to share it with a wife or, worse, his parents. We were six (a perfect number): Douglas, Ben, Jake, Nathan, Nick and me.

It was a fine session with plenty of variations and lots of laughs. The only dissonant note came over the controversial topic of 'moody'.

We've always played that 'moody goes' unless it strays over into cheating. In our set, moody is just another word for backchat, table-talk, even crack. 'That's a bit moody' is as much a compliment as it is a reproach. For us, comments like 'Oh God, why do I always get dealt such shitty cards' immediately followed by a trap-check bet or a raise are part and parcel of a poker game. When a player – typically Douglas – agrees to stay in a hand 'but only because I'm feeling generous', the wise man knows that it's a good time to fold.

The one person to regularly cross the border into Cheatland is Gerard. A typical Bad Man ruse is to use the fact that someone owes him some money to gain an unfair advantage over other players. For example, he'll have a weakish hand in a showdown against, say, Ben (whom he suspects has a better hand than his) and Toby. He'll say to Toby, 'Listen, you owe me money. Don't stay in this hand because I'll beat you and you'll only end up owing me more money.' Like the good boy he is, Toby will fold but so too will Ben because he can't get his head around Gerard's tactics: is it a bluff to force him to fold, is it a double-bluff to persuade him to stay in or what? The rest of us will condemn the Bad Man but (after quickly shuffling his hand into the rest of the deck) he will swear blind that he had a fantastic hand and he only wanted to protect poor Toby.

On reflection, although that has elements of 'moodiness' (and, it must be remembered, moody goes), it also has too many aspects of roguery for my liking. What Gerard's doing there is to use extraneous (to that specific hand) matters to gain an unfair advantage. To claim, as Gerard inevitably does, that if some trickery or deceit is allowed then *all* trickery must be allowed too is so obviously reductive as to obviate the need for rational explanation – except, of course, to the Bad Man.

Tonight's dispute revolved around Ben who, on one hand (of seven-card stuff), found himself in a titanic (well, they were both drowning in booze at the time) struggle with Nick. As he often does, Ben called over Jake to 'have a look at this.' He didn't ask for Jake's advice and neither did Jake offer any but Nick who, it has to be said, was losing heavily at this point, took exception to Ben's actions.

'That is completely out of order,' he said, refusing to see Ben's bet. 'By showing Jake your hand, you've got me not knowing what to think. I know you allow moody but this goes way beyond that.' With that, he threw his hand on the table in anger.

Ben tried to explain himself. 'Listen, Nick, I wasn't trying to gain an unfair advantage, honestly I wasn't. I was just showing Jake my hand because it was so extraordinary.' He then revealed it to the rest of us: it was a royal flush – albeit with wild cards

– but a r.f. all the same. 'If it made you fold – and I'm sure you could never have beaten a royal flush' – Nick nodded to indicate that this was indeed true – 'then I'm the loser but I just thought it was amazing that with such crap showing' (10, 4, 3 and a dooce) 'I had a brilliant hand and I just wanted to show it to someone.'

The rest of the table was split. Nathan, who's a casino regular, was dead against what Ben had done. Douglas, who's also been known to frequent casinos but who's also a close friend of Ben's (with whom he plays tennis and golf), was ambivalent. My view – and it was the one that prevailed – was that although showing people your hand (as opposed to allowing a non-player to see your hand if *he* asks) is a 'bad thing', there was no question of Ben having done so to gain an advantage and that therefore Nick had nothing to complain about.

I didn't add (though I was tempted to) that Nick was being a sore loser: it wasn't bad conduct he was complaining about as much as bad luck. I've been there myself and I don't blame him for losing it but he was wrong to flare up at Ben who's a gentle soul.

Fortunately, the row didn't overshadow the rest of the evening which saw Judicious Jake emerge as the big winner with £550. I won £120. The big loser was Nick who dropped a huge monkey. I don't think we'll be seeing him again.

Once again, I used a late poker game as a pretext for going round to Samantha's. I'm a little ashamed (and, secretly, not a little proud) that I only stayed for an hour – half of which time we spent having sex. In the same way that Mum used to accuse me of using our house as a hotel, Samantha would be entitled to accuse me of using her as a whore but, to her immense credit, she didn't.

SATURDAY, JUNE 5

11.00am. Today is Derby Day – D-Day in more ways than one. Having said that, I've been waiting for this day for so long that it almost feels like an anti-climax.

I've got £200 at 33–1 riding on Courteous. I was going to back it all the way down to twenties but, by the time I next looked at its price, it was already down to 16–1 and I decided that I already had enough exposure to it. Then, after its (winning) trial, it went right down to sixes. Now, today, it's fluctuating around 5–1, 11–2.

After last night's intimacies, I'd just as soon *not* bet at Henry's but to stay away on such an important day would look unnecessarily offish to Henry and, besides, Samantha would be surprised/upset if I didn't come in on Derby Day.

By the time I got there, Courteous had gone in to 5–1, clear second favourite. I had already advised Samantha to back it but she'd giggled delightfully and told me that she'd never placed a bet in her life, so I promised to do one for her – which was another reason to go to Henry's.

6.00pm. It only went and bloody won! At 9–2; at 33–1. I have never before had a winner like it. I am over the fucking moon. I can't believe it. I am gobsmacked, staggered, flabbergasted, overwhelmed, dumbfounded, stupefied. I have won £6,600 (on my ante-post bet) and another £500 on my SP bet which, less the tax and a little prezzie for Samantha (who put up some genuine – and delightful – resistance) has netted me a profit not far short of £7,000. Count it: seven big ones. Well, I will be able to count it on Tuesday when I go to that bookie's round the corner from the office to pick it up.

SUNDAY, JUNE 6

Maggie's at the hospital seeing her mother who is in a very bad way so I had to look after the kids. As Dad says, the more I see of them, the more I like them. Sometimes I look at them as though they're not even my own kids and find myself envying the father until I remember with a warm glow that, hey, I *am* their father. And then I feel guilty that I don't spend enough time with them and I don't take enough part in their development.

The other day, Maggie tried out some 'Are You A Good Father?' quiz from the middle pages of the *Daily Mail*. Unfortunately, it turns out that I am most definitely *not*. I didn't know the name of their form teachers, their best friends or their favourite hobbies.

Maggie berated me when I'd finished: 'Steve, this just isn't good enough.'

'Thanks, Maggie, you're not in school, you know. I might not know much about the *minutiae* of their lives but the one thing I *do* know is that I love my children. I'd do anything for them: I'd die for them if necessary.' How true that is.

'That's not good enough, Steve, you have to live for them too.'

'Come on, Maggie, that's just cute word play.'

'No, it isn't, it's true. Do you remember that film *The Paper*? Marisa Tomei, who's heavily pregnant, is berating Michael Keaton, her husband, because the newspaper he edits always seems to take precedence over everything else in their lives – even at such an important time for them both.'

'So?'

'She gives him a hypothetical – one of many in the film. She says something along the lines of "what if you came home and there's a man with a gun pointed at my head and he says that you have to choose between me and the paper? Keaton replies that that's easy, he'd choose her to which *she* retorts, "That's the whole point, no one's ever going to ask you to make that choice. Life isn't about those sort of life or death choices, it's about a series of individually meaningless decisions and actions, like turning up on time for dinner and appointments".'

'So?'

'So saying that you'd die for your children is meaningless unless you're prepared to live for them too. Playing football in the garden with Jonathan' – she dismissed my attempt to cut in – 'more than once a year, doing a jigsaw with Melanie, being here every evening after six o'clock . . .'

I interrupted her. 'That's because I'm out earning a living.'

She gave me a withering look and, without even bothering to

rebut my claim, continued with her diatribe. 'Look, Steve, children need certainty. They need Mum *and* Dad to be reliable, to be there not just when we want to be but, generally, when *they* want us, when *they* need us.'

She softened. 'You love the kids and they love you. With all their hearts. But they need more from you than you seem prepared to give and that's not fair. Part of the reason I married you was because I thought you'd make a brilliant father. I think you still could but you have to work at it.'

End of lecture. But she's right, I know she is – even if I wouldn't admit it to her. So I welcomed the opportunity to play with the little perishers. We had a trillion games of Frustration (most of which I lost), we ate a prodigious quantity of sweets and we played football in the park (I won). I can't remember when I've enjoyed myself more. Some of it was down to the fact that I'm now richer than I've ever been in my life but there was also something more, something better, something that transcends gambling and money.

When Maggie returned (looking drained: her mother really is dying – I think today was the first time that Maggie's had to accept it emotionally as well as intellectually), she thanked me for looking after the kids.

'You don't have to thank me,' I replied. 'It's my pleasure. They're my kids too.' She didn't say anything – she didn't have to – but, in spite of her anxiety, her sorrow and her tiredness, she did at least manage to smile.

TUESDAY, JUNE 8

Great day which even Phil-in-a-bad-mood couldn't spoil. Went to the bookie's and picked up my winnings.

'Would you like a cheque, sir?'

Would I like a cheque? I've never been asked that before in a bookmaker's; I can't remember being called 'sir' too often either. Would I like a cheque? Well that's kind of you to offer but I think I'll take it in CASH. *Lots* of cash. I want a very large wad indeed. I want to look like one of those flash bastards I've seen in betting-shops peeling off £50 notes. I want to feel like a player, even if it's only for a few hours. Would I like a cheque indeed!

The only time I've had (almost) that much money in my hand was when we bought a car for Maggie so that doesn't really count. But this is MINE, all mine. Sure I'm going to pay a few bills, buy the kids a couple of presents and even put some aside for a rainy day but I'm also going to hit the town and ENJOY myself.

I know what I'll do: I'll tell Maggie I've got to go away overnight for a sales conference – it won't bother her in the slightest. Then I'll book a room at the Swanky De Tutto Swankiest Hotel and treat Samantha to a night of absolute bliss. There will be gambling (at the casino), champagne (not a drink I care for but, well . . .) and bodily fluids will be exchanged. Lucky girl.

WEDNESDAY, JUNE 9

Been wondering where I should hide my money and I've decided to hide it with my diary. Obviously if Maggie finds both then I am completely fucked: it would be a fate worse than debt. But then if she finds this then I'm fucked anyway, so I've got nothing to lose.

Wish I could stop fucking swearing. No I don't. Maggie does though. She often asks me to cut it down – especially in front of the kids, which is, I guess, fair enough. Having said that, there aren't many words they don't know from school. Jonathan even asked me what a 'cunt' was the other day. When I told him that it was a very horrible word for a lady's front bottom, he said the sweetest thing: 'Can I pretend that I never heard the word, Daddy?' Bless.

But Maggie was always on at me not to swear even before we had the kids. Which, of course, only made me want to do it more. 'Do you have to swear in *every* sentence?' she'd ask. So I'd try to compose a sentence without any swear words in it and, fuck me, I couldn't.

Which reminds me of the only joke I can ever remember. This bloke has two sons who are always swearing and he's had enough. So he says to his wife that the next time he hears one of them swearing, he's going to punish him severely. The next morning, the boys come down for breakfast. 'What would you like to eat?' asks the mother. 'I'll have some fucking cornflakes,' says the first boy, whereupon his father thrashes him. The mother asks the second son what he would like for breakfast to which he replies, 'Well, I'd be a cunt to ask for cornflakes . . .'

THURSDAY, JUNE 10

Dropped a fucking fortune on a couple of spread bets this morning. The test match has just started and I thought it might be fun to sell the total runs in the morning session. Usually, it has to be said, there aren't many runs scored at the start of a test: a combination of batsmen's caution and opening bowlers' long run-ups and blistering pace preclude heavy scoring and so a sell is the wise choice. Except this morning England decided to treat the first two hours as though they were the last two hours of a rain-affected one-day international and slogged the ball all over the place.

Obviously, there was more to it than that: in hindsight, England have taken the not unreasonable decision to hit the fast-bowling attack out of the match and, if possible, the series. Those were the England team's tactics; mine were to close my bet as quickly as possible but by the time I got through to the dealers, I was looking at a £300 loss which I wasn't prepared to contemplate for just half-an-hour's play. Oh no, I want more value for money than that from my gambling. So I let the bet run until the session ended and lost £520.

The guy on the news said it had been England's session – well here was one Englishman who could have given him an argument. Foolishly, I decided to chase my losses and did my old trick of buying players for large amounts of money with a view to selling them ten runs later when their spread had moved up.

Unfortunately, four or five quick wickets put the kibosh on that and lost me (just under) another *nine* hundred quid.

FRIDAY, JUNE 11

Shit, I hope this isn't the start of a long-overdue losing streak.

After yesterday's debacle, I managed to lose bigtime at poker – £550. Usually, I don't mind: after all, the money isn't exactly lost, more recirculated, but tonight was meant to be an antidote to yesterday's disasters and instead it merely added to them.

We were six. The same guys as last week except for Nick who, as I guessed, has had enough. In his place was this new guy who Jake brought along. His name's Nigel but he calls himself 'Nige' (ugh).

News from the Bad Man. Apparently, he's losing weight and toning himself up while he's inside so that he can add even more victims to his collage of women that he's 'had'. He's also asked Ben (tonight's big winner with £700 – most of it mine) to organise a lonely hearts ad in one of those free ad newspapers. Ben's also got to record the Bad Man's voice-mail for it too. He's planning to do it in a cod-French Sacha Distel-like ooh la la-type accent. God help the women of Britain.

SATURDAY, JUNE 12

I've been neglecting my spread betting of late and today provided some perfect opportunities to attend to it. Between them, the cricket and the horses tested the battery power of my remote control – although Jonathan did pester me a lot to switch over to the Cartoon Network and I had to let him know who's boss (Melanie was at the hospital with Maggie).

In fact, the cricket was so exciting that there were (one or two) times when I found myself too absorbed to bet. Thorpe was batting so well that it was all I could do to breathe let alone pick up the phone, which was a shame because the way he was going, they were obliged to mark up the spread nice and high whereas anyone watching could tell that he was living dangerously and could hole out at any moment. Which is, of course, what he did – just as I was reaching for the phone to sell his innings. Oh well, you can't win them all.

But, at least, in contrast to my run of the past few days, I can win *some* of them. I sold the total runs in the last session and made ten quid. OK, so it's not a fortune but it's a win and I'm grateful for anything on the credit side of the ledger at the moment. Better than that, I came out £120 ahead on individual players' batting spreads (although I did lose out on wicket-keeping dismissals which are, I suppose, a bit like trading in corners in football matches).

As for the racing, I'd already popped into Henry's to see Samantha and check that she's still on for Wednesday but while I was there, I placed a £10 win yankee. As befits a mug bet (well, why else does Henry offer them tax free?), the yankee perished – although, annoyingly, one of the selections won at 6–1. So it was all down to the trades I made on individual races and across the cards. The horse I fancied most in my yankee (only because the *Post* pointed out that it had made all the running to win over the same distance before) was running at York. I don't normally do belt-and-braces bets, but having lost the first two legs of my yankee, I figured that I didn't exactly have much dosh on the nag and so I backed her over the favourite (with a two-length advantage) at £20 a length. Although my horse went on to lose, it did at least win the match bet for me by seven lengths (net nine) which meant a profit of £180. This more than offset the money I lost selling double-card numbers and selling favourites.

I figured – and with the number of bets I had this afternoon I needed a maths degree just to work it all out – that by the end of the afternoon, I was about eighty quid up. An amazing result on so much turnover.

Maggie returned home looking completely drained, poor thing.

Her mother's not getting any better. It's so fucking remorseless. If there is a God (which, of course, there isn't), he must have a pretty wicked sense of humour. I started to say something along these lines to Maggie but she didn't want to know: she's past trying to rationalise it all. It's gone too deep for that. From here on in, we're into naked, raw emotions, instincts and feelings. No time for wisecracks or challenging thoughts. All Maggie will even begin to accept is homespun philosophy along the lines of 'Don't worry, darling, it'll all be for the best.' Meaningless crap but then, like a dog listening to its master, Maggie's not hearing the words, just the tone in which they're conveyed. If our relationship weren't fundamentally secure, her mother's cancer could jeopardise it. That's why they call it cancer because it's so fucking corrosive. Fortunately, Maggie's an absolute saint while I'm just about intelligent enough to know when to shut the fuck up and to give her the space she needs at the moment. That's why I have no qualms about Wednesday: it will give Maggie the opportunity to do all the things she can't do when I'm around – like read late, fart and sleep diagonally. Ordinarily, I won't let her do the first, the third is impossible and Maggie is strangely reluctant to do the second in my presence. It's not that she's like the Queen who has a special dispensation not to have to do such things, it's just that she believes that it's not something a woman should do in front of a man. It's strange really, given that she's a *Guardian*-reading teacher, but I ain't complaining – even if she does give me a hard time about my own bottom burps.

TUESDAY, JUNE 15

Maggie, if you're reading this then I'm away tomorrow night at a sales conference (boring!) in Birmingham.

Maggie, if you're *not* reading this then I'm away tomorrow night staying at a top London hotel with Samantha.

THURSDAY, JUNE 17

Great night.

Samantha and I checked into the hotel at six and immediately got down to some serious rumpy-pumpy. We then had a drink. This necessitated a raid on the mini-bar and the use of those arsey one-sip-and-they're-gone miniature bottles of spirits.

We decided to have dinner at the casino – on the basis that it is, of course, free – but before we even sat down to eat, I'd dropped a couple of hundred quid. And then, after dinner, everything just came right. I don't know whether I was trying to impress Samantha (by showing her how cleverly/carefully I bet) or whether it was just my night but it really was extraordinary how my luck ran and how I took advantage of it.

I won more than £1,000 at blackjack. I was generally staking between £20 and £40 a hand but, occasionally, I went for the odd £100 splurge. One hand in particular was incredibly lucrative. I put on what I thought was £80 but which was actually £105 because a £25 chip had got mixed up with my £5 ones. I drew 8s against the dealer's 10. Now, although eighteens (as I could reasonably expect to get) aren't much use against twenty (which the dealer could reasonably expect to get), I *always* split 8s – not so much because I'm brave but, in fact, because I'm a coward: because I can't bear the thought of drawing to sixteen. Besides, the principle of always splitting 8s (and indeed aces) applies whether one's playing for a pound or for £1,000.

So I put in another (as I found out) £105 and was dealt a 3 on my first 8. I *always* double down on eleven (unless the dealer has an ace) so there was nothing else for it: I put in another £105 and got . . . a 3. Shit and, of course, I'm not allowed another card on that hand.

On the other 8, I got a 9 which at least meant that I wasn't obliged to draw another card but was still not particularly impressive.

Then it was the dealer's turn. Drawing to a 10, he got a 4

and then – and the bastard paused to really rub in the tension – a wonderful, beautiful, gorgeous 8. He was bust and I won £315 in a single hand!

I left the blackjack table at the zenith (more or less) of my fortunes and went to the roulette table where I covered 26 and all the numbers around it. I guess I was staking in total about sixty quid every turn of the wheel. Twice in a row 29 came in which helped fund quite a few more turns until, joy of joys, 26 came in winning me £1,000.

Of course, I gave back the thousand in absolutely no time at all but still ended the evening £800 up.

Samantha, who'd shown a disappointing reluctance to gamble on her own, was thrilled for me although I did catch her giving me some 'looks' while I was playing blackjack which, rightly or wrongly, I interpreted as 'Christ, you've got it bad' looks.

Having said that, she was warm, effervescent and, yes, yielding when we went back to the hotel afterwards. The only discordant note came when we parted in the morning. She looked me in the eyes – and I swear I could see a tear in her eye – and said, 'Thanks, Steve, it's been fun.' Not 'It *was* fun' but 'It's *been* fun.' Am I being Percy Paranoid to imagine that she's thinking of giving me the old heave-ho?

FRIDAY, JUNE 18

Poker OK. Some laughs, some lagers, some tortilla chips. Lost a couple of hundred quid.

Then I went round to Samantha's. She kissed me when I walked in but I could tell from her body language (and from my suspicions of yesterday morning) that SOMETHING WAS UP. Sure enough, she sits me down and launches into a nervous monologue which, rather sweetly I thought, she'd obviously spent the last twenty-four hours constructing.

'Now listen, Steve, I don't want you to take this the wrong way but I think it would be best if we didn't see each other ever again.' She put up her hand like a traffic warden doing point duty as if to halt my paean of protest but she needn't have bothered, I had nothing to say.

Although slightly flustered that I hadn't followed her script, she continued. 'I've really enjoyed seeing you, Steve, and I think I've got some really hard feelings for you' – I resisted the temptation to crack the obvious joke – 'but I think we'd better stop before it goes too far. You're a married man with children. I know you didn't make me any promises and I don't want you to but it's been playing on my mind. Let's call it quits and be grateful for what we've had.'

She could see that I was looking puzzled and, misinterpreting it as an inability to come to terms with her 'bombshell', she came over to sit next to me, in the same way that a nurse might comfort a patient who's been told they've got a terminal illness. In fact, she misread me: I was just mulling over her extraordinary ability to string so many clichés together. When, I wondered (but only to myself), was she going to tell me that she wanted us to always be friends?

As if on cue. 'I want us to always be friends.'

Something stirred inside me. Pissed off anyway by having lost money at poker, I thought, 'Fuck off, bitch, I was offering you sex not friendship. I've got enough friends but not enough – one can never have enough – pretty young girls willing to offer me their cute, pert bodies.' But I didn't say that. Once upon a time, when I was eighteen or nineteen, I would have done but now I can't be bothered to give as much of myself away. So I smiled and told her that I perfectly understood and would always remember her with affection, blah blah, blah blah. There are words which mean something, words which mean nothing and then there are words you find yourself using when you get the big e. As if it mattered, as if any of it matters.

In fact, the only thing which might have bothered me at all was sorted by her valedictory speech. 'I've told Henry I'm leaving. He went, "You can't, you're too good to leave" but I told him it was for personal reasons and he understood.' Hope Henry won't give me a hard time about losing him his best cashier. Fuck him if he does.

So that's it. *Finito*. Can't say I'm sorry. All good things come to an end etc. etc.

SATURDAY, JUNE 19

Felt a bit blue today. Never mind that I don't care *that* much about Samantha, I just don't like being 'chucked'. There's so much that's wrong that I can't change, that I have to accept: my work, my marriage, myself, that I need everything else to *work*. I hate to think how I'd feel if I weren't still taking the pills.

Didn't fancy going down to Henry's and couldn't be bothered to spread bet or, indeed, do any other sort of betting. So I took the kids and the latest John Grisham to the park and whiled away a few hours watching them and reading him and soaking up the sun.

Felt a lot better by the end of the afternoon but I still feel a bit 'hummie' as Sue used to say when she was feeling (emotionally) out of sorts. I'll try being extra nice to Maggie this evening (God knows she could use some TLC) and see if that doesn't in turn make me feel good but first I'll go out and get us a couple of vids. If I were genuine about wanting to please Maggie, I'd get a Merchant-Ivory film but I'm not feeling *that* altruistic. I'll make it up to her in bed later . . .

MONDAY, JUNE 21

More news from the Gerard front. Apparently, he did manage to get hold of a blow-up doll from somewhere ('Complete with vaginal hair and *three* orifices' as he told Jake on the phone the other day) and he's renting 'her' out for three phone cards a session ('Two if they clean her out afterwards').

TUESDAY, JUNE 22

I did a morning's work at the office and then just took off. This time of the year is always tough for me and I like to reserve a few hours just for me on the day before.

I went to the bookie's and whiled away the afternoon backing second and third favourites in the same race. It's not such a dumb system, I reckon. Let's say there are ten runners in the field and the favourite is 5–4. I back the next two horses in the betting – say at 7–2 and 4–1. If the favourite *doesn't* win (and two out of three don't), the odds are that one of these *will*. On a unit stake of £50 per horse or dog – that's to say £100 a race – I lost about £150: not bad for over £1000 worth of bets.

WEDNESDAY, JUNE 23

Maman est morte. Today was the twelfth anniversary of Mum's death. I still miss her – not so much for herself as for the stability and symmetry she gave the family. When she was alive, there was Mum and Dad, Sue and Steve. We were, to use the current idiom, a functional family. When she died, we all in our own ways went to pieces and the family unity which she prized above all else was itself shattered.

I, of course, had a breakdown. Sue, typically, buried her head in the sand and escaped to Devon, leaving me to deal with the broken shell that had been Dad. Interestingly – and I don't know whether it had anything to do with Mum's death or whether indeed I can take any credit for it – Dad has mellowed a huge amount in the past decade. Maybe it has something to do with growing older or maybe because he's on his own and daren't risk alienating people, he's been obliged to become a more docile, less abrasive, kinder man. I don't know. What I do know is that he and I get on better now than we did when I was at home. Or maybe I've changed, it's hard to tell.

However, Dad becoming so much easier to get along with is the only mitigating feature of Mum's death. Just the memory of what happened makes my heart palpitate and my stomach churn.

I can remember it so clearly: where I was (in school), what I was doing (teaching maths to Tim Buchan's class) – even what I was wearing (blue cord jacket, blue chinos, check shirt from Marks). By contrast, the events of last Thursday, yesterday even, are a distant memory.

I'll never forget being summoned to the head's office to take a phone call. I don't think I'd ever had a personal call at school but it wasn't impossible that one of my friends 'needed' to pick my brains about some social arrangement. I recall my annoyance as I walked to the office and the well-chosen reprimand I intended to give the person who had disturbed me and, effectively, my boss. And then I remember my surprise at hearing Dad's voice on the phone: he'd *never* phoned me at work. Before I could even register that surprise, before I was even fully conscious of it, he'd told me: 'Steve, there's been a dreadful accident, Mother is dead.' There was no moment between me being surprised at his voice and me being shocked by his words. The two happened almost simultaneously: to find any time between them would have been like trying to see the light go out on the fridge door.

It wasn't till later, at the hospital, that I learned that it wasn't an 'accident' – not unless taking eighty sleeping tablets is an accident. She'd committed suicide, topped herself, done away with herself, done herself in. All the hackneyed synonyms for the reality of ultimate self-destruction ran through my mind: I found myself chanting them like an incantation to ward off the horror, anger, tears that I knew would come, which were in fact already there, but which I wanted to postpone until I could get back to my flat where I could give them the individual attention they were sure to demand.

'Committed suicide,
Topped 'erself,
Done away with 'erself,
Done 'erself in.'

'Committed suicide,
Topped 'erself,
Done away with 'erself,
Done 'erself in.'

I remember being angry with myself – I mean *really* angry – that I couldn't find better synonyms, make a better rhyme, make it rhyme at all. I was letting her down. I was her clever son, the first member of her family ever to go to university and I couldn't even fucking chant properly. What sort of fucking cunt was I? What sort of cunting little fucking shitebag was I who couldn't even do that for his mother?

I bit my hand so hard that it not only bled but they had to give me stitches. That'll teach me, I thought, that'll *teach* me for not caring enough about my mum.

And then the tears started and then they never stopped. Not for weeks, not for months. Not really, not for longer than a school period at a time. And then I had my breakdown brought on by the certainty that I too would suffer the same fate. With therapy what I took for inevitability was only ever the possibility of a self-fulfilling prophecy. And yet so sure was I of my reasoning, so convinced was I of my rationale, of my *sanity* that, ultimately, only madness could forestall death.

THURSDAY, JUNE 24

Paid some bills today – felt extremely virtuous.

Went into a bookie's determined to 'earn' some money. I did my 'carry on betting the favourite at double the stakes until you win' lark using £100 stakes. I bet across the cards (dogs and horses). I won the first race at 2–1 (plus £200); lost the second (minus £100); lost the third (minus £200) but won the fourth at 5–4 (plus £500). I won the fifth at 7–4 (plus £175), the sixth at evens (plus £100) and then lost the seventh (minus £100), the eighth (minus £200) and the ninth (minus £400). I bottled it completely when it came to putting eight hundred quid on. Just as well as the next favourite came nowhere. Still, after factoring in the tax, I won about £100 – a much better result than I'd have achieved if I'd been betting 'normally'. This progressive losing system works if a) a favourite comes in within the first few races and/or b) the unit stake is low enough to allow me to carry on doubling my bet if a favourite *doesn't* come in for a few races and/or c) I don't mind walking away after a few races having lost anything up to £1,500.

Melanie's school's open evening. Apparently, she's doing really well and is top of her class in maths (makes one believe in the hereditary principle).

Had a nice chat with Judith, the mother of one of Melanie's classmates. When we first started talking, I didn't think anything about it beyond 'pleasant woman'. But later, when I saw her talking to one of the teachers, I found myself fancying her bigtime. She's really sexy but subtly so and I have an instinct that she's up for it.

FRIDAY, JUNE 25

Exhausted. Whacked. Worn out. Cream-crackered. It's not late – I dunno, two in the morning – but I'm gone. Should leave this till tomorrow but don't really want to go to bed yet even though I'm so sleepy cos Maggie's there and, like Garbo, I want to be alone.

Good evening. Great laughs. Won a hundred (I think) and drank far too much Diet Pepsi – all that phenanyline or whatever the sweetener contains – s'made me feel kind of edgy. Strange mixture, edgy and sleepy.

I'm sorry, Maggie, if you're reading this at the end of the year after I've killed myself. I do love you, honest I do, you're a great person, really you are. It's me I don't like, the me I see in your eyes. I don't like what I see reflected back. I'm not a bad person but I'm not a very good person either. Not an amazing thought. I don't do amazing thoughts at this time of night, at this time in the morning, but you know what I mean. And don't worry about Samantha and all that: she didn't mean diddley squat – or is it squit? I'm too fucked to care. You were always my number one girl (remember?) and I've never betrayed you where it matters most: in that part of my heart where I've always loved you. In that bit of me, no matter what I've said, done or written, I've always been true to you.

Sorry 'bout everything else though. Brain's gone. I'm gone. Zzzzzzzzzzzzz.

SATURDAY, JUNE 26

Even though Samantha's left, I still feel a little awkward about going to Henry's. He's not likely to *say* anything but I just don't fancy getting the *look*.

So instead I took the kids out to the park to play on the boating lake which they absolutely adored and then we went out for a hamburger which they enjoyed even more. I too had a great time.

It meant that by the time we got home, I had 'earned' an afternoon in front of the telly gambling on the gee-gees. Even Maggie who'd spent the morning with her mother (still not good) couldn't and didn't disagree.

I did some trades on individual races and lost about two hundred quid but I made up for it a little with a £60 profit on double-card numbers (not a good day for favourites). I also lost another £20 off my Switch card on a horse which wasn't covered by the spread-betting firms but which I thought might pull off a shock at 50–1. Which is why I only backed it for a tenner each way. I also don't like to bet too wildly on my Switch card: I don't like the bank (and possibly Maggie) to know how much I'm gambling, win or lose. I'm furtive when all's said and done.

SUNDAY, JUNE 27

I took Maggie and the kids to see her mother in hospital. She's not at all well. Although I've known she's had cancer for some time, it's never really sunk in but seeing her in the ulcerated, decaying flesh, there's no doubting she's on death row. Poor thing. She's not a bad old stick, Maggie's mum. I know we've had our ups and downs and she didn't always approve of me – I'm not so sure that she does even now – but we've reached an accommodation of sorts.

Betty, I call her, for that's her name, but I always think of her as Mrs Wallis – not least, I suspect, because that's how she always refers to herself. It's something I hate in people of my age: I find it arrogant – indeed, when someone calls me Mr Ross, I find myself looking around for my father – but it's a generational thing and, in someone of her age, perfectly acceptable.

I have to say it cut me up to see Maggie tending to all her mother's needs. She's truly kind. Poor Maggie. It'll be her next, that's what she must be thinking – that's what'll occur to me when my Dad dies: me next. My mum's death didn't have that effect on me because I'm a man, not a woman but Dad's will, undoubtedly, and the generations will move up a notch. Instead of Dad, me and Jonathan, it'll be me, Jonathan and then Jonathan's son. It's right, it's natural and, barring unthinkable disasters whereby someone dies out of sequence, inexorable. Still, that would be precious little comfort to Maggie – even if I had the insensitivity to mention it to her.

The children weren't fazed by it at all. For them, particularly for Jonathan, it was an opportunity to explore a hospital ('It's just like *Casualty*') and play with lots of things they weren't supposed to be playing with. Of course, they didn't know precisely why Gran was in hospital – no reason why they should – but they, particularly Melanie, had gathered it was something serious.

'Is Gran going to die?' asked Mellie in the car going to the hospital.

'Yes, darling,' said Maggie gently, 'she is, but not yet.'

'Will we see her die?' asked Jonathan.

Melanie, sensing that this was the wrong thing to say, tried to hush him but I gainsaid her. 'That's a perfectly reasonable question. No, we won't see her actually die but one day, hopefully not for a very long time, she will die and then she'll join Grandad.'

'In heaven, Daddy?'

Oh dear, why do children always have to ask such tricky

questions at sensitive times. Obviously there isn't a God. How could there be a God when little children get leukaemia? Trouble is you can't say that to a child when all he wants to hear is that beloved Gran's going to be OK when she died. Also, I don't want to upset Maggie who is something of an agnostic in such matters (she's also a Liberal which makes her something of an expert fence-sitter) and, feeling her eyes boring into me, I chose my answer carefully.

'Gran is a lovely lady' – so far so good – 'and *I* believe that when she finally passes away, her spirit will live on in all of the people who loved her. So she'll be in Mummy's heart and in your heart and in Mellie's heart and in my heart.' I caught Maggie wiping away a tear and realised that I'd said the right thing. The funny thing is, I wasn't being insincere. Sure, I didn't give the kids chapter and verse on what I *do* believe – about corpses rotting away and that's it – but I wasn't lying when I told them that people live on in the people who knew and loved them. That's about the strength of it.

The kids weren't saddened by any of this. In fact, the only reference they made to their grandmother's condition was when they asked her if they could try on her (unbelievably unbelievable) wig. To her credit, Maggie's mum didn't get upset or annoyed but burst out laughing. She's a good old trout: I'll miss her.

MONDAY, JUNE 28

Had a bet at the bookie's and I mean *a* bet. I popped in intending to have a few £100 bets (which seems to be my unit stake these days) and then I had a rush of blood to the head and decided to put the *lot* on just one horse: Jonah Boy which was running on the all-weather at Southwell.

It just seemed to be indicated: improving form, a suitable name (Jonathan's my boy), good jockey, a second favourite and no second favourites had won yet at any of the day's meetings, well-weighted in the handicap, the newspaper tipsters who had backed winners in the earlier races *didn't* tip him while the newspaper tipsters who *hadn't* backed winners in the earlier races did tip him and, best of all, he looked fabulous in the shot I saw of him on the TV screen – all black and shiny and full of beans. Oh yes, I thought, I'll have a bit of that; I'll have a lot of that.

It was a six-furlong handicap and, to start with, he was at the back of the field, a long way behind an outsider who looked to be six or seven lengths clear of his nearest rival but, going into the final two furlongs, the leader came back to the field and Jonah Boy took his place as though the two horses were first magnetically attracted and then repelled. Despite a late charge from the favourite, he hung on to win me £764.

I was whooping/whooshing until a steward's enquiry was announced. Fucking hell, I don't believe it. I was just about to do my pieces when they announced that the enquiry didn't affect the winner.

WEDNESDAY, JUNE 30

June was my best month yet. I won £5,800 which is absolutely incredible given that gamblers are supposed to lose (well how else can bookmaking firms change hands for hundreds of millions?). I know that all of that (and more) is accounted for by my fabulous Derby win but lesser men than me – albeit with less at stake – would have let it go to their heads and gone on tilt.

I'm precisely halfway through the bet and I'm a massive £8,900 up. Reading this month's entries, I think (I hope) I might have done my losing streak. I've got to learn to have the courage of my convictions on the upside but also have the intelligence and the humility not to chase my downside.

In some respects, I'm tempted to close the bet now. Here are the advantages and disadvantages.

Advantages (of closing it now)
I live
The nine thousand I've won won't be jeopardised
No one but me knows that the bet was meant to run for a year
I can start my new life now

Disadvantages (of closing it now)
There's little doubt that I'll win the bet at the end of the year
I might win *more* than nine thousand
I know that it's meant to run for a year
I'm not really ready to start my new life – for example, I've probably left it too late to get into university for this October.

I'm going to keep on going until the end of the year but I will spend more time addressing the question of what I'm actually going to do when, as I now expect, I win. After all, I can't leave *everything* to chance.

THURSDAY, JULY 1

Wimbledon's been going on for a few days now without any participation from me.

Part of the reason why I haven't yet had a bet is that my knowledge of tennis – i.e. Wimbledon (do they actually *play* at any other time of year) – is extremely limited. I simply haven't heard of most of the current up-and-coming players. Consequently, I have a tendency to go for long-priced former greats who are chancing their arms in one final quixotic attempt at glory. Thus, I backed Rod Laver at 50–1 in the middle of Bjorn Borg's run of championship victories and Billie-Jean King in the days of Martina Navratilova's hegemony. I do the same thing at snooker: by the time I've cottoned on to Stephen Hendry (I'm still backing Steve Davis on the basis that a man of his class must get it together again sooner or later), he's lost it.

Maybe I should do what I do on the (rare) occasion that I have a flutter on the darts and only back players at or near the top of the betting who I haven't heard of.

In the end, I restricted myself to buying the red-hot favourites in individual spread matches. My (albeit uneducated) view is that the unhappy clay court specialists who were seeded here because they're so high up the rankings have largely been disposed of by now leaving us with the decent players who will have some sort of run.

There must have been something to my logic as I won a couple of hundred quid.

FRIDAY, JULY 2

I would rather go blind . . .

I've been singing that for the past six hours – thereby annoying the fuck out of myself and everyone else.

Through no fault of my own, I'd been losing steadily for the first couple of hours. The only time I did have a fabulous hand (a pair of 5s in a game of four-card Omaha which saw the flop come down 5–5–3), I played it sensibly and modestly but could I get anyone to stay in with me? Could I bollocks. I suppose it's inevitable that no one else wanted to know: they can see that a full-house is likely to win it and, given that none of them could make trips at that stage, they had no alternative but to fold. My only hope was that someone would have a pair of 3s in their hand but, alas, no one did. The only other possibility, that one of the wilder players would stay in on flush or straight possibilities, also didn't materialise. Where *is* Gerard when I need him?

So when it came to my call (for a whole round), I opted for five-card stud and announced my strategy.

'I'm going to go blind.'

'What's the matter, Steve?' said Ben feigning alarm. 'Have you got glaucoma?'

Jake looked up from counting his stack of chips. 'You should try sleeping with your hands above the sheets.'

'It didn't do Stevie Wonder's career any harm.' Douglas's contribution, of course.

Nathan, the only other player present, just giggled.

'What's the matter, Nathan,' I said, going into Joe Pesci in *Good Fellas* mode. 'Do I *amuse* you? Do I make you *laugh*?'

'Only when you don't mean to,' he said, deadpan. He's a bit of a dark horse is Nathan, our 'good old reliable Nathan' – and not just because he's from the Caribbean.

'You'll all laugh on the other side of your exceptionally ugly faces,' I warned them, 'when I've taken all your money off you.'

More jeers. 'He's so *butch*!'

I started to deal. One card dark and then one open. The other guys all looked at their dark cards; I didn't and made the mistake of reminding them that I was going blind.

'Really, Steve? You should have told us.'

'You are so full of courage!'

'You are so full of crap!'

'OK, fellas, I hear you. I just wanted to be straight with you.'

'Seriously though, Steve,' said Nathan, 'there's no great advantage to going blind in poker. It's not like in brag where you have to pay double if you look at your cards. All you're doing is handing an advantage to your opponents. Not that we're complaining, of course.'

'You watch,' I said, as I dealt another round of cards and, as the strength on the table, raised it the maximum, thereby persuading Douglas and Nathan themselves to fold. 'I'm going to continue going blind until a pair is showing on the table.'

No one else folded and, after all the cards had been dealt, Ben was showing (something like) 4, 9, jack, queen not suited and Jake had 3, 7, 10, queen also not suited. Meanwhile, in front of me (once again not suited) was 2, 6, 8, king. As the strength on the table, it was up to me to bet or check.

'OK, twenty quid. You know you've got diddley squat. *I* don't know what I've got and, more to the point, nor do you. Now you know why I've gone dark.'

Ben folded. I beat him with just the four cards showing. Jake, much to my alarm, raised. Now it was time to look at my dark card. Sod it, a 9. Still, time to put into action part two of my master going-blind plan. I composed a 'Wow-I-can't-believe-my-fabulous-luck-oops-I-better-disguise-it' face and immediately re-raised.

Now it was Jake's turn to look worried. In the same way that I didn't know what my dark card was and therefore was only betting on prospects and/or other people's weakness, he knew that he had good cards. Or maybe he didn't and was only bluffing. That's what I love about poker, there are only so many combinations of cards but the mental possibilities are endless. By the time I get to the third layer of 'Does he know that I don't know that he doesn't know', I've lost it. Maybe that's the difference between a great poker player and merely a good one. Still, the bottom line was that, at best, Jake could only have a pair of queens whereas it was *just* possible that I could have a pair of kings.

So Jake saw me. 'What you see,' I said showing my 9 with a rueful smile. 'Go on, then, hurt me.'

He showed me his pair of 10s and did just that. Bugger.

I carried on going blind for the whole round which was long enough to make me realise that going blind will usually get you into the final two of a hand but will rarely scoop the pot – not unless *no one*'s paired up – including their dark cards. And when that happens, the pots aren't anything to get excited about.

The one exception – and it *almost* makes the whole strategy worthwhile – is when one does exactly as I did (i.e. not look at the hole card until the ultimate showdown) and then actually makes a pair, particularly a big pair. Then the double (or do I mean triple?) bluff really pays dividends because the opponent *has* to take me for nothing.

I finished the evening wiser but poorer to the tune of £410. I ought to register as a fucking charity. All I need is a finer day. If I ever get out of here.

SATURDAY, JULY 3

Popped into Henry's today.

'Hello, stranger,' he said, more friendly than sarky.

'Wotcha. It's only been three weeks, Henry.'

He raised an eyebrow and smiled. 'As you say, Steve.' And then I smiled back: everything was fine. Customers, good customers who lose more than they win are a lot harder to find than cashiers, however honest and pretty they are.

'You're a scallywag, young man.'

'Oh call me that again, Henry, please.'

'What, a scallywag?'

'No, "young man". No one ever calls me that any more.' And I can't use the expression myself without lapsing into Harry Enfield.

'All right, young man.'

'What do you fancy, Henry?'

'A winning afternoon.'

'You and me both, squire.' Why is it that I adopt different speech patterns depending on who I'm speaking with? Am I a chameleon or something? Still, I enjoyed slipping into our standard badinage: it was cosy and reassuring, like tuning into a golden oldies station on the radio.

Mind you, Henry is unlike any bookmaker I've ever met in that he's prepared to share any knowledge he's got. Many's the time he's told me that he's heard a whisper for a horse or that a *spieler* he respects has larged it on an outsider, and I've had a winning nibble myself. Henry doesn't object to his punters winning: what he's looking for is *turnover*. The more money comes in, the more money he makes: it's as simple as that. He's never going to lose because all he ever seeks to do is to balance his book but to make any sort of profit, he needs punters and volume.

Strange business, bookmaking. I think you have to have the right temperament for it: stoic, patient, passive. I'd be totally useless at it.

I stayed at Henry's for a couple of hours betting on absolutely *everything* that came up. Given the number of races I was betting on, I reduced my unit stake back to twenty quid. Apart from anything, I didn't want Henry to think I was on tilt. I have got some pride.

I lost about £350. It would have been more but for a dog forecast. Trouble was I only had a fiver on it. That's the thing with gambling. Not only do you rue the times you lose but also the times you win.

Went home (and played some catch in the garden with Jonathan) to watch the tennis on telly. Fortunately, this is the one sport that Maggie, who'd just returned from the hospital with the kids, actually likes. Although she doesn't understand why I have to have the teletext with all the spreads in running superimposed on the picture. I told her that I'd rather see the teletext than the tennis so a mixture of the two is fair enough.

Her watching with me made it harder for me to close existing trades and open new ones which wasn't necessarily such a bad thing given my tendency to fuck up. So I merely contented myself with following my initial trades in which I'd bought the number of total games across four matches. With two three-setters and two five-setters, I came out (genuinely!) about evens. *And* I spent an afternoon with my wife.

SUNDAY, JULY 4

Maggie's starting to give me grief over the holiday. Up to now, every time she's mentioned it, I've managed to stall her by saying that the tickets would arrive a couple of weeks before we were due to go. But that excuse effectively ends today as the departure date is supposedly July 18.

I do feel a little shitty about it. Not really towards Maggie but more for the kids' sake. They're starting to talk about what they're going to do on holiday and little Jona's even packed his bag! I'll make it up to them.

Meanwhile, I've got to pluck up the courage to tell Maggie that I didn't book the holiday in the first place. It *shouldn't* matter but, knowing Maggie, it will. S'okay though because I've got enough money for us to go elsewhere. Wouldn't mind suggesting Vegas but I don't think Maggie would exactly leap at the prospect.

I'll wait until Maggie says that *she's* going to phone the travel agent/holiday company and then I'll tell her. Just like that. I won't tell her why, but otherwise I'll come clean. 'I'm sorry, Maggie, I couldn't afford to pay for the holiday. At the time I had to pay, it was a direct choice between the holiday and the house. Do you remember the hassle we had with the mortgage? I couldn't tell you because' – fuck, what can I say if she asks? – 'because I couldn't' – useless – 'because I wanted to spare you the distress of making the choice.' Much better. At the end of the day, she'll have to accept it. It's Hobson's choice.

TUESDAY, JULY 6

Phil called me into his office today to congratulate me on the Rouall contract. Truth is, it was a piece of piss but then if I get blamed for things which are beyond my control, I might as well be praised for things which fall into my lap.

Lucky in work; unlucky in luck. Lost three hundred quid on just *one* horse at lunchtime.

WEDNESDAY, JULY 7

Maggie and I had our little confrontation and, in the way that such things never do, it didn't go the way I planned it.

She said that she was fed up waiting for the tickets and that if I didn't do something about it, she would. 'No need,' I told her. 'They won't be coming because I didn't book the holiday in the first place.'

Her face registered the words 'I don't believe it' but before her voice could give them sound, I quickly confessed.

She did me the honour of hearing me out – even up to and including my apology and promise that all was now well financially and that we could book up to go somewhere else, somewhere we *both* wanted to go to, i.e. not Cyprus – and then, when I'd finished, she spoke in an alarmingly quiet and deliberate tone.

'You've deceived me, Steven, and, what's worse, you've deceived the children. I can't tell you how *disappointed* I am in you.'

'Sorry, ma'am,' I said like a naughty schoolboy and tried to give her a cuddle but she rebuffed me in a way that made it perfectly clear that she would rather be intimate with the Yorkshire Ripper.

'I hate you. I really *hate* you. This isn't just about a holiday, this is about my family, *our* family. I won't ask you why you did it: it doesn't matter *why* you did it. It's enough that you did it.'

'I'm sorry, Maggie, honestly I'm sorry. Besides, I didn't think you'd want to go away at the moment, what with your mother . . .'

She put up a hand. 'Don't, just fucking don't.' I was shocked, Maggie doesn't use that word except (very) occasionally if she's dropped something valuable or had an accident.

'I'll arrange another holiday, a better holiday.'

'No, you won't. I will. And you won't be coming with us.'

She walked out without saying another word and now it was my turn to be gob-smacked.

THURSDAY, JULY 8

I was in Reading for the day. I can't say I didn't think about Cathy because of course I did but there was absolutely no question of going round to see her (even though she'd undoubtedly be out at work anyway).

It all seems so long ago. I'm the same age but I'm so much older, so much more experienced, jaundiced, *used*. The early part of this year seems closer to the early 1980s than it does to this month. I was a different person – I *am* a different person – and it's Cathy I have to 'thank' for that. I'm harder now, more impervious to any feeling deeper than attraction, flirtatiousness or simple lust. When I think how well I reacted to Samantha ending our affair. Before this year's reprise of my infatuation with Cathy, I might have blown that up into something so much more . . . I don't know . . . melodramatic. How wonderful, how inevitable, I would have thought, that I am the victim of a 'grand passion'. Look at me, I'm a great lover with all the pain that that entails. Look at me, I'm Romeo, Abelard, Don Juan. Look at yourself, Steve, and see the truth: a furtive fumble on the side, a guilty night of (nothing more than) companionable non-intimate intimacy. As great lovers go, I'm gone: I'm nothing special – just Mr Everyman trying to get away with as much as he can before he gets found out, by the wife, life and detumescence.

FRIDAY, JULY 9

There's a tradition in our poker set that whenever I propose anything – be it new maximum stakes, playing more draw poker or just a break to get some beers – the guys will all cock their heads to one side, think about it, say 'That sounds like an interesting idea' and then change their minds and say, 'Nah!'.

Like I say, it's a running joke and, if I weren't the butt of it, I suspect that I too would laugh like a drain every time I heard it.

But my latest proposal was a serious, important one and not only was it instantly rejected but it actually led to the adoption of a worse poker policy.

What I suggested was that, to end this ridiculous business of dragging and IOUs (which go on from one poker session to another), all players should – I checked myself just as I was about to use the word 'henceforth' – bring along £400 in folding stuff for each session. Then, when they've worked their way through that, they could drag and borrow, if they want to. 'It'll speed up the game no end, honestly it will, guys.'

As I expected, the others – Ben, Douglas, Jake and Nathan (but not Peter, a friend of Nathan who, quite properly, kept shtum) – gave it the big 'Nah!' but I asked them to stop kidding around and give it some serious thought.

Ben, blast him, still said 'Nah' but the others at least kicked it around for a while. Unfortunately, their conclusion was even more unpalatable than the status quo. Table stakes. Once you've played all the money in front of you during any given hand, then you've gone 'all in' and any other betting takes place without you. This sounds fair but all it does is allow people with quite good hands to stay in at little or no risk and thus, effectively, preclude bluffing.

I informed my fellow players of my opposition to this plan in my usual measured tones. 'Fuck off. If we play table stakes, then it'll bugger up our game. I know that that's what they play in casinos but this isn't a casino. They only do that because they can't trust people who've dragged to pay up afterwards, whereas we can.

'The only way I'll play table stakes is if everyone agrees to have, say, fifty quid in front of them before the start of *every* hand.'

'Nah!'

Maybe I should have just walked out there and then but, well, I don't like to make waves and, I don't know, maybe there's a way to turn this to my advantage. Perhaps if we're playing a 'darker' game like Omaha and I'm heavily down, it at least allows me to participate through to the end without having to jeopardise all of my cash – especially if we're allowed to keep cash reserves in our pockets.

Nevertheless, I'm getting a little fed up with certain aspects of our poker crowd. It's just a little prissy at times – especially when we've got guests and we have to pussy-foot around them. Also, I miss Gerard. The *game* misses Gerard. Sure, we've still got Gerard stories but it's not the same. In the words of pompous politicians, I might have to consider my position.

Of course, such world-weariness has nothing to do with the fact that, once again, I lost. Perish the thought. OK, maybe a bit but it's not the entire cause. The guys are changing. Douglas's not quite as funny as he was (although, to be fair to him, he never is when he's sexually satisfied, which he is at the moment thanks to a twenty-five-year-old leggy lovely, lucky bastard), Ben's over-preoccupied with work and Jake is just, I don't know, the word that springs to mind is a Yorkshire one: mardy. It's a mixture of moody and morose and it kind of sums up Jake at the moment. I think he's having a bit of a mid-life crisis is our Jake. Well, welcome to the party, big boy, but I wouldn't begin to know how to reach him even if I wanted to which, to be honest, I don't really. So there we are, the dysfunctionals. See No Evil, Think No Evil and No Thanks, I Think I'll Pass.

Having not thought about it for, literally, days, I find myself once more thinking about the bet. Does this portend anything or does the mere act of thinking about it help reduce the chances of losing it? Or am I talking absolute bollocks because my brain is aching to be switched off?

SATURDAY, JULY 10

Maggie, who's been icy cold with me ever since Wednesday's little 'contretemps', greeted me with what seemed like warmth when I came down for breakfast at eleven o'clock (like you do on a Saturday).

That's better, I thought, maybe she's come round to understanding that there's no such thing as a 'perfect' husband and she'll just have to make the best of what she's got. But, no, the reason for Maggie's change of mood is that she has struck a blow for (her) independence and in doing so has gone from bitch to cat.

Using 'her' money, she's booked two weeks for her and the children at a cheap and cheerful hotel in bloody Cyprus.

My first thought was to forbid it but then I thought about how much of a prat I'd look so I just looked a little downcast. 'Oh come on, Maggie, think how you'd feel if I excluded you from a family holiday.'

'Don't try appealing to my better instincts. I haven't got any as far as you're concerned at the moment.'

'Think of the children.'

She looked at me witheringly and I thought how glad I am not to have been a pupil in her class. 'I have thought of the children and that's why I've booked them a holiday.'

'Yeah, but even so.'

'Look, Steve,' she said softening a little, 'don't worry about the kids. I won't tell them the real reason why you're not going to be with us. I'll just tell them that you're working hard and you can't get the time off. They'll understand.'

'But I don't. Look, I'm even owed two weeks' holiday.'

She took a deep breath. 'Steve, it'll do me good too to spend some time away from you. I need time to think.'

'Oh I see, this has got nothing to do with me forgetting . . .'

'Forgetting?'

'OK, not booking the holiday. This is just a pretext to get away from me.'

'It isn't a pretext, Steve. You not booking the holiday might not be the cause but it's certainly the occasion. We need some time apart. Both of us. We have to do some hard thinking about each other, about our future together. You know what I mean. You do, don't you, darling?'

Congratulations, Maggie, I hadn't figured you for being so perceptive. It was my time to sigh. 'Yeah, I guess you're right.'

We stood there looking at each other and then, suddenly, we found ourselves cuddling.

'I love you, Maggie.' And I meant it.

'I love you too,' she replied through racking sobs.

Oddly enough, I also found myself *wanting* her. Not just 'it' but *her* like I haven't felt towards her for, gosh, *months*. I told her and her sobs turned to giggles. 'Don't! We can't! The kids could walk in.'

'Well then, let's do it upstairs,' I said urgently, tweaking her breasts.

'No, Steve, not now. Let's do it tonight. If you can still remember how.'

Maggie and I spent a really enjoyable afternoon together watching the Wimbledon finals. She knew I was betting (or, as I explained to her, 'trading') but, obviously, she didn't know how much. I found that the easiest solution was to divide all figures by ten. Sadly, I ended up down – £570, or, as far as Maggie was concerned, £57 – thus giving her the opportunity to bestow upon me her disapproving schoolmarm look. But it didn't last long and, at the time of writing (six o'clock), we're still on for, if not a night of passion, then at least twenty minutes of nookie. Reminds me of that old joke: when does a woman make love? While a man has sex.

SUNDAY, JULY 11

Maggie went off to the hospital so I stayed at home to look after the kids. Apparently, her mother isn't getting any better. On the other hand, she isn't getting any worse either. So I suppose there's no reason as far as her mother's concerned why Maggie shouldn't go off on holiday.

I'm not sure though. After last night, which was as intimate and fun as our sex life has ever been (which isn't saying much but even so), I rather hoped that Maggie might relent and invite me to go on holiday with them all. But I've made it an unspoken principle that I ain't going to ask: it's got to come from her. And since it didn't, then I assume that it's not going to. Having said that, the old girl might just have a point – absence making the heart fonder and all that. And it's only two weeks, after all. Other families do similar things. And I don't mean to be nasty but there's precious little chance of Maggie getting picked up on holiday – I mean apart from Cypriot waiters chancing their arms but Maggie doesn't strike me as the Shirley Valentine-type: too suspicious; too self-conscious.

After doing my Daddy bit – cricket in the park, ice-lollies from what the children call the 'green' shop (because that's the colour of the shop, stupid, as Jonathan told me when I had the ignorance to ask) – I made them some lunch and then sat down to watch the cricket on telly.

Since I was in a lighthearted mood, I decided to have a few silly bets (no, not trades, bets). I sold the magic eye index (how often the umpire will ask for the third umpire) and, for a *real* giggle, *bought* Phil Tufnell's runs. Yup, that's how carefree I was feeling: I'm a character in a Bateman cartoon – The Man Who Bought Phil Tufnell's Runs. For good measure, I also bought the total number of runs in the session (despite promising myself that I would never do that again) and bought the number of lbw appeals in the session too.

I think by nature I'm a buyer rather than a seller when it comes to spread betting: I enjoy accumulating each run/wicket/goal/corner, each pound, rather than starting off with everything and then resenting each run/wicket etc. for losing me whatever my unit stake is. So if there's a football match which I genuinely believe will finish goalless, I'd still rather buy goals, goal minutes, shirt numbers etc. rather than sell them simply because I prefer filling an empty glass to draining a full one. The only exception to this is where I sell, say, total points in a rugby game with a view to closing after ten or twenty minutes in the hope that a slow, cagey start to the game will yield dividends. But while my trade is active, I'll absolutely *hate* every minute of the game. In that example, the only time I'm at all happy is when one of the teams regains the ball in their own half for that's what selling goals/points/performances is all about: you can only bear to see them playing in the middle of the park: essentially, the only people who should sell in such circumstances are people who love gambling but hate sport.

My trades lost me over £800, which is on its way to being serious money. Incredibly, it wasn't the (what I thought were) silly bets which let me down (good old Tuffers!) but the 'sensible' trades. There were precious few runs scored and absolutely *no* lbw appeals. From now on, I have to become a seller. That's if I can bear it.

Maggie came back from the hospital looking pretty grim, poor lamb. However, her mother's given her blessing to Maggie going on holiday which is, I suppose, good news of a sort.

MONDAY, JULY 12

Did some greyhound forecasts and made a profit on the day of £186 (give or take a few pennies). 'King magic', as they say down Romford way.

TUESDAY, JULY 13

Jim (in accounts) gave me a ring this morning with a tip for a horse named Mr Chelsby in the 3.30 at Beverley. Now I love tips but I'm feeling a little raw from my recent experiences with 'red hot certainties' so, although I was obviously going to have a punt, I decided to be a little circumspect.

However, by the time I got to the bookie's, I was feeling not a little pumped up (it's amazing what a tinned salmon baguette, a bag of KP Skips and a Diet Coke will do to the adrenalin) and so I gave it the full £100 each-way treatment. I paid the tax but didn't take a price – which was just as well as it drifted from tens to fourteens.

If it had been a four-furlong, 219-yard sprint, I'd have won £1,680. Unfortunately, it wasn't, it was a five-furlong sprint and Mr Chelsby, having led from the off, got beat by the shortest of short heads on the line. I got back £280 which, less the hundred I lost on the win part of my bet, gave me a profit of £180 but I was still disgruntled. There's such a difference between an each-way shot that gets pipped at the post and one that just runs on into third place. Same outcome but with the former, you feel ripped off, while with the latter you feel blessed by fortune. It's the difference between, on the one hand, rummaging through the packet to get a blackcurrant fruit pastille and, on the other, picking one at random.

The knock-on effect of this disappointment was that I gifted my winnings (and two hundred more) back to a grateful bookie. So I'm not just an unlucky cunt, I'm also a stupid cunt.

THURSDAY, JULY 15

Took the afternoon off to go to Melanie's sports day. Well, she is my only daughter and I won't be seeing her for two weeks come Sunday.

There was also the prospect of seeing Judith who was looking rather gorgeous in a simple white shift with her long chestnut hair cascading down the front and back of it as though that were part of the dress's pattern. It was a baking hot day and most of the parents – particularly the dads – appeared to be incredibly uncomfortable, sweltering in the sun but Judith looked totally cool. John and Kevin, the only two other dads from the school I know by name, unknowingly endorsed my taste by hanging round her like bees round a honey pot.

I've been in this situation before and I know the best way to play it is to stand aside and let the others make all the running. It's then only human nature for the object of all this interest to look outwards, beyond her suitors, if only to gain some respite from the attention. I only had to ask myself where Bogart or Cooper or Jack Nicholson would have been standing in similar circumstances to know the best tactics to employ.

'Hello, Judith,' I said nonchalantly and ever so slightly seductively. 'I see you've shaken off Bill and Ben.'

She laughed. A delightful, involuntary spasm which caused her to put her hand to her mouth.

'I'm sorry, you're far too young to remember Bill and Ben.'

She laughed again, but this time it was more of a woman's laugh than a girl's. 'Wish I were.' I like it when a woman uses the subjunctive: it appeals to the pedant in me.

'Anyway, looks like you've pulled.'

'Oh, they're just having fun,' she said with a wave of her hand before adding coquettishly, 'besides, I'm a happily married woman.'

'And I'm a happily married man. We could play happy families together.'

'Sounds fun to me.'

And so on. Oscar Wilde it wasn't but there was some top-notch flirting. Ordinarily, I don't like shitting on my own doorstep but I'm prepared to make an exception – especially as she's got as much, if not more, than me to lose if any subsequent affair were discovered.

FRIDAY, JULY 16

I always thought that you couldn't have too much fun at a poker game but this evening at Ben's (the silver lining to the Bad Man's absence is that we're allowed to play poker at Ben's place) proved that sometimes we can all get carried away and go too far.

Tonight, Peter revealed to us that he's an epileptic. He chose an unfortunate moment to make his declaration because we were in the middle of an exceptionally jolly patch. One or two of us giggled silently and I found myself biting my lip to stop myself going into hysterics – not that epilepsy is anything other than terrible but simply because we were already laughing so much.

It was Ben who cracked us up. 'Saves on an electric toothbrush, I suppose.' Ben says the things the rest of us only dare to think but it was enough to utterly destroy me. So much so that I had to leave the room and go to the loo for fear of wetting myself. Fortunately, when I returned, Peter was laughing along with the rest of us. He's a good bloke and I hope he becomes a regular.

Not that it even mattered but the poker too was great fun. Sometimes it only takes one new person to subtly change the way we play and, with Peter, we're playing much more Omaha, which suits me fine as I think it's probably the best game.

What I like about Omaha is that it offers hope, redemption even, and also great bluffing potential. What I *don't* like about Omaha is that, sometimes, even (what look like) the best hands get fucked. For example, what, on the surface, could be better than, say, four aces? But not in Omaha, oh no! Now I didn't have four aces, nor did I have four kings (etc.) but I did get dealt four 9s and what are they worth? Absolutely nothing because you *have* to play two cards in Omaha so a) two of my 9s are redundant and b) there is, of course, not a snowball's chance in hell of pairing up on the table. It's a case of fold 'em and weep.

Not that I had too much weeping to do tonight (or yesterday

as it now is): apart from all the laughs, I actually managed to make a profit – £30.

SATURDAY, JULY 17

If I could have just one wish as far as my gambling is concerned – apart, of course, from tomorrow's racing results – it's that I could have the right mindset to do longterm bets or trades.

I did the odd one or two when I started spread betting but only because they were given to me free by the company as a gift for signing up to their service. And I did all right with them (although I closed them too early). But there are so many more longterm sporting bets/trades that I call correctly but can't be bothered to actually commit myself to.

'Can't be bothered' is wrong. No, it's more a question of not wanting to have my money tied up for *any* length of time. I have a fear of being trapped in a losing bet or trade that isn't mitigated by either the thought that a) (in the case of spread betting) there is usually an escape or b) my whole goddamn *life* is trapped in one bloody great bet.

Once again there is this conflict between, on the one hand, the sane rational mathematician and, on the other, the emotional, impulsive and (yes) frightened punter. I really wish I could do something about it but, even as I write this, I *know* that the very first longterm trade I did would go humpty-dumpty.

The truth is that my idea of a longterm trade is taking a position on a whole afternoon's racing or football. To start betting on the outcome of a whole season just doesn't begin to happen for me as a concept. If I were prepared to wait that long for a result I'd buy shares.

Dad was over to spend some time with the kids before they go away on their hols. He didn't confront me directly about why I wasn't going – that's not his style – but he did tell me that I could rely on him if I needed him while Maggie's away. He knows the score does Dad. He does worry so much about me and Sue. Actually, I *must* phone her. She's all right is our Sue. No oil painting and not exactly a *Mastermind* contestant (sorry, 'contender') but she's solid and dependable and kind and generous. I wish she didn't live so far away but then that doesn't excuse me not phoning her and I know it's my turn because she's always the one to phone me.

With Dad there, I only did a few trades on the racing but it was enough to puzzle the hell out of him. 'It's all a lot different from the cross-fire half-dollar trebles I used to do. But, still, I'm sure you know what you're doing.'

In the light of my experiences this afternoon, *I'm* sure I don't. I managed to lose a whopping great £840. The truth is I haven't got the foggiest what I'm doing. I pose as a well-informed savvy sort but, in the words of Sergeant Schultz in *Hogan's Heroes*, 'I know *nothing*.' I'd be far better off doing a ten-pee yankee with all the rest of the ignoramuses instead of trying to hack it with the big boys.

Roll on the football season: at least I *understand* football form and if someone's not trying, then the crowd will let him know in no uncertain terms – unlike the bloody horses.

SUNDAY, JULY 18

Maggie and the kids went away today.

I don't feel bereft, just a little panicky in case I *need* Maggie at all in the next two weeks. Damn her – I'm prepared to *die* for her and our children. How *dare* she leave me like this. 'If You Leave Me Now? 'Don't Leave Me This Way', 'Where Do You Go To My Lovely?' – all songs I absolutely loathe – keep playing through my mind. Thank goodness for Prozac. Without it, I'd be fucked, I know I would. I think of it like a chemical safety-net. It doesn't stop me from feeling any of the usual emotions or fears that everyone else experiences and if I don't actually need it, then it doesn't make any difference. However, when I get anxious and depressed, it stops me going lower into a downward spiral and, from there, into agoraphobia.

The funny thing is I miss the kids already. They seemed happy enough as they left the house but I found myself holding back a tear or two. Maggie kissed me passionately in front of the kids – something she's *never* done before. Maybe it is for the best that we separate for a couple of weeks. Though I have to say it would have been good to have a holiday: in fact, I think the only reason I *don't* take any holiday is because Phil's always nagging me to.

It's nice to be able to write my diary without always having to listen out for her Maggiesty. It's four in the afternoon and I'm really letting it all hang out. I'm wearing a baggy T-shirt and a pair of shorts – that's it. I've got the cricket on, a can of Carlsberg going and my feet up, with this diary balanced precariously on my lap (I can't *believe* that I'm going to be able to re-read this).

I'm watching the spreads change on the teletext and I'm feeling far too mellow to do anything about them. What do I care how many runs are scored or wickets are taken – let alone appeals, A-Z indices, magic eyes and ducks?

Later, I'll go out to the newsagent's – not 'our' newsagent's but the one further down the road – to buy a decent jazz mag. That's the one drag about having kids – and, indeed, a wife – you can't keep porn in the house, not even under the bed like I used to do as a kid. Though, looking back, Mum must have known.

Some of the best sex I ever had was with my right hand while my left hand held open a mag. Boy, was I full of juice at the age of eighteen or nineteen! What wouldn't I have done with a plump and luscious forty-year old divorcee? And to think that, judging from the comments Maggie and her mates make about 'young men', I could really have been in there with just about any one I cared to have propositioned! Once again, *Si la jeunesse savait, si la vieillesse pouvait*. Or do I mean *sachait* and *pourrait*? It's a quarter of a century since I did French A Level and I'm fucked if I can remember the subjunctive.

Older women. I even read that awful D.H. Lawrence book because I thought it might be good wanking material. God, I *yearned* for someone to take me in hand – literally. I used to wander around supermarkets just to look at the rich women (I was never interested in common scrubbers) doing their shopping. Take me home with you, *please*. But of course they didn't.

Instead, I had the odd fumble with girls who would (just) allow me to get my fingers all fishy but who were (understandably) terrified of my priapic prick. The odd time that they did allow me to 'go all the way' was invariably a disappointment. For them as much as for me. The venue would usually leave a lot for me to be desired. Their expectations would have been unrealistically high and I wasn't entirely sure of the purpose of it all. It wasn't for the sex: I could do that to myself better and quicker. No, it was partly for the conquest but mainly for my insatiable curiosity. What would she look like naked, what would she be like with my cock *inside* her? But even better than that was the anticipation. From the moment that she said – or, more likely, indicated – 'yes', that was it. I was completely intoxicated with just the prospect of it. The sex itself could never live up to that level of anticipation but it didn't matter; just the *recall* of those heady moments of looking forward to *it* were enough to give me wanking pleasure for weeks to come. I got terrific value out of each lay. The girl might not have done – although none actually complained (to me) and some even made all the right noises (and we're talking post-*The Female Eunuch*) – but it was never about them and always about me. Besides, what did I care? I never came back for more. I'd got what I wanted: my curiosity was sated. Although I'm glad to say, proud to say, that I remained on friendly terms with most of 'my women' even if my desire evaporated once I'd had my fill. Until Cathy.

So my teenage years and beyond were filled with the sound of one hand wanking. The good old five-finger shuffle – sex with someone you love. What beats me is why I (or anyone else) used to buy so many mags? They were timeless so surely I only needed one or, at most, two for the sake of variety. Actually, thinking about it, it was, once again, the curiosity. What I like is the reveal, to see the girl in her normal everyday clothes and then in the altogether. I'm getting all excited. If I could only be bothered to get up off the settee, I'd get down to the newsagent's.

TUESDAY, JULY 20

Popped into Jim's office to thank him for the Mr Chelsby tip.

'Why are you thanking me?' he asked sheepishly. 'It's me who should be apologising to you.'

'That's rubbish, Jim. It's not your fault that the horse got beat.' Why, I wonder, do gamblers – even educated gamblers – say 'beat' and not 'beaten'?

'But I feel responsible.'

'Why? It's not like you *sold* me the tip or put a gun to my head and forced me to back it with my life savings. You were just passing on to me some information and I was – am – extremely grateful for it. What you've got to understand, Jim, is that although I've been backing horses for the best part of thirty years, I'm still pig ignorant on the subject. If I were to tell you the criteria on which I back horses . . . well put it this way, I'm blushing at the thought of them.'

Jim cocked his head. 'That's interesting, Steve, very interesting. You see, for me, racing is more than just a hobby, it's almost what you might call an obsession.' He paused and, in the few seconds before he spoke his next words, I saw him for the first time *outside* of his (to me) customary habitat of the office. I could picture him on the track, in the bookie's, at home with his wife. No, not with a wife. Not because I think he's gay but because he strikes me as the sort of bloke – possibly dismissed by other, less sensitive observers who can't see further than the NHS-style specs and Man-at-C&A suit as an anorak – who's never had much time for women.

He interrupted my thoughts. 'Look, Steve, I don't suppose you'd be interested in coming along to the races with me some time?'

'Interested? I'd be absolutely fascinated!'

He blushed. I don't know, maybe he is a little ginger after all. Nah, much more likely that he's a bit of a loner and he's merely thrilled that he's found a playmate or friend.

Given that I too am all on my lonesome this weekend, I suggested that we went on Saturday.

'Ah, it's Ascot on Saturday,' he said without even pausing for thought. Blimey, this bloke really *is* an aficionado. 'That will be an excellent place to start.'

WEDNESDAY, JULY 21

Can't write for long. (Obviously) this has nothing to do with Maggie and everything to do with the lure of my bed. Popped into the casino this evening. Thought I'd have a go at one of my staple protect-my-upside/limit-my-downside systems. Play blackjack for £200 or one hour, whichever ends first.

Great plan and one which has in the past produced profits. Trouble is, without any *real* deadline – like Maggie expecting me home for dinner – I had no great incentive to stop when I got to the end of my two hundred quid, as I did frighteningly quickly.

Lost another five hundred before I decided to call it a day.

One thing I hate about London casinos: they're so full of foreigners that you can't *talk* to anyone. I got fourteen in one hand and asked the rest of the players if they remembered 'burning' on fourteen or on thirteen and fourteen but they all looked at me as though I were mad. Even the dealers shook their heads uncomprehendingly. Same thing when I mentioned five-card tricks. Surely I'm still a little young to be a nostalgia freak? Maybe I just need someone to share my thoughts with: a soulmate. Tim's dead; Douglas's a little aloof; Ben's good but he's got too many calls on his time. I need a friend, a mucker, a mate. Before that though, I need my sleep.

FRIDAY, JULY 23

For the first time ever (with this poker school at least) we played at my place.

Peter was the first to arrive which gave me a chance to get

to know him a little. He's got a daughter Melanie's age who he rarely sees as he and his wife had an acrimonious divorce – as if there's any other kind. But he's not like Gerard: he talks of his wife with quiet detachment and of the breakdown of their marriage in sorrow rather than in anger.

Peter's as tall as I am, of a similar build and, I should say, of a similar age. In fact, we could pass for, if not twins, then at least brothers. Maybe I'd have been a professional man like him if I too had gone to public school – though he reckons he had a rotten time there, says it put him off buggery for life. I think he was joking; I *hope* he was joking.

Best of all, he had to ring the doorbell with his elbows. He'd brought plenty of beers and packets of nacho chips. I like people to be generous and it's surprising how mean some gamblers are. My old mate Pete used to say that meanness is a disease of the soul and I think that's spot on.

Douglas arrived empty-handed but with profuse apologies. Douglas isn't mean but I'd forgive him if he were as he's so generous with himself. I've never asked him but my guess is that Douglas would regard boring people as the ultimate sin.

Ben showed up with Jake and a guy called Ben who, it turns out, I was at school with, not that I remember him, although he remembered me in the way that younger boys often do. Just as well we didn't go in for the sort of things they did at Peter's school . . .

The poker was a bit like the curate's egg: good in parts. There was far too much high-low which is fine in itself but takes so much bloody effort to sort out afterwards. I'm also no more enamoured than I was of this table-stakes business. I tried switching to our old way on the grounds of 'house rules' but all I got for my trouble was a massive 'Nah'. I noticed Jake leading the 'Nahs' and resolved to take him at some point in the evening.

Sure 'nuff, we're playing four-card Omaha (Peter's call, good man) when, for the first time in ages (to be honest I'd forgotten about it, like one does with such things), I noticed Jake biting the fingernail of the little finger of his left hand, cradling it as he does when he's bluffing. Right, I thought, I've got you, my son.

At the point I spotted Jake's bluff, the flop had come down 10 and 8 of diamonds and 3 of spades and he's put in a big bet, having raised the opening bet before the flop (unusual for Jake to do). I'm holding 6, 7, king and ace, nothing suited but, alone among the other players, I call. The fourth card is the ace of diamonds which means the diamond flush is on. All I've got is a pair of aces and no prospects (unless the 9 comes up and even then I'd only have a low straight). Jake, biting his nail like he's on piecework, opens again and because I think – *know* – he's full of crap, I see him.

The last card is a 3 and changes everything: now a full house is the nuts but I don't take him for that either. No, I think he's got squat – so much so that when he checks, I open and, when he raises, I say 'Aha, a trap-check, that's in chapter four, isn't it?' and re-raise the maximum. My only fear is that he's got trips but all that biting and cradling tells me that he's full of crap.

And so it transpires. His (sporting) congratulations are, unfortunately, drowned by the sound of the other players moaning that they could have beaten both of us. Yeah, tough luck, guys but you've got to be in it to win it, y'understand?

That was, obviously, a high point of the evening and there were other good bits too but there were things I really didn't enjoy – like the needle between Ben and, of all people, Peter. It's Ben's fault, of course, because he's long of three or four beers (which is three or four more than he should drink at the poker table).

I suggested to Ben – gently, I thought – that perhaps he should go easy on the old sauce. He didn't seem to mind but Jake and, to a lesser extent, Douglas most certainly did. I was told to 'get off his back' and to 'shut the fuck up'.

'I don't need this in my own home.'

'So where do you need it then, Steve?'

I didn't dignify Jake's jibe with a reply but instead fell into (what I suppose was) a sulk. All this was towards the end of the evening so there wasn't too much poker left to play. I won a tiny bit of dosh (some fifty quid) but I think I lost overall. Why is it that the things we look forward to most almost always disappoint?

SATURDAY, JULY 24

Was meant to be going to Ascot with Jim today but woke up feeling a bit kind of pissed off about last night and so I cancelled. Luckily he'd given me his home number. He was extremely decent about the whole thing and promised to take me to the races another time.

Sometimes, you cancel things and afterwards regret it. Today was not one of those days. I couldn't even face going to Henry's, let alone Ascot. Even spread betting seemed too much like a big deal. In fact, it was all I could do to phone up a bookie on my Switch card to place some desultory bets on the horses which resulted in – as if I even cared – a loss of about a hundred quid.

So fucking what?

SUNDAY, JULY 25

Not dissimilar to yesterday but everything – me, the weather, the news – was sunnier.

Fancied spending the day with a friend but I left it too late. In most cases, about ten years too late. They're all busy with wives, children, girlfriends. Seems like I'm the only one at a loose end. Maggie and the kids phoned to say that they're having a great time (I'm sort of pleased) but missing me madly (better).

Thought seriously about going down to Ford to see Gerard (or whatever he calls himself these days) but it's far too hot to spend my Sunday driving down to Sussex – not when I've got to be on the road for most of next week. Besides, it would only encourage him. And I know that, one way or another, it would cost me: it always does with the Bad Man. Thought about calling Dad but he'd only be busy or, worse, he wouldn't be and he'd be *too* glad to see me, which would make me feel guilty about all the other times I don't see him.

So I just vegged out in front of the telly for the day, occasionally betting – trading – on the sports, losing about three hundred. Nothing terrible.

MONDAY, JULY 26

I took a little time off from my heavy work schedule (ha ha) to do a bit of punting on the greyhounds. I go through phases like this when I can't get enough of one form of betting – be it football trades, horse racing or blackjack – and at the moment, I'm really into dog racing. There's something blissfully simple about the dogs: short races, no jockeys, fields of six. And I can change my strategy at will and still be no more wrong (nor less wrong) than I would be if I didn't. For, unlike in horse racing where the form and the training work count for so much, it strikes me that in greyhound racing, there's far less to bother about. Sure, one takes note of the times a dog has achieved but since they can vary by more than a second and races are often won by less than a tenth of a second, there's no need to get hung up on them. So one can take a position and indulge in flights of fantasy which are almost creative.

Creative but costly: I ended up losing three hundred and fifty quid.

TUESDAY, JULY 27

I was just about to set off to the office (honest I was) when I got a call from the hospital. Did I know where they could get hold of Margaret Ross? Her mother is *very* close to death. I explained that Maggie was away and asked (very) tentatively whether I should go along as her son-in-law. Fortunately, the man from the hospital said that she's past recognising anyone now and, basically, the only point in going there was for the visitor's sake, not the patient's.

I thought about it for a while and then made the decision to phone Maggie. That's the worst thing about being an only child, she's got no one with whom to share her worries and grief and there's no one else to shoulder the responsibility.

I wasn't sure what to say but the very mere fact that I was phoning on a weekday morning proved to be enough.

'Is it too late?' was all she wanted to know.

'It will be if you're not home by tomorrow. Do you want me to arrange some flights for you?'

'No thanks, darling, but I'd be grateful if you could meet us at the airport. I'll let you know what time as soon as I know.'

I was going to tell her how sorry I am, how much I love her etc. etc. but she didn't need it and wouldn't have heard it anyway. She's in businesslike, pragmatic mode now and has no time for silly old sentiment. If my own experience with my mum is anything to go by, that will come later.

Nothing to be served by me moping, so I took myself off to the office. I went to the bookie's but I did have the decency to take my mobile phone with me in case Maggie wanted to get in touch. As it turned out, I shouldn't have done (gone to the bookie's not taken my mobile phone) as I lost £600 in no time at all.

WEDNESDAY, JULY 28

They managed to get home on another tour-operator's charter. I picked them up from the airport. Poor old Maggie, she just flopped into my arms. I had such a sense of *déjà vu* – I'm even getting it again as I write this – it's almost overpowering.

Mellie's upset too although Jona's largely oblivious to it all. He was just pleased to see Dad. As well he might be. They'll be fine, especially once they're home.

I asked Maggie if she wanted me to find someone to look after the kids so that I could come to the hospital with her but she said she'd rather go alone but could I stay at home with the kids in case she needed me. It's self-serving but it's good to hear her acknowledge that she *does* actually need me sometimes.

Took the kids home and spent the rest of the day in a kind of limbo until Maggie came home to tell us that her mother was 'critical but stable' whatever that means. Poor her. Poor Maggie.

FRIDAY, JULY 30

Came home in the middle of the afternoon so that Maggie could go to the hospital. She also asked me not to go to poker tonight and so I didn't. It's so rare for her to ask me to give it up that it would be worse than churlish – unforgiveable – to refuse. Apparently, her mother's hanging on to life by her fingernails.

After I'd picked up the children from school, there were a couple of hours of Test cricket for me to negotiate. I don't know whether it was just reward for my altruism or whether it was just good luck but everything I backed turned to gold. I really got into the right groove – the gambler's equivalent of line and length, middle and off, pitching the ball on a sixpence. As soon as I sold a batsman, he was out; as soon as I closed a position, I was vindicated in a matter of seconds.

Because I was in cautious mode – I don't know why – I 'only' won (just over) £900 and immediately got into that compulsive gambler shit of 'Why didn't I put more money on'. You just can't win – literally – when you get into that and the best thing to do is to have a few belts of whisky but, being responsible for the kids (not to mention Maggie later) I couldn't really do that. So I switched off the telly and challenged the kids to a hot session of Frustration which, in my current form, I won by a street. Still, I let them have their sweets anyway. They are children, after all.

So now we're waiting for Maggie to come home. Her mum must still be alive or we'd have had a phone call but it's a close-run thing. She's not going to recover – she's really not – so it seems such a bloody tragedy that they can't give her something to put her out of her misery. I don't believe in euthanasia as such but you wouldn't treat a dog like that.

SATURDAY, JULY 31

10.00am. If it's not today, then it will definitely be tomorrow. Doctors say that it's a miracle that she's lasted this long. Some miracle.

Before Maggie set off for the hospital, we had a brief discussion about what we should tell the children. We agreed that we should hold the line that Granny's poorly until she actually dies when we'll tell them just that. No point in distressing the little mites: far better for them to picture Granny alive and only 'poorly' for as long as possible. Actually, the amazing thing is that Maggie and I have adjusted so quickly and well to the developments in her mother's condition. Never got the chance to do that with my mother. Wish I had.

Normally, I'm terribly conservative and cautious when I use my Switch card to make bets but, today, with Maggie's mum hovering between life and death, I just didn't care any more. This was reflected in my losses: a nasty £700. Didn't give a damn though: it's only money, isn't it? You can't take it with you. And if Maggie notices the entry on my bank statement, I can always use her mother as an excuse. That's not being cynical, just honest.

Today's been a microcosm of the whole month. It's been a shitty month 'bet'-wise. I've lost £4,800 which means I'm now only £4,100 up on the year.

7.00pm. Maggie returned and, amazingly, her mum's still hanging on in there. Makes me feel guilty to even *think* about killing myself.

SUNDAY, AUGUST 1

Maggie's mother died this morning. We were woken up at five in the morning to be told. Obviously I didn't say anything but they could have waited until a more sociable hour like, say, eight o'clock. After all it is a Sunday and there wasn't anything we could actually *do* with the knowledge that she'd passed away at 4.52am precisely.

Maggie got off the phone and snuggled up to me for reassurance, warmth, consolation – all of which I gave her. She was crying but not weeping: more of a gentle sobbing, I should say. To be honest, I reckon she's relieved more than anything. She's had her mother's imminent death hanging over her like a, well, sentence of death for the past few months and there's been no real hope of remission, let alone a cure. Her death is a merciful release, best thing that could happen, now do you mind if I just go back to sleep because I'll be a lot more use to you later on if I'm not feeling so ragged?

Left the kids with Karen and took Maggie to the hospital so that she could pick up her mother's things. They said we could go and see her but I managed to talk Maggie out of it – partly because I didn't fancy seeing a corpse but also because I don't necessarily know it's such a healthy thing for a daughter to do anyway.

We left the hospital with all of my mother-in-law's possessions in a pair of matching Sainsbury's bags. Strains of 'Streets of London' . . . First song I ever learned to play on the guitar. I'm amazed my mum didn't commit suicide earlier.

Told the kids about Grandma and they took it very well. Mellie shed a few tears and then said a prayer for her. Bless. Jona said he'll look at the sky the whole time to see if she's gone to heaven.

Bless bless. Though it has to be said he was watching Cartoon Network within just three minutes.

MONDAY, AUGUST 2

Don't mean to be callous – and, to be fair to me, no one could deny that I've been Mr Supportive in the past few weeks – but it's great that it's over (apart from the funeral on Friday) and I'm free to get on with my life again. I've been so preoccupied with death that I've neglected my own life.

I'm still ahead on the bet, which I think is extraordinary with less than five months to go, and, perhaps even more amazing, I'm actually ahead of target for this quarter. So much so that I decided to (basically, apart from a couple of calls) take the day off. I'll say this much for Phil: he may be a snide cunt and a management lackey but so long as you're keeping up with your target, he'll leave you to do your own thing. When I compare – or rather contrast – him to Greg at Leaver's . . . well, he doesn't bear comparison. Whatever I think of Phil, he is at least a professional. Greg, on the other hand, was a fucking amateur and, like so many incompetent people, mistook activity for action. So he'd spend all day badgering his salesmen – whether or not they were meeting target or, indeed, exceeding it – almost entirely for his own need to be involved than for the sake of results or anything.

Decided to make a virtue out of a vice by telling Maggie that I was hanging around home just to be near her (and the children). Truth was, of course, that I would be 'hanging around home' only if Henry's could be described as 'around home' which, I suppose, on the broadest of definitions it could be.

It was good to see Henry again – especially as the last time I saw him was on a Saturday when he never has much time to chat. Judging by the welcome he gave me, he seemed even more pleased to see me. I remember thinking, I wish someone important (at least to me) could see me being greeted so effusively. It really made me feel grown up. Like the first time a pub landlord didn't laugh when I invited him to have a drink with me.

'Samantha popped in yesterday,' he said with a sly grin.

'Oh yes.'

'Just wanted to see how I was but she managed to mention you three times.'

YES!

'Oh yes. What did she say?'

'She just wanted to know that you were well.'

'I am thank you very much. Please pass on my best if you see her again.'

Henry laughed. 'You are a naughty boy, aren't you? Can't say as I blame you myself although she's not my type: I like 'em with a bit more meat on 'em.' I've never thought of Henry in terms of his libido but it seems he has one – or *had* one.

With time on my hands, I found myself looking at the phone-line tipsters' adverts in the *Racing Post* with their big promises: 'guaranteed winner', 'maximum bet advised', 'absolute steamer'. God I hate those bastards: if they know so much why aren't they sunning themselves on their private Caribbean island instead of flogging tips? They know no more – and probably less – than the newspaper's own tipsters. It's just that people don't value information unless they're paying for it. Well, I don't pay – except in my losses – and I don't think I'm any worse off.

This afternoon, I was in an indiscriminate mood. There was flat racing at Ripon and national hunt at Newton Abbot but I treated them as though they were both the same, not bothering to look into the form or even to notice the distance any race was being run over. And why should I? What possible difference does it make to me whether a race is being held over five furlongs or three miles, over the flat or over the jumps? What business is it of mine? So long as the jockeys know and so long as they communicate it to the horses, then that's fine with me.

As a mathematician, I'd rather look at the odds, at the probability. As a gambler, I'm always more interested in unproven horses or ones that haven't been properly tested. Who knows what they can do? Fine criteria, I know. Where I run into trouble is with what experts call the 'cunt factor'. I simply can't bear being a cunt.

I guess that's how betting works by making you feel like a cunt if you miss *your* bet. I'll sit there at the roulette table for an hour religiously backing 26 and all the numbers around it in the *certain* knowledge that the second I leave the table, 26 will come up. Of course, it doesn't but just the thought that it might, that I would feel like a cunt, is enough to keep me glued there for at least ten more spins than I'd planned.

Similarly with horses. You *have* to stay to the end because if you're backing, for example, second favourites through the cards, how could you bear it if a second favourite came in *after* you'd left? You'd feel a cunt. Hence the cunt factor.

However, that's not the extent of it. It doesn't just operate in the breach. No, the moment you have even the scintilla of a thought that a horse *might* win a race, you have to back it for fear of being a see-you-next-Tuesday. Then when you add this to the usual gambler's crap of going with your first fancy for fear that if you didn't and it won . . . you find yourself trapped by more superstition than a witch in the Middle Ages.

Why do you gamble, Steve? It's for pleasure, for recreation. Like fuck it is. I gamble because I am (frightened of being a cunt); I am (a broke cunt) because I gamble.

Fortunately, no horses fucked me over personally in the sense of, e.g., a top weight coming in the race *after* I'd backed a top weight. Unfortunately, I only backed two winners out of the twelve races I was there for and those were at odds of 11–4 and 3–1. So I ended up losing about six hundred quid.

Some day off. I'd have been better off taking the children out on the most expensive treat imaginable.

WEDNESDAY, AUGUST 4

Maggie was having a bit of a weep about her Mum this evening. Pissed off as I was by my near miss this afternoon, I am sensitive enough to know the difference between losing money and losing a mother.

'Come on,' I said giving her a cuddle, 'tell me all about it.'

'I never got the chance to tell her how much I loved her.'

'She knew,' I said automatically and then, thinking about it, I saw it all with absolute clarity. 'If you hadn't loved her then you would have had to tell her that you loved her. Only lies have to be articulated; the truth can remain silent.'

THURSDAY, AUGUST 5

Met a great bloke today. Was on the road for most of the day and only had time for lunch on the run so I stopped off at this kebab restaurant and asked for a doner with all the bollocks. Just as this bloke – a genuine bubble, I think, or possibly from Turkey ('*Midnight Express*? That'll do nicely') – was stuffing the pitta bread with cabbage and lettuce and chillis and that, I asked him what the kebab was actually made of. I mean, nothing personal, just an intellectual question.

This splendid man answered me in an accent that was pure Stavros: 'Sir, if you're sober enough to ask what's in it, then you're not drunk enough to eat it.'

FRIDAY, AUGUST 6

Maggie's mother's funeral this morning. Kids off school. Mellie sad; Jona excited.

Lots of seventy-something women all of whom had dyed their hair unlikely shades of brown. Big day out for them. They'd seen off yet another of their contemporaries: the thrill of the survivors with none of the guilt. Yet who could deny them their joy at their friend Betty's demise? At their age you must take your pleasures where you find them.

Maggie's colleagues and (most of) our friends had also turned out which was pretty decent on a Friday, although of course so many of our friends are teachers and are therefore on holiday. It was strange to see Jim and Sophie again after all these years. I haven't seen them since I quit teaching. Sophie's no less ugly than she was – 'Hi, Sophie, nice to see you, shame about the circumstances' – but then neither is she any more ugly. Jim's got less hair on his head (haven't we all?) but more on his chin. Why do blokes – particularly teachers – do that?

I was there for Maggie of course, as was my father, though, to be honest, I don't think she needed us or anyone. She looked cool, almost detached, as if she were focusing at some point several yards – or, indeed, hours – away.

Nevertheless, I found myself watching her, not so much for her sake but, I have to confess, out of curiosity. It's not often that I get the chance to observe her legitimately – particularly while she's under such strain. It sounds selfish, intrusive but it's not (although neither is it unselfish nor unintrusive), it's just curious: I might get some clues; I might just get to 'read' her.

In the event, I learned nothing but there was a truly scary moment when I suddenly noticed her resemblance to her mother. No, I'll go further than that: momentarily, temporarily, she *became* her mother. Strange that because she's always looked more like her father. God, I hope she *doesn't* become her mother because although one doesn't like to speak ill of the dead and all that, I'd leave her so fast that it would make her head spin.

It's extraordinary – even unsettling – how one can contemplate such thoughts whilst otherwise conducting oneself as a husband, father, erstwhile son-in-law, son and mourner. I wonder what terrible thoughts the others are harbouring.

If the bet goes against me, before I kill myself I will leave instructions that I don't want *anyone* to attend *my* funeral.

I didn't dare ask Maggie whether she minded me going out to play poker tonight. She'd have doubtless said she did mind but, worse, she might have said she didn't and I'd have had to live with the guilt. Besides, now is not the time in our relationship for me to hand her another gold-plated shout line with which to be able to slag me off to everyone we know (not that it would matter) and, if she chose, to our children (which would matter a great deal). 'Do you know, he went out to play poker on the very evening of my mother's funeral?' or, almost as bad, 'Do you know, the very day of my mother's funeral, he asked me if he could go out to play poker?'. No thank you. Insensitive and selfish, I might be. Stupid and shortsighted, I'm not.

SATURDAY, AUGUST 7

I went to Henry's with the betting equivalent of a full scrotum having not had a bet for at least three days. Dangerous mood to go gambling in and so it proved. In three or four hours, I lost eight hundred quid on a mixture of horses, dogs and lack of control.

One race in particular really summed up my afternoon. It was a hurdle race at Stratford. The first three races had been won by outsiders (16–1 plus) and so I decided to back the 6–4 favourite, Juggler's Fate, on the bases that a) it was time for a favourite to come in, b) it was absolutely rock solid in the betting, c) it had been tipped by most of the 'experts' but not napped by any of them (usually a good sign given that most of them get their naps wrong) and d) it had some genuinely good form.

Having just won £400 on Larksbeek in the 3.30 at Ascot, I decided to put the lot on Juggler's Fate and, for the first two and a quarter miles of the two-and-a-half-mile race, I was absolutely justified. He (I assume it was a he: I always think of racehorses as males unless there's evidence to the contrary) was jumping without any problem and had been in the lead since the start of the second mile when his jockey kicked on, presumably because the pace was too slow. With two furlongs and one hurdle to go, it looked to be all over: Juggler's Fate was some twenty lengths ahead of his nearest challenger, whose jockey had been whipping him for the past half-mile. I was – fatally for me – working out my returns (not especially hard at 6–4 for a stake of £400) when my horse stumbled at the final hurdle. Didn't actually fall but it slowed him down enough for the horse that had been in third place to pip him right on the line.

MONDAY, AUGUST 9

It's been a traumatic time and I'm really not good at trauma. Some people are (Sue for example) but I'm not. I cope at the time but it eats away at me and I pay for it later. Hopefully, since it wasn't *my* trauma but Maggie's, it won't take its toll on me. Not that I want Maggie to suffer but it wasn't *my* mother who died, well not this time, and poor old Maggie is going to suffer soon enough – though I have to say she's bearing up quite remarkably: if anything there's a real spring in her step although that could just be out of relief that it's all over. Perhaps I'll take her out one evening this week.

High turnover (in terms of volume of cash staked) at the bookie's but I emerged with a loss of only (about) one hundred and ninety quid. Not bad for bets; useless for 'the bet'.

TUESDAY, AUGUST 10

Was in the office today. Jayne's got a new hairdo and her tits look as ripe as ever. She even seems to have done something about her 'tache. We've always flirted – nothing more than office banter really – but I wouldn't mind taking it a stage further. Except that she's married and I don't know whether I'd be able to gaze at her lips without looking for hair.

Funny thing about Jayne is that she's also got great legs – not that I'm much of a leg man myself – but she never wears an outfit that shows off both her tits *and* her legs: it's always one or the other. Apparently, William, the north-eastern rep, has made Frank (Technical Support) promise to call him down if ever she turns up at work in anything that reveals paps and pins. Top man, William.

There's a new bonus on offer which I'm really up for: the Exec. Club, which I've never bothered with before (just as well really as

I've never qualified for it), are doing five-star long weekends in Portugal for anyone who gets in the top ten per cent. That would do wonders for Maggie – and it wouldn't do me too much harm either. Thing is, with Bolland's and J.H. Wozencroft coming on line, I'm almost there. Just a little push and we'll be there before I can say Quinta Del Largo.

Saw Jim – we went out together for a pie and a pint at lunchtime – and we're going to Sandown on Saturday week. It's something to look forward to. I like Jim but I'm not entirely sure we're on the same planet, never mind the same wavelength. For example, he's on a charity committee. Fair enough but the charity in question is for cats. Cats! Worse, he invited me to join the committee.

After telling him just what I think about cats, I told him precisely what I thought about committees.

He laughed politely but didn't try to gainsay me. He's a thoroughly decent cove or good egg who's a keen member (or so he told me) of his school's old-boy association. He even wears the tie. The 'town' tie, he was at pains to inform me, not the 'country' one. He edits the old boys' newsletter and never misses a reunion. I'm now absolutely certain that he's a virgin. I can't make up my mind whether the fact that he's (evidently) happy with his life makes him a sadder bastard than if he *knew* how pathetic he was. I can actually feel tears pricking my eyes as I write this. The pleasure that he derives from such childish pursuits. He's still only a prefect but now he's got extra privileges. He can go into betting-shops! He can go into pubs! He can wear coloured shirts! How tragically ridiculous that he should be so contented with his (what looks like a dismal) lot while I, who have so much going for me, might very well top myself in a few months' time.

FRIDAY, AUGUST 13

Friday the thirteenth. Like I give a fuck. I'm only superstitious about gambling.

Played poker at Douglas's. It's been a few weeks since I last played with the boys and that's given us all the opportunity to put that little contretemps at my place behind us.

The usual suspects: him, me, Jake, Nathan, Peter and Ben. Ben's invited a friend of his – Robert – who's Welsh. I tell him authoritatively that, apparently, the Welsh have found a new use for sheep: wool. Robert raises his eyes to the ceiling and the others (except good old Peter who has himself been the butt of my 'humour') glare at me. As if I could give a fuck.

One Omaha hand stands out. I get dealt ace of diamonds, ace of clubs, 9 of diamonds and 9 of clubs. Fantastic hand and, although I know full well that the flop can fuck up everything, I bet the maximum before the flop. Everyone groans but no one folds, a) because we're not, apart from Jake and Nathan, great folders (we've come to play, not to not play) and b) however bad their hand is, no player wants to feel like a cunt by stacking (what turns out to be) the nuts. In similar circumstances, I've stayed in with, say, 3, 6, 9, ace all in different suits and been rewarded with a flop of 6, 6, 9. The truth is that, in our game, we don't tend to go in big pre-flop which is silly if one's got good cards.

The flop comes down 4 of clubs, 9 of spades and jack of clubs. Absolutely fantastic. I've got trip 9 for openers and great house possibilities if *anything* pairs up. There's also a good chance of getting the nut flush. So, on the basis that they've already all committed themselves to the hand, I bet the pot. Fifty quid.

'You're full of crap!'

'Pot buyer!'

'This is so clearly a bluff, Steve, you've been bluffing from the start.'

'Have you got a good hand?' This from Douglas.

'Guys, guys, guys,' I interrupted, 'this is poker not happy families. If you want to know, show the dough.' This line, that I'd just made up – 'If you want to know, show the dough' – became the line of (the rest of) the evening. With variations like 'If you want to go, don't be so fucking slow', 'If you want to crow, win the dough' etc. etc.

With varying degrees of reluctance, three of them – Douglas, Jake (worrying) and Peter – called.

Fourth card was the ace of hearts. Not *brilliant*, but I've still got the nuts: three aces. So I larged it once more by betting the pot. Two hundred and fifty quid. Douglas goes all in for £30 and Peter goes all in for £90. Normally, I hate 'all in' but if it means the difference between merely buying the pot (i.e. no one seeing me) and an extra £120 (i.e. what the two of them paid to see me) then I'm all for it.

Fifth card was the 2 of diamonds – making the best possible hand an ace-5 straight. I didn't have the nuts but surely neither of the others did? They wouldn't have stayed in after the flop just on the off chance that those two specific cards would come in?

They fucking would. Well, Peter would. Douglas, who was also waiting for the (king) club flush, conceded. Good bloke, Douglas. Why is it that the first person to show his cards in a hand of poker is invariably the loser? I showed my three aces and was about to rake in all the chips when Peter quietly said, 'I think that these might just do it' and put down the 3 and the 5 to claim the hand.

'Important question for you, Peter – and for you too, Douglas. If we weren't playing table stakes, would you have paid two-fifty to stay in? Be honest.'

Douglas: 'No way. For thirty pounds, it was worth my while staying in just in case the flush came in – although, of course, you had me licked there – but for two hundred and fifty . . . there's no way I'd have risked getting my butt busted.'

Peter looked more pensive – as well he might, given that he had at least wagered three times more than Douglas. 'On balance, I don't *think* I would have done. Before the last card, I had three jacks and a chance of a straight – the straight that eventually came in – but I think there was more chance of the flush coming in than the straight. No, ninety pounds was *just* enough. I'm not risk averse but two hundred and fifty pounds would have been too hazardous.'

So that's it. I make a decent poker bet of two-fifty. At the time I made the bet, I hoped that they would call but, after all five cards, I'd have been glad if they had folded. What I couldn't – and can't – accept is this 'third way' of seeing a sixth or a third (or whatever proportion of £250 they happened to have in front of them) of my bet. For thirty quid, Douglas was almost getting a free look at both the fifth card and my cards. This table stakes/all in is going to bloody bankrupt me. I can see the value of it in a casino game where drawing and IOUs are clearly unthinkable but in a friendly game? How can it be OK for players to draw money – even from out of their pockets – *after* a hand but not during it? It's a joke. Or would be if it hadn't cost me so much money.

Amazingly, I actually finished the evening *up* – about £100. Like the good player I am, I've only remembered the bad hand.

SATURDAY, AUGUST 14

1.00pm. I only woke up thirty minutes ago. Thank you, Maggie, Melanie and Jonathan for allowing me the luxury of a lie-in, although the fact of the matter is that nothing short of a towering inferno would have woken me earlier.

The football season's started again (properly), thank God. I love cricket – much more than I do football – but, as a medium for betting, it's not in the same league as footie.

I think I may have stumbled across a clever way of gambling which, if it doesn't eliminate risk (what would be the point?), at least mitigates it. Better still, it guarantees that one of my betting accounts gets credited. On the other hand, one, of course, gets debited. Goes like this. One of the spread-betting firms offers what it calls 'Saturday Shorties'. Three teams from the Premiership which you'd expect to win their games. If all three win, the bet makes up at 50 points, with a 10-point bonus for any of the three teams scoring four or more goals. If one or more of the three teams loses or draws then the whole bet makes up at zero.

Today, it's Arsenal and Chelsea (at home) and Liverpool (away). The spread is 17–19. I'm going to sell and if just one of the games ends in a draw, then I get seventeen times my stake of £50 (£850). If, however, all three teams win, then I win thirty-three times my stake – £1,650 – possibly more if any of them score four goals. Now here's my 'cunning plan'. I'm going to back the same three teams to win in a treble with a bookie (using my

Switch card – I don't want Henry to know what I'm doing. Least not yet).

6.00pm. Did it and got a result! I placed my trade and then phoned the bookie and got odds of 2–5 (Arsenal), 1–2 (Chelsea) and evens (Liverpool) – i.e. just over 3–1 in the treble. I put on £400 (plus tax) on the basis that if I won my trade, I'd finish over £400 up and, if I didn't, I'd win my bet and 'only' lose £450. Point is, it's *not* (as I know Henry would say) backing two horses in a two-horse race, it's just covering my position – which is based on empirical experience gathered over a lifetime of losing football betting: namely that you're bloody lucky (or, in this instance, unlucky) to get three results correct.

Anyway, the ends justify the means and I did indeed win £414 on that trade and bet. Trouble is, I also sold goals, performances (in some of the other games), and double card numbers at Newmarket and bought Division Two (i.e. what *they* call Division One) goals and the SPs at Ripon – bad trades all – to leave myself £1,200 down on the day. I think I'm going to concentrate on this Saturday Shorties thing: if I can get it right, I might just get out of jail.

SUNDAY, AUGUST 15

Great day: one for the scrapbook.

Ben, Douglas, Jake and I went down to Ford in Douglas's mega-horse-power-dick-compensating BMW which, fortunately, he doesn't refer to as a 'BM' or, worse, as a 'Beamer'. Gerard's allowed to go out for the day as he's coming to the end of his sentence. Doesn't time fly – not for Gerard, I'm sure – it seems like only yesterday that he was being slammed up for the first time.

Anyway, big-hearted Jake (he's visited Gerard regularly) persuaded us all to go down and take Gerard out for the day.

Initially, the plan was to take him to a local restaurant, give him a good feed and then bugger off home. But in the car on the way down this simple scenario metamorphosed into something much more elaborate and exciting.

BRIGHTON! We decided to take him along to a hooker to get him laid and then rent a hotel room for the day to play POKER!

We picked him up at the prison's reception. Jake and I had already visited him so we weren't surprised by the casualness of the regime but Douglas, who comes from a country where they still have chain gangs, couldn't believe that prisoners were allowed to move about so freely and without any supervision. Ben, meanwhile, was absolutely fascinated. It's the first time he's ever been to a prison and, ideally, he'd have loved to have stayed for a look-see. I told him that I too had wanted to look around but that you're not allowed to. Presumably, they're worried in case visitors try to stay there.

It took us forty minutes to get to Brighton where we parked in a multi-story car park near the railway station which is apparently the best place to find any town's red-light district. And so it proved. Even on a Sunday morning, the public call boxes were absolutely choc-a-bloc full of hookers' cards.

After much debate, we selected an appropriate card and rang up on behalf of the Bad Man who was charmed, excited and appalled (but only at the thought that *we* should think that *he* would need to pay for sex) in equal measure.

We walked to the address – the basement of a grotty house in an unremarkable road – and sent in the Bad Man to do whatever it is that bad men do in such circumstances.

The rest of us went to a pub just down the road and had a few giggles at Gerard's expense. Well, *we* were paying for it, after all – surely that entitled us to *some* enjoyment?

'At this precise moment, what do you think Gerard is saying?' asked Jake.

'Ugh, ugh, UGH!' grunted Ben in an approximation of the unsophisticated noise that chaps are wont to make during intercourse.

'You love me,' I ventured.

'*I* love me,' guessed Douglas.

Gerard himself arrived at the pub to catcalls. All of us had enjoyed some sort of vicarious thrill from what he'd been up to and we wanted to hear the grisly details.

As a student of irony, I also enjoyed the subtext of the four of us each trying not to let on to the others just how exciting we found it – even though our *machismo* would only allow us to express our contempt. Having said that, the whole area was incredibly seedy. Personally, I have no *nostalgie pour la boue*: my whole life's been one long attempt to get out of the *boue* – and the *merde* – but I quite like the idea of uncomplicated, transactional sex.

The other guys all belong to the 'I don't have to pay for it' school. Which is pathetic. You can pay for it without *having* to. The way I see it, sometimes you eat in (and don't pay) and sometimes you eat out (and do pay). There's nothing more to it than that (although, in practice, I'd rather Maggie caught me having a quarter-pounder with cheese than a knee-trembler with a hooker) and for grown men to pretend otherwise is nothing less than disingenuous. Truth is, we *all* pay for it one way or the other at some time in our lives. With prostitutes, you pay before; with wives, afterwards: it's called alimony.

My thoughts were interrupted by Gerard's boasting. 'She said I was really well hung.'

'No,' said Ben, 'what she said was that you should be well hung.'

Even more extraordinary, the Bad Man claimed that the girl had given him his money back. Absolute bollocks, of course, that sort of thing doesn't happen outside of Hollywood movies but, amazingly, he then produced sixty quid out of his pocket that he certainly didn't have when we walked in so maybe, however unlikely it seems, he did get a refund. The thing with the bad man is that you *just don't know*.

After an hour in the pub for a few drinks (with Douglas complaining about having to drink what he called 'plastic' – i.e. soft drinks) and some not-too-bad pub grub, we found a two/three-star hotel which allowed us to take a room just for the day. They looked a bit surprised – even nervous – at the sight of five men taking one hotel room but I explained what we were doing and they couldn't have been more cooperative, even down to removing the bed and supplying us with a suitable table and chairs.

The poker was, inevitably, a bit patchy – especially as Douglas had forgotten the chips – but just to play poker again with the Bad Man was a total joy. He was up to all his old tricks: declaring late (and changing his mind) in high-low games, dragging from the pot and then conveniently forgetting about it after the hand and, as Ben pointed out, being so moody that he should be renamed Tom, after the Australian cricketer (a gag that went right over Gerard and Douglas's heads). Gerard also managed to conveniently 'mislay' the £60 we had given him in the first place to get laid and which he had had 'refunded'. Consequently, he was playing with our money which meant that we were on a hiding to nothing.

But then that was the whole point of the day: to show the Bad Man a good time and what better time could we have given him than to indulge all of his vices (we had also supplied him with a few bags of his favourite taco chips – although, it has to be said that Gerard is a good two stones lighter than he was before he went inside).

It was a happy Gerard who was returned back to Ford Open at the close of play. And will any of us – even Douglas – get a thank you? Does k.d. lang have a boyfriend?

TUESDAY, AUGUST 17

Jonathan's birthday today. He's seven. It seems like only yesterday etc. etc. and yet he seems to have been around for ever.

I've been a little worried about Jona recently. It's been since he returned from holiday really. He seems to be suffering from separation anxiety. In its gentlest form, it's more sweet than worrying: always telling me how much he loves me and how he wants to be with me all of the time but it does get more serious than that. The other day, he screamed when Maggie and I left him with a babysitter just to go out for a drink. He was truly inconsolable, apparently, the whole time we were out. And the funny thing is he's more clingy to me than he is to Maggie, which I can't make out at all given that he spends so much more time with her. A bigger bastard than me might even find it flattering.

But that's not all. He's also started twitching. Maybe it's more of a wink than a twitch but it's still disconcerting – especially in front of strangers. Maggie's ninety-nine per cent certain it's psychological and I'm a hundred per cent certain but that doesn't mean that we're not pissed off when well-meaning friends – aye, and 'friends' whose boring lives are uplifted by the prospect of meddling in other people's problems – suggest that we take him to Moorfield's to have his eye checked. As if . . . We *know* it's psychological so what's the point? To which we get the reply 'Then take him to a psychologist' to which I would desperately love to respond 'Fuck off and mind your own business' but usually just say, 'It's a possibility we're considering'.

WEDNESDAY, AUGUST 18

I can't believe it. I set off another fucking speeding camera. I was doing, I don't know, 44mph on a 30mph section of the A316 that drives 50mph no problem. So that's it. I'm going to get banned and lose my fucking licence and then get sacked from my job without any compensation. And all because I was going a tiny bit faster than a speed limit set artificially low so that the police or the local authority or whoever gets the money can raise as much revenue as possible. It's a fucking scandal.

I wouldn't mind – well, I would but it's a figure of speech – if they, the authorities, punished other 'crimes' a tenth as vigorously but they don't. Burglars are routinely let off with a caution, muggers are given a bit of community service and other criminals are released because the Crown Prosecution Service thinks that prosecuting them wouldn't be 'helpful'. Well what about me, you bastards? I'm not a bad man. I might be a lousy husband but I'm a good father and a decent law-abiding member of society. Doesn't that count for anything? Don't I deserve some leniency, some compassion, some *mercy*? For sure as eggs is eggs, if I get a speeding ticket I will lose my licence. My other points are all far too recent for the magistrates to let me off.

My only hopes are that the camera was out of film, or that it didn't catch my registration number or, unlikely but still possible, that they decide only to prosecute drivers who were going in excess of, say, 45mph. In short, I've got two hopes: slim and none.

FRIDAY, AUGUST 20

I really *do* hate it when Ben drinks. It's not because he loses: that's an excellent policy. No, it's because he sometimes wins – at my bloody expense.

We were playing at his place – which perhaps explains why he was drinking more than he usually does. I was maybe a couple of hundred quid down when he and I went head to head in a game of seven-card stud, nothing wild.

After all four open cards had been dealt, I was showing the 4, 8, 10 and queen of diamonds and had the 9 of clubs and the 4 of hearts in my hand. Ben was showing the 7 of hearts, the 9 of clubs, the 10 of spades and the 10 of clubs. The others (Douglas, Peter, Jake and Nathan) had all stacked.

As the strength on the table, it was Ben to bet and he opened £50. Looking at my cards through his eyes, knowing that even if I didn't already have the flush, there was still one more card to come, I decided to go in big. I saw his fifty and raised him one hundred and fifty. Being drunk, Ben's problem was less a question of whether (to go in) than how (to count out £150-worth of chips).

Last cards dark. Mine was the jack of hearts. OK, no flush but at least I got the straight. Ben checked to me. I looked at him and went all in with £180. Ben giggled and asked Jake to help him count up sufficient chips to see me.

'Queen high straight,' I said laying down my cards.

'Two pair,' said Ben and laid out his cards showing his hole cards: the 2 of clubs, the 7 of clubs and the jack of clubs.

I was just about to scoop the pot when Jake, damn him, said, 'Wait a minute. Ben's got a jack-high flush.'

I couldn't believe it. 'Aw, come on, guys, Ben thought he had two pair. He can't beat me now.'

'You know the rules, Steve, the cards talk.'

'Yeah, but even so . . .'

'Bad luck, Steve,' said Douglas. 'I have to say I took you for a flush.'

'Me too,' said Peter.

'Flush?' asked Ben. 'What flush? I thought you had nothing.'

I really felt sick. Not only did he not realise that he had a flush, he didn't even realise that I almost certainly had a flush – and, potentially, a better one than him.

If I didn't like Ben so much, I'd hate him.

That was it for me. I lost the best part of five hundred quid but, more than that, I lost my fucking spirit on that hand.

SATURDAY, AUGUST 21

Went with Jim (he drove) to Sandown on our rearranged trip to the track. Thought of taking (at least one of) the kids with me to give Maggie some time off but, luckily, they're going to her friend Helen's house for her daughter's party and Maggie's keen to go too. Still, she appreciated the offer and I earned some brownie points.

It was funny to see Jim in (what one might call) mufti. He was wearing the sort of home-knitted pullover that made me think of Howard in *Ever Decreasing Circles*. Lucky it was only twenty-one degrees in the shade. I half expected him to have brought a thermos flask full of soup and meat-paste sandwiches wrapped in silver foil – he reminds me of Murray Stevenson with whom I used to go to county cricket matches when we were thirteen. Still, there's something reassuringly anoraky about him: he seems to know what he's doing.

For starters, we went to the paddock where he showed me what I should be looking out for. 'A decent professional can, over a period of time, beat the bookies just by looking at the horses in the paddock. If you look around you, you'll see plenty of people looking at the horses but they've got no idea what they're looking at.' I looked around me. He was probably right: my fellow racegoers were mostly women who were oohing and aahing at how lovely the horses were. Didn't look too scientific to me.

'Now what *we're* looking for is a horse that is ready and willing to race. It should have a shiny coat and a fit, well-defined physique. Don't laugh, Steve, you want your horse to be an athlete.

'Don't worry if the horse looks a bit excited: that might just mean that he's really up for the race. What we're really looking for is a horse that has that little bit of arrogance, that marches around the paddock as though it owns it. Think of a great heavyweight boxer entering the ring: strong, his body gleaming, supremely confident and light on his feet.

'By the same token, we're also looking to eliminate other horses from our consideration. We're not interested in any horse that's really sweating.' I indicated that I knew this. 'Yes, that's usually the only thing that people look for and yet, paradoxically, a little bit of sweat doesn't necessarily militate against a horse.

'I'm more bothered about a fat horse, one that's carrying too much lard beneath its girth. I also don't like horses which are clearly frightened by the whole experience or, worse, angry about being at the races. You can tell the latter by its ears which may very well be stuck right back. It's also likely to be seriously uncooperative with anyone who has the misfortune to come into contact with it – including the jockey. Above all, always avoid horses wearing bandages – particularly on their *front* legs. It's the same as, say, rugby players wearing knee bandages: it's an admission before the off that something is wrong or has the potential to go wrong.

'I'm also against horses running in blinkers for the first time. They rarely win. If blinkers are going to make a difference at all to a horse's form, it's more likely to happen *second* time out in blinkers. But basically, blinkers are a bad thing and you should avoid horses which wear them.

'That's what *not* to back. What we *are* looking to back are big, fit horses which are, to coin a phrase, up for it. In a sprint, like this first race, I'm looking for a nice muscly sort with really powerful hind-quarters.'

'Point taken. But surely if what you say is true, then that should be reflected in the ring?'

'You'd think so, wouldn't you? Unfortunately – well, actually, fortunately for us – it doesn't work like that otherwise only horses that shortened in the betting would win and that's not the case.'

After all that, we decided to back Barshava. I was all for it for another reason too: it's owned by an Arab sheikh and you've got to figure that these fellows don't buy nags.

We went down to the ring where the best price we could get was 7–2 – although that was a whole point better than what some of the board bookies were offering. God, some of those guys really get on my tits: they lose absolutely no opportunity to tell the world how broke they are etc. But they seem to spend their whole time laying off bets to each other. It's like a game of fucking pass the parcel and the one who's left with the biggest liability on the winning horse loses. Except it doesn't work like that because, in practice, they simply end up betting on the rails with the big boys who then end up passing it on to we poor saps: the punters who get given nasty pinched odds. Thing that really gets me is that a horse *starts* a race at, say, 9–2, but if it actually wins, it gets 'returned' at 4–1. That shaving of half a point is a tax by any other name. I put this to a bookie once and he told me that I was imagining it. Yeah, right . . .

Another thing that bothers me about racetrack bookies is knowing which bookie to bet with. It's fine when one is offering a better price than another but what if they're both offering the same? I can't believe how pathetic I am. I find myself trying to distribute my favours equally between the bookies and even avoiding the eye of any bookmaker with whom I haven't had a bet. It's all part of my desire, my need to ingratiate myself with people. Even bookies.

However, such thoughts vanished as soon as I saw Barshava cantering down to the start. Even to these untrained eyes, he looked like the donkey's bollocks. Jim was positively purring and both of us were well chuffed to see the price going into 9–4 and even 2–1. A shortening price could mean that 'serious', informed money is on the horse or it could merely just be a self-fulfilling prophecy, that when the price goes in, more people back it, like a snowball gathering more snow as it rolls down a mountain. Either way, it's good to have your judgement endorsed. The only trouble is that, down on the track, everything is so magnified, so intense. So a horse goes from 3–1 to 2–1 – it happens in so many races at so many meetings – so what? But when you're there, caught up with the excitement, it's all so desperately important and you find yourself piling more and more money on just because you can get a bit of 9–4 when you were rejecting 100–30 not ten minutes earlier.

By the time the race actually started, I had persuaded myself that Barshava was totally unbeatable. So much so that, without realising it until afterwards, I managed to put twelve hundred quid on it in about seven or eight different bets on odds ranging from 7–2 to 9–4. Ridiculous when I'd 'only' brought sixteen hundred with me in the first place. Reminds me of how I always used to finish all my Easter eggs by the end of Good Friday.

Race started and Barshava was held up in the middle of the pack until they hit the two-furlong mark and then he was given his run. I can't remember the last time I screamed so much but if vocal power counted for anything, I'd now be celebrating a massive victory. Unfortunately, it doesn't and it didn't: Barshava just lost it a couple of yards before the line.

'One for the notebook,' said Jim, actually taking out a bloody notebook.

'One for the fucking glue factory,' I muttered, more to myself than to Jim but he heard me and laughed nervously. He didn't know just how much I'd put on. It's not necessary either: after all, he is a colleague and however discreet he might be, I wouldn't want anyone at work to know my private business.

I now only had four hundred left so, although I did the whole paddock and form thing with Jim (who'd obviously been up all night putting his form guide together), it was with a very heavy heart. Nevertheless, there was one more point of interest. I'd told Jim all about my wonderful experience at Fontwell where I'd been on the line to see for myself (and then bet on) the winning horse in a photo finish and we agreed to stand as close to the winning post as possible, notwithstanding the extra charge.

Anyway, in the third race, there was an incredibly close photo-finish between Whizzall and Kallottie Bay. From my position, I was *certain* that Whizzall had just shaded it. Jim confirmed it. I rushed round the betting ring like a loony and was amazed to see one bookie offering 4–1 against Whizzall. I absolutely emptied my pockets and put on everything – £210. Being the decent sort of bloke I am, I even told the bookie what I'd seen and asked him, gently like, if he was mad. No, he said, he'd just taken too much on Kallottie Bay and he was trying to balance his book. No skin off my nose.

And then I saw other bookmakers offering similar odds against Whizzall. They couldn't *all* be trying to balance their books, could they? I started to panic. I could feel the nasty seafood sauce from the shrimp cocktail I'd eaten an hour earlier rise in my gorge. And then the result was announced. 'First, number three, Kallottie Bay; second, number . . .'

I couldn't believe it. I still can't.

Fortunately, I did a trade on the Saturday Shorties. The teams this week were Leeds United, Manchester United and Arsenal and the spread was 16–18. I sold at 16 for £60 a point (not for the first time, I had to give them authority to take money out of my bank account via my Switch card in case the bet made up – as is hypothetically possible – at 80).

I then did a £500-win treble on the same three teams which, I am delighted to record, lost – leaving me with a profit on my football betting of £960 (for the trade) minus £545 (for the bet plus tax) equals £415. I'd have done better to have nixed the races and stayed at home but then hindsight makes geniuses of us all. Next week, I'm going to go in big on these Saturday Shorties and maybe not take out so much insurance via the win treble.

TUESDAY, AUGUST 24

I was meant to be in Aldershot this morning before going on to Portsmouth this afternoon but the morning appointment was cancelled and so I decided to go to Portsmouth early and spend some time at a bookie's.

The few people hanging around looked more than a little strange – as though their parents had been related before they'd married – but no one bothered me so I couldn't complain.

The other thing I noticed was the fabulous deal that the bookie was offering his customers. As an independent, he offers money back if the horse is beaten a short head or if it falls in a hurdle race or if it is beaten less than half a length in a chase or if it is found guilty under the non-triers rule. He also pays out on disqualified horses, while both horses in a dead-heat are treated as outright winners and are settled in full. Plus, in sixteen-runner handicaps, he pays out on the fourth if there's a withdrawal – and doesn't that happen too often to be coincidental?

I asked the bookie – nice bloke – how he could afford to do all this. His reply was, 'I can't *afford* not to do all this'.

Having said all that, I wasn't even taking advantage of his largesse since I was doing my doggie bets for later. I've got a new system if such a dumb m.o. can thus be honoured: back the three outside traps in every race across the cards at Hove and Sunderland in £5 forecast combinations and £3 tricast combinations. £1,152 staked and more losing bets than even I could be bothered to count but it only needed one decent winning tricast to make it work.

In the event, I got two tricasts and three forecasts. One tricast paid £60.08, the other £72.40 but the forecasts were pathetic so all I achieved was a £319 loss.

WEDNESDAY, AUGUST 25

Don't know what I did right but I actually had a winner today. It was only – only! – a 4–1 shot and I 'only' had a oner on it and I managed to give back three-quarters of my winnings to the bookie and so I 'only' made a profit of a £100 on the day but it'll do me.

FRIDAY, AUGUST 27

Good poker session. They say if you can remember the sixties then you weren't really there. Same thing's true about poker games.

Don't normally drink so much – can't afford to in case I lose my licence – but since I'm going to lose it anyway, what the fuck do I care? So I'm a bit tight, squiffy, rat-arsed. Christ alone knows how I got home without killing myself or being stopped by Plod. Lucky they didn't stop me cos I'd have definitely lost my licence and this way there's still a chance I won't. I think I know what I mean.

Can't remember the last time I drank so much. I feel a bit pukey if truth be told so I think I will go up to bed and be a sleepy bubble. I might even give one to my lovely wifelet.

SATURDAY, AUGUST 28

2.00pm. I've just about recovered from last night. I didn't throw up but it was a close-run thing. Funny thing was, I finished a massive forty quid up last night which is better than I usually do so maybe I should play drunk every week.

I've decided to really large it on the Saturday Shorties. Nothing else, because that's been my problem: not concentrating on a single strategy. So just the Saturday Shorties and nothing else. The three teams this week are Manchester United and Newcastle United at home and Arsenal away. Man. U. look like home bankers (not rhyming slang) and it's hard to argue against the Gooners but

Newcastle look incredibly vulnerable – even at home. The spread is 18–20 so I've sold for a massive £100 a point. As for my back-up insurance bet with the telephone bookie's, I've restricted myself to just £600 which is just one third of my upside and an infinitesimally small proportion of my downside.

This is it. This is real excitement. This is going to the wire. I'm not Steve Ross, I'm Steve McQueen in *The Great Escape*.

When I decided to do 'the bet', I envisaged days like this. A huge amount of money at stake and an afternoon spent watching the teletext. I feel so extraordinarily *alive* that I'm almost tingling. If this trade works today – and it's *got* to – then I think that this might be the way forward for me: large bets on (what are effectively) short odds. That's why I like spread betting so much: one can bet odds-on without feeling like a mug for doing so because the 'odds' are expressed so differently. For example, towards the end of the season, a football team might be, I don't know, ten points clear of its rivals. Its odds are 1–6 which, bearing in mind tax of 9% (disgraceful when the bookies themselves only have to pay over something like 6.75% to the Treasury), makes it a prohibitive bet. However, a spread-betting firm offering an index of 75 for the champions, 50 for the runners-up, 25 for the team finishing third and 10 for the fourth team might offer a spread of 69–71. The upside is only four times the chosen stake – while the downside, assuming that they only finish second, is a massive twenty-one times the stake – but it's still a feasible bet, especially if one goes in really big. It may not sound like the most exciting way to bet but when your arse – and your life – is on the line, it's got to be the most sensible. Just a few of those and I'll be home and hosed. Meanwhile, I'm reminded of the archaeologist who dug up an Egyptian mummy. Inside the wrappings was a man in perfect condition. On his face was a look of total shock which, assumed the archaeologist, must have been the cause of his death. And then in the man's hand the archaeologist noticed a piece of paper which he managed to prise away and read: 'Goliath, four hundred shekels to win.'

* * *

4.00pm. It's half-time and the portents are pleasing. Newcastle United are 3–0 up and are therefore (for me) a lost cause but Manchester United are drawing 0–0 and, hoorah!, Arsenal are a goal down. In the words of my mate Clive who'd backed Seve Ballesteros for (what was in those days a massive) £5 at 66–1 in the 1976 Open and was now just eighteen holes away from over three hundred quid, 'I'm feeling quietly confident.' The fact that Seve went on to finish second and Clive, who'd decided against backing him each-way, never quite got over his disappointment doesn't mean anything. I hope.

6.00pm. Complete sickener. I can hardly breathe let alone write so I'll just record the facts:

Manchester United scored a goal in the 90th minute to win 1–0.
Arsenal scored two goals in the 77th and 83rd minutes to win 2–1.
Newcastle United scored one more goal in the second half to win 4–0 which adds another 10 points to the 50 awarded for all three teams winning.
I have lost forty-two times my stake or £4,200.

SUNDAY, AUGUST 29

I was meant to go to the casino with Douglas tonight but I'm still reeling from yesterday. Best I don't go. Douglas is one of those people I prefer to see when I'm feeling good about myself. Besides, I'd only be chasing my losses because today is still part of the same weekend that I lost. 'The lost weekend' – I like it. I fucking hate it. I can't be a compulsive gambler because, according to all the 'experts', compulsive gamblers secretly want to lose. Well, not me, buddy. I can't *bear* losing, I really can't. I couldn't sleep last night just thinking about it. Sure, I don't mind losing a few hundred quid, that's recreational and, were it not for 'the bet', a fair price to pay for an evening's entertainment, especially as on another occasion, I might win. But £4,200 goes way, way beyond that. I'm not the sort of man to hypothecate his money but, even so, I am acutely aware of just what, and how much, £4,200 can buy. With that size of loss, I think I've crossed a kind of gambling Rubicon. I'd say 'never again' but I know that I can't do that and, besides, I'm now so down, down, down – by how much, I'll know on Tuesday, a day I'm not looking forward to – I don't have any other choice.

So, sorry Douglas, but I can't make it because . . . er, one of the kids is ill – no, best not tempt fate – Maggie wants me to take her out to a family function. Douglas's been married, he'll understand and, if he doesn't, then fuck it because, me, I'm out of it. It's all I can do to play Frustration with the kids and then only for very small stakes.

TUESDAY, AUGUST 31

Wouldn't have been such a bad month if it hadn't have been for Saturday: £4,200. I still can't believe it. What gets me is that Newcastle scored *four* goals. No, I'm not being paranoid: I don't believe that they did it just to piss me off – though they did piss me off – but that's just my luck, isn't it? Not only do I lose 32 points but, just to rub it in, I have to lose another 10 points on top.

After totting up my losses for the month (bearing in mind that there are days when I haven't recorded my gambles because they resulted in wins or losses of less than a hundred and I couldn't be arsed to list *every* last little wager) the net result for August is that I lost £7,800 on the month which means that I'm now £3,700 down on the year.

If only I hadn't *sold* the Saturday Shorties and had bought them instead – even at half the stake – I'd be quids ahead.

That does it. New strategy. Well, actually, it's my old strategy which just goes to show that what goes around, comes around. No more odds-on chances – even on spread bets. I'm not going to bet on anything where the downside is greater than the upside.

WEDNESDAY, SEPTEMBER 1

It's two weeks to the day since that speed camera went off and – touch wood – I haven't heard anything. I've forgotten who it was told me that more than half the cameras were dummies and that, with the 'real' ones, you always heard (the bad news) within a fortnight (like I did last time) but, whoever it was, he seemed to be bloody certain about it. So that is one hell of a relief. I'm also glad that I wasn't stopped for drink-driving the other night – God, how ironic that would have been! I'm now going to be Mr Keep-To-The-Speed-Limit and if anyone who finds themselves behind me on a single lane road doesn't like it, they can kiss my arse. I've got enough going against me without losing my mobility. I certainly wouldn't want to have to rely on Maggie for transport.

Actually, she's being very offish with me at the moment. I know she's still mourning her mother and all that but that's no excuse for treating me like shit. Example: I've made every effort to be really (physically) affectionate to her in the past couple of weeks but she's been completely frigid. Example: Jonathan's a normal seven-year-old and, like any normal seven-year-old, likes to get up to mischief but she's always screaming at him and telling him off. It's not right and, given the lad's problems, not fair either. I hope for her sake – and for all of our sakes – that she gets out of this mood soon. Apart from anything, the lack of a love life justifies my straying which is, in itself, a threat to our marriage and the family. She'd only have herself to blame.

I don't think the amount of money I spend gambling is out of order but the squandering of it on stupid selections most definitely is. I ought to gamble less often but in bigger denominations. Find a likely winner and then really large it.

Did that today, in fact. I only had two hundred quid in my pocket and, rather than divide it up among three or four bets only one of which might have come in, I put the lot on Pater's Pride to win the opener at York.

I thought long and hard before deciding to go for it. I read everything I could about the horse and all his rivals but what finally made my mind up was the fact that no fewer than three different national newspapers' course correspondents had made him their *only* bet of the day. I mean, never mind naps and next bests and all that, these fellows, these *professionals*, were prepared to let their reputations for that day rest entirely on Pater's Pride. What did I *know* to the contrary to gainsay them?

I took a price at 13–8 and, after digging around in my pockets for loose notes and change, managed to pay the tax. Ordinarily, taking a price *and* paying the tax is a recipe for disaster but, in my new incarnation as Pro Gambler, I've got no time for all that superstition crap.

Six-furlong race. Notthetarget, the second favourite, raced into (what looked like) an unassailable lead. Then, suddenly, with one and a half furlongs to go, a horse literally burst through from the pack to take up the running. I couldn't hear the commentary as something was wrong with the sound but I was pretty sure that it was Pater's Pride. Damn it, it *had* to be. Just to make certain, I had a quick glance at the betting screen to confirm that number three was indeed Pater's Pride but, no, it was some nag named Cocumber, a 33–1 shot. I felt sick at the thought of having the prize grabbed from me like that and my attention must have been diverted for some time because the next thing I remembered, the sound had returned and Pater's Pride was being called as the winner. Apparently, or so I learned later, he had made his run even later than Cocumber and had caught it on the line. I had won and not even realised it! Over three hundred quid as well.

I'd like to record that I did the sensible thing and exited pronto but obviously I didn't and managed to fritter away two-thirds of it in the ten minutes I had available. However, I *did* leave with a £100 profit.

FRIDAY, SEPTEMBER 3

I very rarely have a bet on a Friday because Friday night is always poker night (except when Ben's missus won't let him and/or Jake's in a strop and/or Gerard's in the jug) but I had a spare ten-fifteen minutes so I decided to have a bet. Wish I hadn't: lost £300.

That's why I don't bet on a Friday: it does my head in when I need all my wits about me. I also have to go to the bloody bank just to get enough cash to play.

The game was at Ben's which was good, although now he's smoking again the fact that he's the host means that there's nothing to inhibit him (and Jake) from lighting up. Douglas, like me and Peter, is a confirmed non-smoker but Nathan, although not a smoker himself, is much more tolerant than we are – if only because he's an habitué of casino card games. Which reminds me, I must give Douglas a ring to rearrange – to go to this 'new' casino of his to play poker.

The great news is that the Bad Man's been given his release date: October 12. With Gerard away, I've had to be the lavish one at the poker table. Sure, Ben can be relied upon to large it – especially when he's drunk a couple of beers – but he's not in Gerard's league when it comes to pot building. The trouble with percentage guys like Jake, Nathan and, increasingly, Douglas, is that they only go in when *they've* got a hand; I want them in when *I've* got a hand. Obviously, they're doing the 'right thing' but it ain't half boring and meanwhile Gerard, Ben (with beer) and I can at least be relied upon to go along for the ride – even with just 'prospects'. Bloody Nathan only comes in with the fucking nuts. In his defence, Jake does occasionally bluff – although, of course, I've got him there. Actually, Jake announced – in the sort of embarrassed look-it-doesn't-mean-anything way that guys do – that he's getting married to Sally (whom I've only met once but seems eminently suitable) *next* month.

Peter, who's incredibly curious to meet this 'Bad Man' we keep talking about, asked whether Gerard would be on probation which caused Douglas to wonder aloud about the qualifications Gerard's putative probation officer would need.

'He – I say "he" because twenty years of legislation against sexual discrimination in the workplace is rendered meaningless by the prospect of Gerard – would have to have the forensic skill of Inspector Morse, the saintliness of Mother Teresa of Calcutta and the forbearance of Job. He would also require the cunning of a fox, the heart of a lion and the hide of a rhinoceros. Added to that, he would need to relinquish all his other "clients". And even then he might find himself retiring early through ill-health.'

Jake thought about this for a second and then said: 'Say, Douglas, you're a bit like a friend only without that loyalty bit at the end.' Even Douglas giggled.

For some reason, we were switching games an awful lot which meant that the quicker-witted (Douglas and Ben) had an advantage over the 'better' poker players (Jake and Nathan) while Peter and I seemed to do well at our favourite games (respectively seven-card stud and four-card Omaha) irrespective of what we were playing before or after. I had my fair share of wins but that's to look at it quantitatively rather than qualitatively: I'd rather have had half the wins if the pots could have been three times larger.

I lost the £250 I came with plus another £250 I borrowed off Douglas who was happy to lend it to me because he was the big winner with £640.

SATURDAY, SEPTEMBER 4

Watching an afternoon's racing is like reading a whodunnit. In both cases, a plot unfolds which the reader/gambler tries to predict while the eventual outcome always looks so obvious with hindsight.

A typical afternoon's racing at any one meeting – e.g. Epsom – is going to yield a couple of favourites, a couple of second/third favourites and a couple of outsiders. Just as the thriller will have a couple of murders, a couple of red herrings and a couple of near misses. In both cases, the question is 'How and in which order will all these ingredients occur?' As with so many things, God is in the details.

Don't know why I'm feeling so philosophical, unless it's because I'm completely sated. Maggie's taken the kids out for the day (like I know where) and so I've indulged myself on every front. I've demolished a six-pack of Carlsberg (the ordinary stuff, not the Special Brew), I've eaten a whole pack of smoked salmon and earlier I discovered Maggie's horde of chocolate and wolfed the lot. I also took the (rare) opportunity to have a good old five-finger shuffle using an old jazz mag. and – for the first time in ages – a one-to-one wank line (though I have to say I've had sexier voices phoning up to tell me that they're installing kitchens in my area). I'll have to remember to hide the telephone bill when it next comes as I *know* that Maggie would query any premium-rate number ('We don't use such things,' she'd say; 'No, madam, but someone in your home did,' they'd reply and, by the process of elimination, she'd quickly work out who that someone was).

In between all those other activities, I had a massive splurge on the horses and the football. Knowing I'd have the house to myself, I decided not to go to Henry's but to do some serious spread betting. After my last debacle, I avoided the bloody Saturday Shorties but I think I got involved in just about every other trade on offer besides.

One football trade that really paid dividends was the Premiership Multiples where the home goals scored in the Premiership are multiplied by the away goals. With eight games being played, the spread was 130–140. Accurate enough, I guess, but from what I could gather, nearly all the upside had been assumed – rather like those multi-corner bets which invariably seem to make up below the spread but for which the spread is kept high because, as I've noted before, punters would rather buy than sell such indices – and so I sold the spread for £10 a goal. Sure enough, although there were twelve home goals, there were only eight away goals and so I won £340.

In the event, I narrowly lost on my horse bets but more than made up for that with my football bets. Did I say bets? I'm sorry, I meant 'trades'. I'm feeling like a dealer today, not a punter and, as such, I recorded trading profits of £622 on the day. If only I had the braces, the greed and the front, I could get a job in the City.

MONDAY, SEPTEMBER 6

I have to say that with my losses of the past few weeks, I'm having to make tough choices between paying the bills and funding my gambling. Actually, there's no choice really since if I don't allocate money to gambling then I can't win the bet. So it's back to binning the bills (which means getting up early to catch the post before Maggie does) and making each pound count in every gamble. Besides, what matters more: me and my family or the profits of the gas, electricity and telephone companies?

Maggie wouldn't be at all happy if she knew but then she's by way of being a miseryguts at the moment anyway so what difference would it make? If I were more of the he-man, caveman sort (instead of a sensitive new man), I'd just grab her tonight and, not to put too fine a point on it, give her one. That would sort her out one way or the other. Trouble is I'm just not like that. Also, I can't bring myself to even *think* about Maggie in a sexual way at the moment: I find the thought of it totally repulsive. Having said that, I feel I ought to be there for her in her hour of need as she was for me when I needed her.

Sometimes I wonder why life didn't turn out like I planned it. It was all going to be so much more – I don't know – exciting? Fulfilling? At the very least, I expected to know more of the answers but, shit, I don't even know the *questions*. Seems like the more I know, the less I really *know* (I know what I mean). Every day, I feel just a little more inadequate and that's in spite of twenty milligrams of Prozac coursing through my veins.

I need the love of a good woman, that's what I need. Not Cathy – not just because she won't have me anyway – but because even her best friend (if she's still got one after the way that she treated

Lois that time) wouldn't call her a good woman. Maggie's a 'good woman', I suppose, but, in the words of my old school reports, I could do better. Samantha? I wonder where she is now? She's undeniably 'good' and a damn sight sexier – and younger – than Maggie.

Poor old Maggie. I couldn't do it to her. Not yet, at any rate, not before the bet is settled either way. But if I win – and it is a big but – I might just treat myself to a newer, younger model. Well, why not? If I'm prepared to leave Maggie all that money if I lose, then I should be allowed to chose my prize if I win. Which reminds me: if I do have to top myself, I *must* destroy this diary first. I can't even begin to imagine how hurt Maggie would be if she discovered this after my death – she might even want to kill herself and where would that leave the kids?

WEDNESDAY, SEPTEMBER 8

Sue phoned last night and we talked for hours. I do wish she lived nearer so I could just pop over and see her. I know there's nothing to stop me arranging to go down to Devon but that's the thing: I'd have to arrange it, I can't just see her spontaneously. And then there's Dave. God knows he's a fine man and I couldn't wish for a better, more decent husband for my sister but he is so fucking *dull*. I don't think I've ever heard him express an opinion: I've certainly never heard him contradict Sue – which, as her brother, I approve of but, as a bloke, I just can't handle. It's not natural.

Sue and I were talking about Dad. I was saying how much I respect him and she was agreeing but then she added something that really shocked me. 'Of course you weren't so keen on him when you were a boy.'

'What are you talking about? I loved him, I hero-worshipped him.'

'Yes you did but you were also terrified of him. You used to go and hide under the bed whenever he came home from work and you'd misbehaved and you were worried that Mum would tell him and he'd beat you with that walking-stick.'

'Fuck, you're right. Do you know what, I haven't thought of that walking-stick for over thirty years? I'd forgotten all about that. Did he used to beat you as well?'

'No, only you.'

'But he's so sweet and gentle now. You know, all "if you're happy, I'm happy" and all that.'

'That's because he reinvented himself as Gramps' – what her kids call him – 'after Mum died.'

'I thought you loved him.'

'I do but I'm under no illusions.'

We talked some more but I was still cogitating on what she told me about Dad. She's right though, I *was* terrified of him. Physically, he's nothing now – never was much to look at – but I can remember now the sheer terror of him shouting at me, bellowing at me, to come downstairs and 'explain' – that was his word – my 'behaviour'. And then, whatever I said, even if I cried and begged him not to, he would get out the walking stick and really wallop me with it.

I guess he stopped doing it when I was, I don't know, eight or nine, and I'd completely forgotten all about it until Sue reminded me. What a cunt he was: I can't *imagine* doing anything like that to Jona. I mean, I've hit him but only with my hand and only in the heat of the moment. What kind of man, what kind of *monster*, could inflict such pain on his own son?

How could I have forgotten? Could that have helped trigger my breakdown? No, that was Mum not Dad. How could he have changed so much?

Well, that does it. I did feel guilty about borrowing that money from him. I have been paying him monthly interest but now, in the light of what Sue was saying, fuck him. He can go sing for it. I also reserve the right to borrow more from him.

Tuned into the televised football halfway through the first-half. It was still nil-nil so, looking to profit from my tardiness, I sold the first goal. Game finished fucking goalless so I lost £360.

* * *

Thought occurs to me. I always assumed that Sue moved down to Devon because Mum killed herself but, thinking it through, it had much more to do with *Dad* than Mum. By going so far away, she made sure that she wouldn't be lumbered with him. Funny the way I completely misread that.

FRIDAY, SEPTEMBER 10

The talk at the poker table turned to advertising. I think Douglas was winning at the time and the subject of advertising is as good a way as any of putting him on the back foot.

'Tell me, Douglas,' I said, 'do you lie as successfully at the boardroom table as you do at the poker table?'

'Unfortunately not,' he replied, 'which is why my child only eats on alternate days.'

Jake's turn. 'You deal with products, don't you, Douglas?' Douglas nodded. 'Then why is it lemon juice contains mostly artificial ingredients, but dishwashing liquid contains real lemons?'

'You're the scientist, aren't you, Dr Sanghvi?'

'My doctorate was in astro-physics, Douglas.' That's news to me: I didn't know that Jake was a doctor. He's gone up in my estimation – not just because he's a PhD but because he doesn't use his title in everyday life. Actually, that's something I hate when medical doctors introduce themselves by their titles in social situations. Solicitors don't say, 'How do you do, my name's Egbert Molesworthy, solicitor-at-law,' so why do doctors wear their job titles like fucking campaign medals?

One trick of mine when I meet a particularly vain doctor is to say, 'I'm in the medical world myself.' Their pompous little eyes light up: marvellous, a chance to talk shop! I give it a couple of seconds and then add, 'Yes, I'm a hypochondriac.' I'm not, but it's still fun.

I must have missed a couple of crucial lines of dialogue because the next thing I knew, Douglas was telling us all about all those awful TV commercials for washing-up liquid/washing powder featuring a mother and daughter (both inevitably from the Home Counties). According to Douglas, such commercials are known generically as '2CK ads' which stands for – and I couldn't believe it at first but I suppose all 'professions' are entitled to their own gallows humour – 'two cunts in a kitchen'.

Douglas confirmed that he can make it on Sunday to go to the casino. Despite the bad time we – or, at least, I – had last time, I'm really looking forward to it. Besides, it's a different casino with – or at least so Douglas avers – 'regular guys': though what their bowel movements have to do with poker I have no idea.

Just as well that I'm playing again the day after tomorrow (actually, it's tomorrow now) because I didn't exactly cover myself in glory tonight. I 'only' lost a couple of hundred quid (unlike big winner Douglas who won the best part of five hundred) but I played like a complete tosser. I stayed in every game we played. Nothing wrong there: that's the whole point of playing a friendly game of poker, to *play*. But I was staying in far too many pots – purely out of boredom – on *nothing*. Seven-card stud (nothing wild), I'm there right up to the penultimate card on one pair when there are (almost) certain straights and flushes on the table. OK, so that's curiosity maybe but what about when, with kings and queens suited, I stay in an Omaha hand which flops 3,4,7 (i.e. a low straight) and develops into a flush (not in one of my suits) on the last card? What's that if it's not a fear of being bored?

SATURDAY, SEPTEMBER 11

I wish I had a 'mate', a 'mucker', a 'best friend'. Just someone to hang out with, to confide in.

I'm not lonely. How could I be with Maggie and the kids at home? But I'd like a pal to go out with, who I could just phone up without going through the fucking phony charade of 'How are you?' and 'How's your family?' and all that.

I've got a lot of, I don't know, 'friendly acquaintances' – at work, at poker – but sometimes I need more. But hanging around Henry's this afternoon, I'd have even settled for an f.a. (apart from

Henry himself and he doesn't really count on a Saturday). I found myself thinking 'I wonder how Tim is?' when, obviously, I know he's dead. Funny that, I keep on expecting him to be there, in his tracksuit and trainers, when I walk in.

As it was, I found myself going in and out of Henry's – a bit restless, like – and wandering up and down the high road, popping into shops, the pub, a cafe (full English breakfast at ten past three – 'andsome), but never staying anywhere longer than (at most) twenty minutes. There was a new Dorothy Parker collection in the bookshop. I could have bought the fucking book for twelve quid rather than stand there reading it like a surreptitious schoolboy but I didn't want to waste good gambling dough on non-essentials like books and so I ended up losing £300 instead of £288. Fortunately, Henry takes my cheques.

SUNDAY, SEPTEMBER 12

Douglas and I went to 'his' casino this evening and, I have to say, the players there were a lot classier, friendlier, *nicer* than the last casino Douglas took me to. So much so that I filled out an application to join as a member in my own right.

Ostensibly, we were there to play in a Hold 'Em tournament – £20 and unlimited buy-ins – but the *real* purpose of our visit was the cash game afterwards (i.e. after we'd got knocked out).

Douglas and I were drawn at different tables for the tournament. At my table, the other eight players were the sort of people I expected to meet, only less repulsive. Nevertheless, they were still identifiably 'casino types'. Where do these people live? What do they do when they're not playing poker? Where do you go to my scuzzies when you're alone in your bed? The casino is a different country: they do things differently there. Gamblers – real gamblers, not part-timers like me – inhabit a different universe. In its own way, it's quite a benign universe: you pay your tournament fee (or, during the cash games, £5 an hour) and you get your free drinks and reality – in the shape of . . . well, everything else – never intrudes.

They make friends. Sort of. But they're only poker friends: *casino* poker friends – not like Jake and Douglas and Ben but relative strangers only brought together (and defined) by their shared vice. They might spend (the best part of) nights together, drink together, eat together, whinge together and even – on designated casino golf days – play golf together but it only goes card deep.

When people go away – for whatever reason: jail, work, bankruptcy – they effectively become 'unpersons'. Someone might ask after them ('seen Paul recently?') in a desultory way but, pretty soon, they're forgotten about until one day they reappear and it's like they've never been away. In its own way, it's the ultimate existential relationship: these people only exist for each other when they see each other.

The other eight at my table all seemed to know each other, to belong. Last time, I was proud of the fact that I didn't belong: anything that set me apart from that flotsam was fine by me but tonight, I felt a pang of alienation. Although part of me is still hanging back like a married man outside a brothel, another part of me wants to be one of them, to be accepted – ultimately even respected – by them.

We had a girl at our table which is always bad news for me: I just can't bet against chicks, I always blow it (fnarr, fnarr). She was Italian but, incredibly, had no trace of a 'tache. Luckily, I didn't remark on this to any of my fellow players as two of them turned out to be related to her.

The guys on either side of me couldn't have been more sociable or helpful but, unfortunately, both smoked (almost incessantly). Worse, the people in charge were loath to put on the air-conditioning on the basis that 'it blows the cards around on the table immediately underneath it.' Sounded like pure bollocks to me: much more likely that there's a directive from head office not to use the air-conditioning any more than is absolutely essential (i.e. to save money). Organisations have become extremely skilled at finding excuses for their tightness: the last time I stayed in a hotel, I noticed a 'message' in the bathroom along the lines of 'Like everyone else, Rip-off Hotels are really worried about the environment. Unnecessary washing of towels will completely fuck up all wildlife as we know it . . . pollution . . . global warming . . . blah blah blah. So please don't leave your towels out to be washed unless you are a complete bastard who doesn't give a damn about fish and wildlife and 'ickle furry creatures. Thank you for your cooperation. The Management.' The fact that the hotel saves on its laundry bill has, of course, nothing to do with it.

So there I was, gasping for breath, drinking more mineral water than my bladder could hold just to counteract the smoke, and dying the death of a thousand lost poker hands.

Basically, I fucked up bigtime in the tournament. It has its own pace and demands and I just couldn't get to grips with them. Everyone gets £500 of chips and when (and only when) they're exhausted, can you buy in for more. I'd have thought that £20 buy-ins wouldn't see me lose too much but I did £160 in the first hour. The thing is, out of nine players, *someone's* going to have a good enough hand to go all in, which means that you've really got to pay to play. However, unless you've got the nuts – or damn near – you're not going to win and I can honestly say I got rags the whole time. Truth is, I was happy when they announced that there were no more buy-ins and I could join the other failures – including, I was secretly pleased to see but managed to look as though I wasn't, Douglas – in the cash game.

Douglas told me that you only needed £50 to 'sit down' in the cash game and, strictly speaking, that was true but the real *players* had serious stacks of chips in front of them. I mean, we're talking *hundreds* of pounds which made my £200 look positively puny. On the other hand, given that we were playing table stakes, it did mean that I couldn't lose more than that – at least not in just one hand.

We played dealer's choice although we were restricted to a choice of Hold 'Em, Omaha, Irish (like Hold 'Em except you get dealt *three* cards one of which has to be discarded after the flop) or seven-card stud (nothing wild). In the event, everyone was so attuned to Hold 'Em that no one (except me) chose anything else.

Although I won a small pot early on, I managed to get through my money in little more than half-an-hour. Douglas lost too so there was no point in trying to touch him for a loan. I suppose I could have used my Switch card at the cashier's but I didn't fancy the idea of either Maggie or the bank seeing the casino's name opposite a £250 cash withdrawal, so we left with our tails between our legs, regaling each other with war stories which, by Friday, will have been so embellished that we'll make Amarillo Slim look like Fatboy Slim.

The fact is that, for all our post-match bravura, we – although maybe I'm misjudging Douglas who *says* that he often wins there – were hopelessly out of our depth. Those guys we were playing with were simply lethal. They could toss in a £500 chip – *just like that* – on mere prospects. Me, I need to have the nuts and even then I require a week to deliberate over my bet.

See, for these guys chips are just that: chips. If it takes a dozen £100 chips to buy/bluff/*win* a pot, then so be it. The key is to play the hands on their merits and to treat the chips merely as counters or tokens: as a means to an end. The second you stop to think about how much they're *worth* and, by extension, what you have to do to *earn* them, you're dead.

TUESDAY, SEPTEMBER 14

I had a couple of bets and lost two hundred. Stupid betting; dumb criteria. Was about to leave when I heard the first show for the next race at Yarmouth so, in a Pavlovian response, I had a peek at the form and noticed something that made my nose twitch: the favourite had never been in a race before. OK, all the horses were two-year olds but this isn't the beginning of the season and many of the other horses had already had an outing. So how could anyone justify this unraced horse's favouritism? Even if its breeding is immaculate and its work at home is fabulous, there's no telling what might happen during an actual race. I know that trainers are adept at putting their horses through their paces in as realistic a way as possible – they even have mock starting stalls – but surely nothing can prepare a horse for the hurly-burly of a *real* race.

The favourite was priced at 11–10 and its price was holding steady. The second favourite in the nine-horse field – and, at 11–4, the only other real contender in the betting – had not only had a run before but had actually finished in the frame. So I thought about it and then put two hundred quid on its nose. I didn't take a price on the basis that the horse, Green Court, didn't seem to be coming in at all. Also, having paid the tax, I didn't want to tempt fate any further.

The race started and Green Court was prominent in the first three (of the six) furlongs which, in my experience, is usually a bad sign but, amazingly, while the other horses faded, Green Court just kept on and on. I waited for a challenge from the much-vaunted favourite but it never materialised – the so-called wonder horse finished well down the field – and Green Court won with ease. Better still, it was returned at 3–1 so it won me six hundred quid or a profit on the day of four hundred.

SATURDAY, SEPTEMBER 18

What the fuck do I know about Ayr? I mean, beyond the fact that it's in jolly jockoland? Fuck all. And what do I know about a horse named Leadwall? I mean beyond the fact that it's got four legs and will one day end up as cat food? Once again, fuck all. And what do I know about horse racing? I mean beyond the fact that, outside of a casino, it's the fastest means of losing money known to mankind? For the last time, fuck all. So why did I spend £500 (plus tax) backing Leadwall to win a race at Ayr?

Because I'm a complete cunt.

The thing was, *everything* – and I do mean *everything* – was in this wretched nag's (may it be boiled down for glue slowly and painfully) favour. It was running in the last race at Ayr. It was 6–4 favourite. All other favourites in the card had lost (so it was time one won); three newspaper tipsters who hadn't won a single race all afternoon had backed it; it was a course and distance winner; neither the jockey nor the trainer had won yet today; its nearest rivals in the betting were all on the drift; from what I could hear, the other punters in the shop all seemed to be opposing it; its best form was its most recent form; I had spent three hundred quid backing losers in the three previous races and so I was due a win – and so on. Even Henry, who'd taken my cheque, nodded appreciatively as though he reckoned I was on to a good thing. I'm not totally sure I didn't hear him laying it off on the phone.

And yet it not only lost, it didn't even get in the frame. What's the fucking point of backing horses if they don't run true to form? It's fucking pointless. I might as well throw my money straight down the drain – at least I won't develop a fucking ulcer watching it disappear.

If I end up dying, the trainer and jockey of Leadwall deserve custodial sentences for being fucking accessories.

Earlier, I'd done my trades on the football and, unbelievably given my current luck, I had a few results. I'd decided to concentrate on just a few specific matches buying/selling the mini-performances. What I like about this is that, unlike the fixed odds, one match isn't contingent on another but stands alone. I'd bought Liverpool, West Ham and Coventry City and sold Aston Villa, Wimbledon and (from a ridiculously high quote for the spread) Manchester United. Five out of six obliged – the exception being Villa who *always* seem to scupper my plans – and I ended up winning £494. A plea in mitigation for the day.

MONDAY, SEPTEMBER 20

Lost two hundred in a bookie's in South-East London. I don't know precisely where I was: one unlovely town/district elides seamlessly and grottily into another so that you can't tell (or care) if you're in New Cross, Elephant and Castle or Catford – why don't they just test a nuclear bomb on the whole of the region and build a twelve-lane motorway instead?

TUESDAY, SEPTEMBER 21

I'm bothered. It must be clear to Maggie that I'm going for it bigtime at the moment. Damn it, I *know* she's seen the odd red bill and she *must* have noticed me getting up early to grab the post but she hasn't said a word. Now why would that be? If there's anything more disconcerting than Maggie nagging me about my gambling, it's her *not* nagging me about my gambling.

I just can't read her at the moment. All the old 'tells' have gone. She's like a Stepford wife. She's Maggie on the outside but someone entirely different on the inside. I wonder if she's going through her menopause? Nah, she's far too young. I *know* she's not having an affair – well, I'm pretty sure. She takes a bit of fancying even at her best and now is definitely not her best. Could she be having a breakdown? It's not impossible and it would be just like the old girl to have a breakdown and still function perfectly well as a housewife, teacher and mother.

Shit, I hope she's not having a breakdown. For her sake, obviously, but mostly for *my* sake. I have my own problems to contend with: I don't need hers as well. That sounds heartless, I know, but that's the deal *we* have: *I'm* the one who has the problems in that direction whereas Maggie's the 'coper/carer'. We can't start swapping roles.

WEDNESDAY, SEPTEMBER 22

I managed to lose a couple of hundred quid on three races before I had to leave the bookie's to go to my next appointment. Clever thing would have been to leave it at that but on my way home, I realised that there were still a couple of races to go and so I stopped off at the nearest bookie's I could find.

I arrived just in time – or so I thought – to get on to this 6–5 favourite in a seven-furlong race at Chester, the last race on the card there. But no, as I put my betting-slip down on the counter, they were off and the cashier wouldn't take it. I appealed to the bloke sitting down settling the bets but he wasn't having any of it. I asked him to get the manager but he explained – in a tired, bored, job's-worth voice – that he was, in fact, the owner and that rules are rules.

'But I wanted to bet three hundred pounds – that's a lot of money you're potentially losing.'

'We'll just have to live with that,' he said superciliously.

And then the penny dropped. The cashier looked over to him before turning me down: she must have indicated that it was a large bet and he must have taken me for a member of a sting operation trying to cover as many betting-shops as possible and attempting to get on as near to the off as possible so that the price isn't forced in.

The fact that I knew *nothing* whatsoever about the horse did nothing to allay his suspicions – especially as it romped home by six lengths.

So in order to prove to him that I wasn't a scamster – anything I might have said would just have seen me falling into a Billy-Bunter-I-didn't-steal-the-doughnuts-and-anyway-they-didn't-have-enough-jam-in-them trap – and, in a valiant (in other words, foolhardy) attempt to win back some of my losses for the day, I placed a massive £400 on the next red-hot favourite, an 11–10 on chance in the last race at Goodwood.

It lost.

FRIDAY, SEPTEMBER 24

There were just five of us at Ben's – the man himself, Jake, Douglas, Nathan and me – which suited me fine as I think that's the optimum number provided that there are at least two *spielers* playing who will bet on absolute rags.

I won the first three hands but, sadly, after that I couldn't win a pot all night. I tried buying them but someone always ended up seeing me and taking my balls for ludicrous (in terms of bet-to-pot ratio) sums. It didn't matter what games we played – Omaha, Hold

'Em, five-card stud, seven-card stud (with and without wild cards), Southern Cross, Funday Times, Spit, Baseball – I lost them all. Hell, I even lost every hand of high-low and that's with two people (usually Jake and Nathan) routinely folding. It was just horrible. There I was, the original third man, shovelling in £20 chips as though I was on fucking piecework, in the certain knowledge that the two other players in with me would end up splitting the pot. As Douglas said, 'Steve, you're so unlucky, if Pamela Anderson had triplets, you'd be the one in the middle on the bottle.'.

There was one hand where I really thought I had it made. It was seven-card stud, high-low (without the wheel) and after six cards, I was showing a pair of kings and other high cards, while Douglas and Jake were both showing low. Fabulous position to be in – not as good as being the only lowball because that's easier to ascertain than being the only high hand but it still gives me the opportunity to really milk the other two as they vie for the better low hand.

So I'm giving it the maximum raises and re-raises and assuming that the other guys are betting heavily only to knock each other out – hell, they're even *complaining* at my big bets, but I'm losing hundreds and having none of it.

The last card's dealt and mine's a third king. Fucking brilliant. As the strength on the table, I open. Douglas calls. Jake raises, I re-raise. After much talk about his 'bleeding butt', Douglas folds. Jake calls. 'OK, Jake,' I say, 'I'm obviously going high and you're going low, shall we split the pot?'

'No,' he says.

My sphincter tightens. 'What do you mean "no"?'

'No. What part of that word do you have trouble understanding, Steve?'

Fuck. What's he got, apart from quite possibly the nut low? A straight? Possible, but would Judicious Jake possibly risk losing everything on that – especially as I could well have a 9-to-king straight? Not a flush? No, he's showing two diamonds, one heart and a spade, he can't have a flush, can he? Yes he fucking can, the cunt. I was suddenly conscious of the coincidence that my face was flushing just at the thought of his flush. Ha, fucking ha.

And then we had to declare and he came up high and low. He pulled three diamonds out of his hand and showed me his fucking flush.

I couldn't believe it but, hey, all credit to Jake, well disguised and all that.

I felt sick. Sicker than a parrot with terminal psittacosis.

I was done. Eight hundred quid – I didn't bother to hide it – and fucking out. The guys didn't object to me leaving before eleven. We're not great ones for punishment beatings and I'd had my fucking kneecaps removed. And no, I didn't want their credit and I certainly didn't want their fucking sympathy.

SATURDAY, SEPTEMBER 25

Still suffering from last night. I don't play poker to lose. For me, poker's about fun: I don't mind if I drop a couple of hundred – especially as, ordinarily, I'd expect to win it back the following week – but eight hundred is massive moolah.

So I'm looking for a little bit of luck, aren't I, and what happens? I only bloody get some! I'm down at Henry's and I've got a £20 reverse forecast on traps four and six in a dog race. I've chosen four because it's got three of the best six times of all the dogs in the race and yet it's only 7–2 and I've paired it with the dog in trap six because it's the only dog taking a step down in class in this race and that's something I like in a pooch.

It's a short race (380 metres) and what usually happens is that a dog takes the lead and, er, wins. Which would have been bad luck for me if it had happened here as the one dog was winning from trap to final bend when – glory be – it collided with its nearest rival (trap three) to leave them both sprawling and gifted the race to trap six with trap four second. The BAGS paid out £19.72 which meant that I won more than £350.

Had a few more bets at Henry's – winning an additional sixty or so – before retiring to the comfort of my lounge and the TV.

Like last week, I went big on the mini-performances – not least because I just *love* tracking the matches on the teletext.

Unfortunately, my judgment was as bad this week as it was good last week. However, a buy of the total points in the (televised) rugby won me £225 and so my overall spread-betting losses were limited to £310.

If I'm not careful, I'm going to have to find some more money to put into my spread-betting account(s). It's going to be tough – might mean not paying the mortgage for a month or two – but it's a question of priorities.

SUNDAY, SEPTEMBER 26

Went back to (Douglas's) casino but this time on my own. *All* the same people were there. Shit, how *do* they afford it? Some of them are quite openly unemployed and many of them are clearly unemployable. There's no question that, for more than a few of them, gambling is their occupation – in the true sense of the word – but how on earth do they make it pay?

Similarly, it's impossible to find a happily married man in that card room. One fellow was talking about a game that went on at his place till five in the morning yesterday/today. 'Didn't your missus mind?' I asked, just trying to find out a little more about these people who are almost a race apart, like aliens from the planet Ante. 'Nah, I'm not married,' replied the bloke in a tone which implied that he *had* been married but wasn't now.

The fact is that the sheer time it takes to play poker – especially if you do it six or seven days a week – precludes doing a serious job or conducting any sort of meaningful relationship. My initial instinct, I have to say, is one of puritanical revulsion; my second (and third and fourth etc.) instinct is to say, 'If you can't beat 'em' and, at the moment, I don't seem able to, 'join 'em'.

And so I did. I didn't do too badly in the tournament: I managed to get down to the last dozen or so – with just one buy-in – when I lost to (or, to use an expression I heard tonight for the first time, 'got seriously outdrawn by') a full house when I had trip 7s. Still, I could hardly begrudge forty quid on such great entertainment.

The cash game went less well. Once again, I just lack the reserves, the ability, the balls to succeed. There was this bloke whose name was Mike – least I *think* his name was Mike: half the blokes there seemed to be named Mike – and every time I started to get into a hand, he simply bulldozed me out of the way with £500 chips. He wasn't unfriendly or anything – on the contrary – he was just doing what alpha males do throughout the animal world: he was seeing me off his territory.

Truth is, I ended up losing the five hundred quid I brought with me but, worse, I also feel like my self-esteem's taken a hammering. Even in *my* fucking area of expertise – mathematics – I was left looking like a plonker. Whenever I went all in and tried to count out the pot I was participating in – as opposed to the side pots – another player would invariably beat me to it. I guess it's a case of practice making perfect but that didn't make me feel any better.

Last time I noticed the way that the players talked to the waitresses – and these girls are, of course, not hard to notice, as they're wearing short skirts and skimpy tops which leave little to even the most unimaginative man's imagination. This time, I was struck by the relationship between the gamblers and the casino staff who organise the poker tournament. They seem to know each other really well: it's like they all work together. Which, in a sense, they do.

Such familiarity didn't militate against that curious meanness that (some) gamblers are prey to. While they're quite happy to toss £100 chips into the pot on *nothing*, they'll complain like mad at paying £2 for a prawn sandwich or £3.50 for a steak baguette. It doesn't seem to me that it's unfair for the casino to charge such reasonable sums for food when all they're getting from the poker players is 'rent' of £5 an hour – but try telling that to the mean sods I was playing with.

TUESDAY, SEPTEMBER 28

Saw someone today who took me right back to my misbegotten youth. Colin King. Good old Colin. I hadn't seen him for twenty-two years. Never fell out, just lost touch. Last time I saw him was at the Oval at a county match and we found that we didn't actually have that much in common any more. But he's a nice fellow.

Colin was my best friend from about ten to fourteen. He was – still is, obviously – two years older than me but I was much cleverer than him so I led, he followed.

I bumped into him in a bookie's on the Edgware Road when I was on my way to a (rare Tuesday) call. Christ, he looked bad. I hope he didn't think the same about me. At least I haven't put on four stones, lost my hair or generally gone to seed.

Apart from that though, he was still the same old Colin, grinning from ear to ear at . . . what? . . . the sheer joy of being alive, of not working, of *spieling*.

So there we were again: Colin and Steve; Steve and Colin. In a bookie's. Colin and I popped our gambling cherries together. Summer of 1970. I was fourteen but looked older; Colin was sixteen but looked younger. Indeed, it was him who was challenged (half-heartedly) by the betting-shop manager.

We didn't really have much idea what we were doing – *plus ça change* – so I took command. I watched the men. And what men they were! With their cigarettes clamped to their lips (I'd already started to smoke but I couldn't yet inhale let alone 'wear' a cigarette in my mouth), their easy banter with the cashier and their erudite discussion of how anyone could and should have known what was going to win the last race. How I longed to join them, to be as respected by others as I respected them.

The men looked at the newspaper pages dotted around the office and wrote down their selections on betting slips, so I did the same. Piggott. Yes! Lester Piggott, I knew that name. Who didn't in 1970? 'Don't worry, Colin, just do as I do' and what I did was to back Piggott's horses for a shilling a race for the next four races. My first time in a bookie's and already I had a system. And 'the long feller' didn't let us down, he won three of the four races, giving us a profit of eight or nine shillings on the afternoon.

I was hooked for life and so was Colin. We spent the rest of that summer in betting shops. And every other school holiday thereafter. We would have gone there on Saturdays too throughout the year but the betting shop manager(s) decided that we were, in fact, too young to be there on Saturdays, although it was fine any other day. Bit like the barber's, I suppose, where they'd never cut your hair on a Saturday except on the afternoon of the FA Cup Final when, of course, every self-respecting man – and boy – was stuck in front of the telly.

We lost more often than we won but persuaded ourselves that it was the other way round. Christ, what a great business bookmaking is: you take your customers' money and they leave convinced that they've taken yours.

Good luck was our right; bad luck was merely transitory. It would eventually come right if only we could find the secret. To which end we would ape our elders and pore over the displayed racing papers after each race to see what it was the winner had over its competitors and how we too should have known beforehand.

We drifted apart around the time I went to university. Colin was working in a local menswear shop and I guess we had increasingly less in common. In fact, he'd been working there since the age of seventeen after failing his O-level retakes. At first, I was proud to have a friend in full-time employment: it made me feel more grown up but the novelty soon wore off – especially after I got a Saturday job there and saw just how boring and soul-destroying it was. The shop owner was a middle-aged loser – I could see it even then – who liked to take out his own shortcomings on his wretched staff. He'd spend most Saturdays teasing me about my academic prowess: 'Your mother must be *so* proud of you, Professor, now take these boxes up to the stock room and make *me* proud of you'. It wasn't so much what he said as the venom with which he said it. And I put up with it for two years – throughout my A levels until I went off round Europe –

for £4.75 a day. The fucking skinflint never once gave me a whole fiver even though I regularly sold more clothes in a day than poor old Colin did in a week. The last day I worked there, I told him he was a complete cunt and that I was leaving. Amazingly, his reaction was to send Colin round the next day to ask me to come back but wild horses etc.

Colin and I filled each other in on the intervening years. Lost jobs, lost marriage, lost kids and – although he didn't mention it – lost bets. Still, he seemed happy enough, the poor sod, but then he always was low maintenance. Whenever I read about some multi-millionaire rock star who's depressed, my mind always turns to happy-go-lucky Colin: give him a bookie's and a couple of bevvies and he's like a pig in shit. Wish it worked so well for me.

For old time's sake, we backed the same horse. I wasn't sure how much to stake in case he noticed: too much and he would think I was flash; too little and he would see me as a failure and I couldn't lose face with my former acolyte. So I bet fifty quid. The horse lost, of course. So much for nostalgia.

Colin left before I did. After he'd gone, I rummaged around on the floor until I found his betting slip. He'd bet twenty pee. Poor sod.

THURSDAY, SEPTEMBER 30

I thought it'd been a really terrible month but actually it wasn't so bad. Yes I lost – £3,200 – but that's not nearly as much as I'd feared. I honestly thought that I'd lost anything up to ten grand.

The fact is I'm now £6,900 down on the year and yet I don't feel 'down'. I honestly believe that I can win this bet, I really do.

FRIDAY, OCTOBER 1

I think that what I like best about being a bloke (rather than a chick) is our ability to apply rigorous intellect to seemingly banal subjects. During the course of tonight's poker game (at Douglas's) the conversation turned to The Corrs.

Inevitably, there wasn't even a nano-second between the word 'Corrs' and the word 'cor'. I think it was me, if I'm honest.

Then all of us (Ben, Douglas, Jake and Nathan) – except Peter who hadn't heard of them – went into sad-sack-middle-aged-men mode. To be honest, I don't think any of us knows which girl in the group is which – although I have a vague idea that the one who plays the violin is my favourite – but that didn't stop us giving it/them our full consideration. And then after someone said in a typical unthinking scattergun way 'I'd give 'em all one', Ben gave us the poser that tested our intellects to the full. 'There are three beautiful girls in The Corrs and one, as far as I know, heterosexual man. In order to sleep with one – or more – of the girls, would any of you agree to sleep with the man first?'

Silence and lots of chin-wagging.

'I would,' said Jake – but then, as I didn't hesitate to point out, he'd shag anyone.

'I would if I could be given an amnesia pill immediately afterwards,' said Douglas.

My answer was more complicated than that. 'I'd take my chances by putting the names of all four of the group in a hat and taking out one of them. That's to say I'd go with a one-in-four chance.'

'Yeah but what if you got the bloke?'

I thought about it for a few seconds. 'OK, I'd draw out two names and agree to shag both of them.'

'But then you're doubling your chances of getting the bloke.'

'Yes, but I guarantee getting at least one girl.'

'But what if you drew the girl first and then drew the bloke. Wouldn't that be a complete sickener?'

'Hmm. OK, then, here's how it goes. I'd draw *one* name. If it's a girl, then fine, thank you very much, that's the end of it. If, however, it's the bloke, I'd shag him and then draw *two* names next time round.

The worst that could happen then would be that I'd draw him and a girl. Sure, I'd have to shag him but then, having shagged him, it wouldn't be such a terrible thing to shag him again and it would guarantee me a shag with one of the girls.'

The others laughed but otherwise all indicated their agreement (although Douglas did offer his immense sympathy to the poor Corr bloke who'd have to be shagged by me). It really is one of the great things about being a bloke, talking seriously about silly things.

I have to say that the poker wasn't as much fun – at least not for me – although I won £70. Once again, I couldn't find anyone to come in with me whenever I had a decent hand.

SATURDAY, OCTOBER 2

I really enjoyed last night/this morning so much. I wish *all* of my life could be that much fun but wherever I turn, I get hassle. I get hassle from Phil (the cunt). I get hassle from Maggie (the bitch) and I get hassle from the fucking credit-card companies (the tossers). And to add to my problems, I've got Dad hanging around me looking like a worried cow and Jonathan's still got all sorts of problems which I rather hoped would fade away once he got back to school but which seem, if anything, to have intensified. I mean, I love him – I *adore* him – but I can do without being woken up at two in the morning almost every night just to reassure him that the toys in his play box aren't going to come alive and kill him (I blame that *Toy Story* video).

Maybe I should *take off*. Just like that. Fuck off to, I don't know, Vegas. Why not? I've never been there. I've never really been anywhere. I've gone on plenty of holidays but I haven't actually *lived* somewhere without a return ticket tugging me home.

On the other hand, that wouldn't help me with the bet. With the end of the year approaching, I find myself thinking about it more and more. The big question I have to ask myself is, will I actually *do* it if I lose? The truthful answer would be no, not at all . . . were it not for that fucking insurance policy. I mean, two hundred thousand is a fuck of a lot of money – especially by comparison with my current net worth. How could I *possibly* throw away that chance? Especially as it's not as though I've got much to live for. Especially as it is, after all, a gambling debt and, therefore, a debt of honour.

So I'm going to plough on but one thing's for certain, I'm going to have to increase the stakes and if it means that I die owing thirty, forty or even fifty thousand, then at least the policy will still yield a minimum of £150,000. Enough for the kids to have everything they need. Enough to make up for a worthless father.

No, not worthless – feckless, that's better. Still, it amounts to the same thing as far as they're concerned. Hope they know I love them though. I love the way the pupils of their eyes dilate when they look at their Daddy; I love the smell of them when they've just come out of the bath; I love them jumping on to my lap for a cuddle. All reasons to live, I guess, but for how long? How long will it be before Jona pushes me off when I go to give him a cuddle because 'Hey, Dad, I'm a big boy now, you can't cuddle me'? Or Mellie looks at me with her mother's disdainful eyes instead of her own loving ones? Yeah, sure I could kill myself *then* but only after I've blown the chance of giving them £200,000.

Only thing I slightly regret is leaving the money to Maggie. Not because I think she'll blow it (if I thought that, I could leave it in trust to the kids) but because I don't really fancy leaving her *anything* at the moment. She's so fucking remote, aloof, distant, she's almost hostile. It's extraordinary how a supposedly intimate relationship can be conducted in such a cold, sterile atmosphere. She's completely unapproachable. She doesn't initiate any conversation and won't answer anything other than a direct question.

It goes without saying that we're not 'enjoying sexual relations'. Haven't done so for a couple of months which gives me all the justification I need to screw around (not that I ever bother myself about such things – although I do think that sex is a pretty good indicator of the state of a marriage and that once intimacies are suspended, so too are any obligations of fidelity). Maggie's welcome to screw around too – if she can find anyone sufficiently indiscriminate.

I think I know how I'd kill myself. I did consider the idea of jumping off a high building or bridge or something but I don't think I could bear the drama. Better – much better – would be simply to take an overdose of diazepam (I must have enough in the medicine cupboard to see off half an American cult).

I'd wait until Maggie and the children were out and then make sure that Dad found me dead. Tough tit but someone's got to. The condemned are entitled to some last requests. To drink: vintage champagne which, apart from anything else, would help wash down the pills. To eat: standard Death Row fare: three Big Macs followed by a massive tin of Quality Street from which I'll pick all the purple ones and the toffees. As for music, I thought about Leonard Cohen but much as I like his music – particularly his more recent stuff – it's far too cliched to check out to. Better pick out some mid-period Joni Mitchell: 'Jericho', 'Furry Sings The Blues', 'The Last Time I Saw Richard', 'Help Me' or anything off 'Mingus'. *That's* the way to go: like a hippie taking an accidental overdose, the last words I'll hear in this life will be Joni's.

Shit, this really is something I hope I can avoid but I am prepared to do it if I have to. I really am. Just the thought of it freaks me out but it's the only constant in my life. That and losing on the horses – which is what I did *again* this afternoon. I lost three or four hundred quid (all right, £400) at Henry's on a succession of losers. I then returned home to lose more money – another seven hundred (plus) – on football spread-bets.

MONDAY, OCTOBER 4

Money's tight. I can get round it to a certain extent by greasing on my credit cards but, sooner or later, I'm going to have to actually *do* something about it. Like take out a big loan – secured or otherwise – to take me through to the end of the year.

In fact, thinking about it (as I increasingly am), it makes no difference to me whether I lose by £100 or £100,000 and I can quite easily imagine a scenario whereby I'm, say, fifteen grand down and borrow another twenty grand to win it back. Well, anything's better than topping myself without first exploring every potential avenue for success.

Comforting thought and one that sustains me after my latest spread-betting debacle. I turned on the TV football twenty minutes into the game. It was still goalless so I asked for the first match goal spread – 51–54 – and sold it at 51 for £20 a minute: a potential profit of £600. There's also the extra few minutes you get for 'free' in injury time at the end of the first half.

Unfortunately, despite a lot of goalmouth action, two decent penalty appeals and one goal ridiculously disallowed for offside, the match finished goalless. So the bet made up at 90 and I lost £780.

WEDNESDAY, OCTOBER 6

Given that I've had (more than) a few losers recently, why did I blow six hundred quid on a horse at Beverley this afternoon? And, almost as pertinent, where the fuck is Beverley anyway? Bird's name, isn't it? Bit like going racing at Karen or Sandra. Fucking serves me right, it does. I should stick to betting on horses I know something about running at race tracks which I know actually exist.

Bollocks, of course, but it might explain – nothing else fucking does – why I staked six oners on Petallard and why it went on to lose.

I was in this bookie's in Hayes, not far from the airport. Didn't have much time and, because none of the staff there knew me, I didn't feel at all constrained from betting the (i.e. *my*) maximum on each race. Point of fact, there were only two races, for me at least. First one was a six-furlong jobbie at York. I had £250 in my pocket and put the lot on the favourite whose name escapes me.

Incredibly, it won – by a street and in a canter – and so, after tax (winning horse, *ergo* didn't pay tax), I was left with six hundred quid. Felt that it was 'my day'. *Knew* that for every pound I held back in the next race – which was the only race I had time to stay for – I would feel a complete cunt when the horse came in. So I fucking larged it. Rolled along to the counter like the Hofmeister bear and put six big ones on the nose of Petallard. Asked for a price at *7–4* and was immensely gratified to see the cashier go to the manager to okay it like it was a *real* bet and I was a *real* punter. 'This is betting, my son,' I told myself in a voice at least three postal districts more common than my own. Still, if that sort of money doesn't buy me ten minutes self-delusion then it's poor value.

Race started. Five furlongs. God, I *love* sprints. There's no worrying that a horse might be running too fast or won't have anything left for later: it's just hell for fucking leather.

Petallard started a bit sluggishly but gradually got into his stride and, by the end of the third furlong, was one of three horses which had gone clear of the field. His jockey – guy I'd never heard of: proves that Beverley doesn't exist – was the only one of the three not to have gone for his whip. Good sign.

Fourth furlong and one of the other two horses dropped back so dramatically that it looked like it was running backwards, leaving Petallard and his hard-ridden challenger.

As they went into the final furlong, it was absolutely neck and neck. A thrilling race with the two horses absolutely locked side by side together. Would I settle for a dead heat? NO, I 'KING WOULDN'T! COME *ON* MY SON! GAWN!

They passed the line almost together but, from the photo, it was clear that Petallard had just inched it. Yes, indeed, I had won – £1,650 less the tax because, quite rightly as it transpired, I didn't want to tempt fate.

I rushed around in the way that punters do when they're on a lap of honour in the bookie's, looking at all the form guides and checking in the racing papers to see how clever I was to have spotted the winner's potential. Hee hee, *that* paper didn't get the winner and nor did *that* pundit: tch, they should employ me instead. Look of – yes, definitely – admiration, respect on cashier's face. Fancies a tip, she does. Well buy some fucking Clearasil, that's my tip, pet.

And then the dreaded words: 'Steward's inquiry'.

No! NO! *NO!* This can't be happening to me. It is *so* unfair. I find it hard enough to pick winners as it is without having them snatched away from me.

Other people in the shop who'd seen me celebrating the nag's victory tried to console me by telling me that it was only a formality but I've said the same thing myself to other people in my position: it's meaningless drivel uttered by zombies who, at no cost to themselves, are trying to come across as decent human beings. Fuck off. What do *you* know, losers?

And now they're showing the incident on the monitor and it's transparently clear what the basis of the objection is: the jockey on my horse has clearly obstructed the other horse. Absolutely no doubt about it. The fact that my horse would undoubtedly have won without breaking the rules is irrelevant. The fucking inexperienced jockey screwed up and I've lost fifteen hundred quid. The cunt.

Couldn't believe it. Still can't. We live by a thread. My whole life is subject to a steward's inquiry. It's a *leitmotif* for my entire fucking existence. What I want to know is why no steward's inquiry has ever disqualified the winner in favour of *my* selection? If life can be unfair, why can't it sometimes be fair too?

FRIDAY, OCTOBER 8

Our last poker game without Gerard and I, for one, can't wait for next Friday. Ben and Douglas were talking about Jake's stag night later this month and the moment I opened my mouth to ask an innocent question, Ben squashed me by saying, 'It's OK, Steve, we're up to speed on this one.'

Well, gee thanks, guys, I was only going to ask which restaurant we were going to.

Actually, I don't know if it was me (and I don't know Nathan or Peter well enough to ask them) but I found the three of them (Ben, Douglas and Jake) more than a little *conspiratorial* tonight. Like, they're in the *stag night gang* or something. It all felt a little like playground politics again and, I don't know about them, but I'm getting a little old for that sort of thing.

On the other hand, it's entirely possible that I'm just like the sergeant-major who says that everyone's out of step except him.

So I didn't join in with their plans except to comment *sotto voce* when I heard them talking about a lap-dancing club, 'That's just licensed prick-teasing'.

Feeling a little alienated didn't do me any harm though as I was the big(gish) winner with £310, while the giggling girls all lost.

SATURDAY, OCTOBER 9

This year – more than any other year I can remember – I've been very conscious of trying all different sorts of betting systems: almost as though I'm 'road-testing' them or something. But then since I'm literally staking my *life* every time I have a bet, I can be forgiven for trying anything.

Nevertheless, there are some systems to which I'm fatally attracted and one of them is my old pal 'carry on betting the favourite at double the stakes until you win' bet. This is, of course, a progressive losing system but what it has over its even-money casino counterpart is that it only needs a winning favourite at better odds than, say, 2–1 (not impossible) to make some really decent profits even to (relatively) small stakes. The downside, as with all progressive losing systems, is that in doubling the stake after each loss, the money just haemorrhages.

I decided to do it for £50 stakes to give me more chance of winning or, at least, getting my money back. I also decided to back across the three (televised) meetings on the anecdotally understandable – though scientifically unsound – basis that even if one meeting yielded no favourites, the others were sure to make up for it.

I really can't *believe* I've just written that. Surely I'm not that lame-brained. But, no, wait, it appears that I am. It is not 'anecdotally understandable', it is idiocy and I am a fool. Why is it that when it comes to gambling – with my *very existence*, goddammit – all my intelligence, all my education just goes west? Do I have a death wish or something? Or do I just leave my brains outside when I go into a bookie's?

Actually, today I didn't go to a bookie's (so I really don't have any excuse) but did my betting on the phone. Yeah, I know that Maggie might see my bank statement but, frankly, I don't give a fuck *what* she thinks any more. I've come too far with this bet – and with our marriage – to give a damn about her bourgeois dislike of gambling. That's my vice, woman: accept it, if you want me.

For what it's worth, Maggie seems a lot better. We don't really communicate that much at the moment but I've caught her smiling – rather than scowling – at the kids recently and I'm not totally unsure that she didn't (accidentally?) cuddle me the other night in her sleep. Hell, I'm all for good marital relations – just so long as I don't have to curtail my freedom to achieve them.

Meanwhile, when the racing goes on, Maggie goes out. As soon as she hears that admittedly annoying 'sting' on the Channel 4 racing ('der der der der der dum di dum'), she's reaching for her car keys and bundling the kids into the car. Who knows? Maybe she doesn't want them to be corrupted by Daddy's gambling habit?

There were, in total, ten televised races and, to offset my potentially huge losses, I sold the favourites' spread indexes at all three meetings (taking care to do so just *before* the first televised race at each meeting so that I didn't get caught between two stools). The first race yielded a 5–2 winning favourite (plus £120 after tax). I lost the next three races (minus £381) but won the fifth – thank God! – at 4–7 with £400 on the nose (plus £192). The sixth saw the favourite get touched off in a photo-finish (minus £54) but the seventh produced a 6–5 favourite (plus £111). The eighth, ninth and tenth all lost (minus £381).

So, all in all, I lost £393. Not terrible and, it has to be said, I wasn't losing any other money in that time but it's no way to gamble – not unless I can guarantee winning on the *last* race. Which, of course, I can't. The main trouble with any progressive losing system is that, ultimately, you're playing to your absolute limit (in my case, £400 a race) just to win back the original losing bet of, in this instance, fifty quid. No, it's no way to carry on unless I'm going to allow myself to place bets of – gosh – £1,600 or even £3,200.

Meanwhile, the spread bets were disappointing. Where the favourites hadn't won, they still managed to get in the frame which meant that they got 10 or 5 points allocated to them, so the favourites' indexes still made up at roughly the original quoted spread.

MONDAY, OCTOBER 11

Lost £400 in two races in just ten minutes. Wish I could *earn* money at the same rate.

TUESDAY, OCTOBER 12

Maggie 'reminded' me that we're going to the parents' dinner at the school on Saturday. First thought was 'Fuck off, I'm busy' but I've learned to swallow my first thoughts with Maggie. 'Sorry,' I said with a grimace, 'I'm busy.' I'm not, in fact, but that's nothing to do with her.

Maggie bestowed upon me the look of condescension she's bestowed upon generations of schoolchildren. 'I've already bought the tickets.'

Bad luck, bitch. Pause. 'Can't you give them to someone else?'

No pause. 'We haven't got the money to start *giving* things away, remember?'

Through gritted teeth. 'All right, can't you *sell* them to anyone then?'

'Why should I? What are you doing that's so important on Saturday.'

Deep breath. 'I don't see what business that is of yours.'

'I do happen to be your wife.'

Sotto voce. 'Oh, so *now* you remember.'

'And what's that supposed to mean?'

'Nothing.' Which is precisely what it does mean. I tried to be more conciliatory. 'Listen, can't you go with a friend or something.' But even then I couldn't resist sneering when I used the word friend, although, to be fair, she *does* seem to have no shortage of friends.

She looked at me as if I was a lump of cold sick that she was going to have to clear up. 'I don't know. I just don't know.'

'Look, Maggie, what would I want to spend a Saturday night at the school for? I've got nothing in common with any of . . .' And then, finally, I remembered Judith. She'd be there: she's always there. She's one of those mums who talk about 'supporting' the school – as though it were a fucking football team. How is that women can speak so much without using *any* irony? Still, notwithstanding her irony deficiency, she is undeniably fit.

I launched into a coughing fit to mask my change of heart. When I finished, I couldn't have been nicer. 'Maggie, you're right. I *should* spend more time up at the school. They're not bad people and I can postpone what I was going to do on Saturday. So it'll be my pleasure to go with you.'

Maggie happy – or relieved more like (she obviously didn't like the idea of other mums knowing she couldn't get a date on a Saturday night) – and not a little puzzled. Keep her guessing, I say.

WEDNESDAY, OCTOBER 13

Gerard was released from jail yesterday. God help society; God help us all. Incredibly, he's already up to no good. While he was inside, he advertised for women (using Ben's voice) and, unbelievable but true, he got a few hits – even though he was totally upfront about being a con (-vict, not -man).

In the past month, Gerard has managed to pile on the pounds – about *thirty*, apparently out of 'boredom' – and so, having arranged to meet one of these wretched women last night, he phoned her and told her that he would be round 'after dark' and that he would slip into her bed while the lights were off and, er, 'make love' to her.

Sounds crazy, of course, but apparently it happened – or, anyway, something very much like it happened. The chronology *seems* to be as follows.

10.00pm. The Bad Man turns up at this woman's house and enters the open front door.

10.02pm. The Bad Man sprays his mouth with breath freshener

(I'm guessing now) and goes into her bedroom and talks to her.
10.30pm. He's shagged her without either of them actually having seen each other – although Gerard did slide a photograph of himself (from when he was seven years younger and four stones lighter) under the bathroom door.
11.00pm. Gerard phones Douglas – *from his girlfriend's bed* – to boast about his 'conquest'. From this point on, I have Douglas's word for what happened which means that, unlike earlier, it definitely happened.

Gerard tells Douglas, 'Heh heh', that he's just 'had the most beautiful girl in the world', explains how this act of coition came to pass and asks Douglas whether he'd like to talk to her.

Without offering either of them the choice, Gerard puts the two of them together.

'Hello,' says the girlfriend.

'Listen,' says Douglas. 'You don't know anything about Gerard . . .'

'Gerard? I thought his name was Marcel?'

'OK, Marcel. Have you given him any money?'

'No,' she replies nervously.

'Well, don't and, while you're at it, put some clothes on and get the hell out of the place.'

The girlfriend giggles nervously as though Douglas's ribbing her which, in a sense, he is. Sort of.

Sensing that the conversation is not going the way he planned, Gerard grabs the phone and, after joshing with Douglas for a couple of minutes, rings off.

Even though Douglas was actually asleep when the phone rang, he had the presence of mind to dial 1471 after putting down the phone to get the woman's number. The next morning, he called her back and asked her how on earth she could trust a complete stranger in such an intimate situation. 'Aren't you afraid that he'll slice off a chunk of your arse and fry it in a wok?'

Anyway, she's duly chastened and, as such, tells Douglas what 'really happened'. According to *her*, although she did allow Gerard to come round 'in the dark', they only talked and then 'petted a little'. More to the point, she reveals in passing that, whether or not she's beautiful, she's certainly not a 'girl' but a woman of forty-nine. Evidently with low self-esteem and without very much self-respect.

So, he claims he's 'done' her; she claims he hasn't but what is beyond doubt is that he has been to her place in the dark and intimacy has taken place. What does this say about her? What does this say about him? What does this say about his *friends*?

THURSDAY, OCTOBER 14

Since I started losing a bit, I've been taking out £250 a day with my cash card. It's the easiest way for me to get hold of money without much effort and without anyone asking me any difficult questions. I don't *spend* what I take out every day on the day itself and this self-denial enables me to splurge more on other days.

Today, I had five bets – each for a £100 (no tax paid for superstitious reasons) – on five (clear) second-favourites in five different races. Unbelievably, I didn't have a single winner – just three seconds, one third and one unplaced.

Sometimes, when I've done all my money I wish I had more to try to win some back. Today, I was only too glad that I didn't have any more as I would only have lost it. It was one of those days.

FRIDAY, OCTOBER 15

It was Gerard's first poker session since enjoying Her Majesty's hospitality and he left us all in no doubt that he preferred ours to hers – particularly as there's little doubt that Her Maj. would have even less interest in the Bad Man's sexual (or not) exploits than we have.

Knowing what we did – unbeknownst to Gerard – it was difficult for Douglas and I to keep straight faces as Gerard attempted to regale us all with his nocturnal accomplishments.

'I've done it before, you know,' he bragged at one point.

'Oh really, Gerard,' said Ben, 'and here was me thinking that you were a big "v".'

Gerard smiled uncomprehendingly as though he had been paid a compliment in a language he didn't understand – which, in a sense, is about the strength of it because sarcasm and irony are entirely foreign to him.

'No, I did this once before. A few years ago, I advertised for a girl in *Time Out*. I got a few replies and then with one of them I had a sort of "telephone romance".'

'You mean, you had free sex chats down the phone,' said Jake.

'That's the sort of thing,' said Gerard without any sense of shame or embarrassment. I swear that if we caught him *in flagrante* with a sheep, he'd finish off and then boast about the sheep's appreciative 'baas'. 'Eventually, I went over to her flat and we talked in the dark as though we were still on the phone but of course we weren't so we could make out at the same time.'

I couldn't help asking him whether this woman – these women – didn't feel cheapened by the experience.

'No no, not a bit of it. What you have to understand is that there's nothing *sordid* about it.' Even Gerard could sense that he hadn't entirely convinced us and so he tried another tack. 'Look, what you have to understand is that I'm constructing a fantasy for them.' That did it. We all of us – even Peter – just creased up. The Bad Man's self-image is that, contrary to the impression we've formed, he's not a scuzzbag but is actually providing a service to women. I love him, I really do.

Meanwhile, he's already got his all his plans for the future mapped out. He's taken a lease on a huge warehouse – with a flat *underneath* – in what he calls Maida Vale (the rest of the world knows it as Kilburn). Still, good luck to him, especially as his new 'operation' (as he insists on calling it) *sounds* as though it's on the level. He's going to run (what he calls) a 'super agency' providing every imaginable service which punters pay to access and which the service-providers pay to join. Since it's Gerard, there is of course some spin to it. All the phone lines into this 'super agency' are charged at premium rates in exchange for which he's promised to underwrite – i.e. guarantee – *every* job. For any legitimate businessman, it sounds like a potential minefield.

For someone like Gerard, who'll be off at the first hint of trouble, it's probably a licence to print money. Shit, I don't live in Kilburn – and nor does anyone else I know (apart from, I think, Mary Cash) so what do I care?

Gerard was prepared to talk about his new business all evening but we weren't. So we played poker and it was fucking brilliant. It seems extraordinary that just one person can make such a big difference but when that one person is Gerard . . . He bet big at the beginning. He bet big when he was down. He bet big when he was up. Man, he just bet big all the time. Which meant that *anyone* who wanted to play poker just had to bet big too – yup, even Jake and Nathan. 'You gotta pay to play' was Gerard's motto for the evening.

I loved it. Although Friday nights are much more about fun than finance, it sure does spice up the proceedings when someone bets the pot on – like – a single pair. Especially, when it's accompanied by catcalls (often in absurd American accents) like 'Yo, Bad Man, some jailbird's rammed his cock so far up your ass that you ain't *thinking* straight.'

Although they tried to keep up, when push came to shove, Jake, Nathan, Peter and Ben found themselves stacking (what turned out to be) winning hands because they weren't prepared to call on 'prospects'. So, ultimately, they all lost. Only Douglas (£320), Gerard (£410) and I (£150) held our nerve and therefore cleaned up.

SATURDAY, OCTOBER 16

I get down to Henry's at two o'clock only to find that there's been a huge coup on a 7–2 winner – 7–2! Shit, I can't remember the last time when I had a winner – let alone a 7–2 winner.

I love betting-shop coups. It isn't just the winning – although, obviously, that's the most important part – it's also the taking part. The sense of being united with other gamblers, the promise of beating the odds. When a piece of information comes into the shop, it's like the illumination of a dark room, and the pooling of that information intensifies the sense of anticipation at no real cost to the informant – how much can one betting shop alter the price of a horse?

In my experience, only about half of all betting-shop coups actually come off. The trouble is you don't know which half it's going to be. But I'll willingly put up with the losses in return for the winnings and the crack.

I call them 'coups' but this of course covers everything from a little stable information to (glory of glories) a full-blown fixed race.

I had my first encounter with the latter when I was still a student. The horse was called Purple Branch and it was running in a five-furlong race. A 'face' in my (then) local bookie's took me to one side and advised me in the strongest possible terms to 'get on this horse, pay the tax and don't take a price.' I did precisely as I was told, putting the entire contents of the pockets of my student jeans on the nose – £4.50, as I recall – not much now but a fortune back in 1976 to someone living on £10 a week.

Purple Branch opened at 6–4 but then drifted out – alarmingly, as it seemed to me at the time – to 8–1. The race started. In those days, of course, there were no TV pictures in the bookie's, all we got was commentary on the blower. Purple Branch wasn't mentioned at all for the first four furlongs. The blower went mysteriously silent. I was just about to screw up my betting slip in that quasi-cathartic way that punters do when the 'face' winks at me. I hold my breath for what seems like an hour, trying to come to terms with the prospect of raspberry jam sandwiches until the end of term, when the blower comes back on to apologise for the silence and to announce the result: 'First, Purple Branch . . .'

Thirty-six quid! Pound for pound, in relation to my income, it was – until this year's Derby – the biggest win of my life. I couldn't work out how the coup was done but I was just grateful to be in on it.

Often when I've related that story, I'm asked – usually by a 'civilian' – what I think of the morality of it. The truth is, I don't. I don't think of the morality of it and, if I did, it wouldn't bother me. I start from the assumption that many horse races are bent anyway and so what if I don't have the good luck to be in on a coup myself? My bad luck for not being in the right place at the right time. I'd just blow my money anyway, wouldn't I?

I'm a little more dubious about stable information, but only from the point of view of efficacy, not from the standpoint of morality. The word leaks out of a yard that a horse is doing good things in training. Yeah, OK, but you can't infer from that – as some punters try to do – that it will necessarily win the big race on Saturday. There might be other horses in the race which are doing even better things in training. At best, all that stable information – as opposed to the fixed race scenario – can give you is, say, a ten per cent edge. Which might just be enough.

I was so pissed off at missing out on the coup that I couldn't really face betting at Henry's. I had a couple of (losing) hundred quid bets on a 6–1 and a 7–1 shot and then went home to have a real blast at some spread betting.

I did some football trades (bought Newcastle United and Leeds United mini-performances; sold total Premiership goals; bought Division One goals) but, as far as the horse racing was concerned, I decided to bet on each race as it happened on the basis that trends develop and pointers are given so it's stupid to commit myself in advance.

I was pottering along quite happily – losing a couple of hundred but no more – when I noticed an old friend running in the 4.05 at Newmarket: Barshava. That was the horse that Jim and I did at Sandown. True, it lost but only just and I do recall Jim saying something about 'one for the notebook'.

Barshava opened at 9–1. It hadn't run since that defeat. As I was saying earlier, who *knows* what it's been doing since then in training? For all *I* know, it's been hotter than the ringpiece of the curry-eating champion of New Delhi. Maybe it is itself the subject of a coup. Even if its price doesn't go in significantly, that doesn't prove anything as its 'connections' might have been keeping the information to themselves.

So I went after it BIG TIME. On the 50–30–20–10 index, it was quoted at 8–11. I bought at 11 for £100 a point. For the first time ever, the guy on the phone had to go to his superiors to clear my trade which made me feel simultaneously intrepid and trepidatious. He came back to say that since they had my Switch card number that was fine but since this could happen again, would I be interested in a credit account? Would I be interested in a credit account? Does Dolly Parton sleep on her back? The fact is, I've really been beating my brains out trying to get money together for my spread betting. I've always operated on the understanding that it was a question of depositing money or using the old Switch card. I didn't realise that credit was possible. I'll phone them on Monday.

Meanwhile, there was the small matter of Barshava and a potential £4,900. Now that's what I call an upside! Second place would have given me £1,900, third £900 and even fourth place would have seen me only losing a oner.

Unfortunately, Barshava trailed in a disappointing second-last losing me £1,100. Never mind 'one for the notebook', that's one for the pet-food factory. My football spreads lost me another £440 so the whole day was a bit of a bummer.

SUNDAY, OCTOBER 17

Last night was OK. Maggie and I went to the PTA do at the school. Shit, I hate to sneer but Maggie was so pathetically *excited* by it all you'd think we were going to the Duchess's Ball or something. Maggie spent ages getting ready, which would be fine if it showed but, sadly, it didn't. Still, I wasn't about to rain on her parade, so I made all the right noises and even offered to help her put on her necklace.

The other parents are all right. The (few) snooty ones make a point of never attending while the (not so few) really common ones accidentally-on-purpose never get to quite *hear* of it, which leaves 'ordinary' parents like us.

Like any one-night stand, the evening meant different things to different people. Understandably, to the organisers (and spouses) who'd invested all their time, it was the highlight of their calendar while to the rest of us, it ranged from something to be endured to something to be enjoyed. I found myself veering towards the former until I spied Judith and . . . well, it made the whole evening a lot more tolerable. Even down to the bearded men in the chunky jumpers drinking ale.

There wasn't much time so subtlety was an unaffordable luxury. Hence my 'Hello, gorgeous.'

She fluttered her beautifully long eyelashes and demurely placed a hand across her mouth as though embarrassed by the outrageous compliment. Normally, I don't remember what women wear – what man looks at a woman's clothes when all we want to do is look *through* them? – but I couldn't help it in her case. She was wearing a red shirt – I don't know, maybe it was a blouse – and a slit black skirt with knee-length black boots. If she'd been wearing a black hat and eye-mask, she'd have looked like Zorro but, even without them, she still looked fiery, adventurous, *different*.

'It'd be great to be with you somewhere else, somewhere more private, maybe fifteen years ago,' I was both shouting (to get over the noise) and whispering (for the sake of discretion).

She tugged at the sleeve of a brown check sports jacket. The wearer of this jacket, a thin, fair-haired bloke – no, 'chap' – with a neat moustache/beard combo flecked with grey, wheeled round. She introduced us: 'Steve, this is Roger, my husband. Roger, this is Steve, who wants to be my lover.' I kept my cool and gave a little bow. Roger smiled and said, 'You're welcome to her, she snores.'

Before I could think of a reply, Maggie dragged me off to talk to the head and I didn't get to speak to Judith again but, to be honest, I don't think there's any future for me there.

MONDAY, OCTOBER 18

Got in touch with the spread-betting firm's administration department and told them I'd been recommended for a credit account.

Before we even got on to the only important question (how much credit do I want?), I had to undergo the third degree. Shit, they asked me questions that even Maggie's never asked. And then they gave me the SP. Basically, my credit limit would be set at a quarter of whatever funds I had in the bank or building society. Aaaarggggh! But I don't have any funds in the bank or building society or, indeed, anywhere. Couldn't I still, please, have some credit?

Grudgingly, they told me that I could so long as a) the credit check comes out OK (which, given that I haven't got any CCJs outstanding, it should) and b) I get a letter of reference from a bookmaker. I was about to panic and then I remembered good old Henry. He's never been much in favour of me spread betting but he couldn't deny an old friend – a valued *customer* – a reference, could he? Not if he wanted that old friend to remain a valued customer?

WEDNESDAY, OCTOBER 20

Ordinarily – and I'm damned if, in this context, I know the difference between 'ordinarily', 'usually' and 'normally' – I don't back horses I've backed before (Night Nurse honourably excepted). Either they won for me last time in which case I shouldn't push my luck or (more often) they didn't in which case there ain't no point in making a fool of myself again. Why, it's less than a week since that fucking nag Barshava (may its bones even now be holding together some lad's model aeroplane) lost me over a grand. And yet, familiarity can breed content as well as contempt and Arctic Gnome, despite being a grey, falls into the former rather than the latter category.

I was in a bookie's in South London when I heard the name Arctic Gnome over the blower. Arctic Gnome, Arctic Gnome? Sounds familiar and then I remember him obliging (t'ain't so hard to recall my winners: there haven't exactly been many) for me way back when. Now, here he was running at Chepstow.

I had just two hundred quid on me which I absolutely *ladled* on to Arctic Gnome at 7–4.

He set off as if he were running in a five-furlong sprint (instead of a two-and-a-half-mile hurdle), took an immediate ten-length lead and never surrendered it. Judged purely as a race, it was probably the most boring contest since, since . . . I don't know, the last Grand Prix I watched on television but £350 profit was enough compensation for me.

FRIDAY, OCTOBER 22

I'll say this much for the Bad Man: he doesn't let the grass grow under his feet. He's already got his operation under way. It must be true because Jake's been there and seen it happening. Apparently, there are six or seven telephone operators (women, natch) and workmen coming in and out. Jake says it *looks* like a regular business.

Gasps all round the table – even from Peter who's only met Gerard once. It was Douglas, of course, who asked Gerard the leading question: 'OK, where's the catch?'

Gerard giggled: he doesn't mind being quizzed on his favourite subject (his life and times) and he just *loves* being the centre of attention. 'There's no catch.'

'*That's* the catch,' quipped Ben.

'Come on, Gerard, there must be a catch.'

I was the one to spot it. 'How much are you actually paying your staff, Gerard?'

'*Paying*?' asked the Bad Man with mock (I think) horror.

'You're not ripping them off, are you?' asked Jake who's a bit of a bleeding heart. Also, he's met them and perhaps feels more of a pang than the rest of us.

'Of course not,' said the Bad Man in the sort of 'reassuring' voice that sends any sane person running for the hills. 'All my girls stand to earn thousands.'

'"Stand to earn"?'

'They're all on a complex commission structure.'

I couldn't help it. 'Is that the sort of "complex commission structure" where they don't get paid?'

'How can you say that, Steve? I'm famous for my ingenuity.'

'I think you mean "integrity",' corrected Ben, 'and, believe me, you're not.'

Laughter ensued which allowed Gerard to change the conversation to a more fruitful topic. 'Listen, boys, I've got the most fantastic poker room in my new flat. Jake's seen it. It's fantastic, isn't it, Jake?'

'Fantastic, Gerard, fantastic.'

'It's absolutely huge.'

'Size isn't everything, Bad Man.'

Gerard wasn't to be diverted from his theme. 'I'm going to get *two* proper "professional" poker tables specially made. Then I'm going to hire some dealers and operate a *serious* big money game with some *real* spielers.'

'What's in it for you?' asked Ben, as curious as the rest of us.

'I'll take five per cent of every pot. It's called "tax".'

'I bet it is,' said Ben.

'Oh well,' opined Douglas, 'that's probably less than you take out of our pots.' More gasps. Gerard grinned.

'Come on, boys,' he said rubbing his hands together as though he were Fagin's illegitimate great-great-grandson (could be), 'let's play poker.'

And so we did. I don't know what else Gerard learnt when he was inside – I mean, apart from French – but he's certainly improved his poker playing. I reckon the months he spent in chokey were as close to a post-graduate course in bad-mannery as makes any difference. Lucky he didn't stay in any longer. He's still extraordinarily reckless – as he showed last week – but there's more steel now. He won't stay in *every* hand if he's really got nothing or if he suspects that someone else might have something. Similarly, when he does stay in to the end of a hand, he does *sometimes* fold which at least keeps us all guessing. Also, 'all in' suits him because he uses it in a moody way, as in 'OK, how much have you got in front of you? Forty-two pounds? All right, I'll bet forty pounds.' Well, what the fuck does that mean? And when his victim, having tried to work it out, ends up stacking, Gerard will reveal, say, two pairs. Gerard has no problem whatsoever in showing his cards when he's not obliged to: for Gerard, it's not the winning that counts but the rubbing it in.

So it wasn't surprising that he took the spoils this evening/last night with a haul of nearly five hundred quid. I broke even – or at least that's what I declared: I think I must have lost about eighty. Jake lost big time. Maybe it's the thought of married life that's making him go on tilt. Which ties in neatly with my theory that marriage is like a pinball game.

SATURDAY, OCTOBER 23

Henry's agreed to be my referee – although he did sigh and give me an 'it's your funeral' look as he did so. I don't mind if he disapproves or not. Shit, *he's* the one who makes his living out of other people's weaknesses not me: it's not for *him* to judge me. I don't know: maybe he's just trying to look out for me. Well, I don't need it.

Thing is, since Tim, since Samantha – since spread betting – I haven't had that much time for Henry's. In this technological age, it feels increasingly like an anachronism. I swear they'll keep the last bookie's as a museum: it can only be a matter of time.

Sometimes, I find the old-fashionedness of it all reassuring – reminding me, as it does, of my youth. And then someone like Nigel, the half-witted ex-squaddie, will come up to me for the third time that day to tell me how I should have known all along that the winning horse was going to win and I start to yearn for my armchair, the remote control and the cordless phone. History's passed Henry and Henry's by.

So I had a couple of bets – as a way of saying thank you to Henry for his letter of reference – and then skidaddled out of the place for the comfort of my smoke-free lounge. Funny thing was, I actually walked away with more money – £47.50 – than I walked in with.

* * *

Trading's the future. They're even offering financial betting now on stocks and shares. It goes to show what I've always thought, that the stock market is just a glorified casino. I'd have a go at it if I had the *remotest* idea what it was all about.

At least I *understand* football. Even if I do support Chelsea. Sort of. I don't really see how *anyone* can support a football team any more when their line-up changes every bloody season. When I was a boy, you knew where you were with your team. We had Barry Bridges and Bobby Tambling. We had Harris, Hollins, Hinton. And Peter Osgood and Peter Bonetti. And then Alan Hudson and good old Charlie Cooke. There was a certain *type* of Chelsea player. I suppose there still is but it's not the same type and, like as not, the individual will move on – to Europe – after a season or two.

There's an age thing as well, I think. There's something a little *sad* about middle-aged football supporters: hero-worshipping is a young man's game. Perhaps I'll take Jona along and see what he makes of it all – although he's a Manchester United fan. Well, he is this week, at any rate.

In his honour, I bought Man U's performance and I also bought the Premiership goals at 24 for £20 a goal (the most they'd let me bet until my credit is finally approved).

I enjoy trading on the football because I get a whole afternoon's entertainment for my bet – which I don't on a single horse race.

As it was, there were only fifteen fucking goals scored in the Premiership – and none by Manchester United, damn them. So I managed to lose three hundred quid without any difficulty at all.

MONDAY, OCTOBER 25

Got a letter from Mr Watson this morning. Apparently, he's 'very worried' by my mortgage arrears. *He's* worried? What does he think *I* am? Most important thing is that Maggie didn't open the letter – even though it was addressed to both of us. Not that I care what she thinks but I can do without the hassle.

I can do without *any* hassle. My whole life is fucking hassle. Not a day passes that doesn't bring half a dozen bills of one sort or another. Women – certainly women round this way – talk a lot about 'juggling', their lives and careers and things like that. Well, I could teach them all something about juggling. What I've been doing with bills and final demands these past few weeks would qualify me for a gig at Barnum & Bailey's.

The key thing is how long will it be before the 'balls' (i.e. 'bills') all fall on the floor?

TUESDAY, OCTOBER 26

Went to the office today in a pretty good mood. I've been working (for me) really hard for the past few weeks – not least because I've been hoping to make the Exec. Club.

Well, today I discovered that I just missed out and I'm as fucked off as it's possible to be. I've done my bit and I can't help feeling that head office has moved the fucking goalposts in extending the time limit to help those people who took time off in August.

I said something of this to Phil but he just gave me a tight grin and wished me better luck next time round. The cunt.

That does it for me. I've busted a gut over the summer to meet the Exec. Club target and what do I get – apart from a *little* extra commission (big deal) – for my troubles? Fuck all. From now on, I'm just going to do the bare minimum. Not that I can live off my basic but the fact is, I can achieve at least three-quarters of target on hardly any work but to earn the extra quarter takes a disproportionate amount of time: at least half as much again and it ain't worth it.

The money I earn isn't going to make a ha'pporth of difference to the bet – either way. If I win the bet, the first thing I'm going to do is junk this fucking job and, if I lose . . . I could quit now but I'm damned if I won't squeeze the last easy penny out of the bastards first.

WEDNESDAY, OCTOBER 27

I thought that Maggie hadn't noticed Mr Watson's letter the other day but she had. 'What do the bank want, Steve?'

'Oh, it was just a standard letter inviting us to apply for a loan if we want a holiday or anything.'

She looked at me – just looked at me – for perhaps only seven or eight seconds but it was just long enough for me to blush. Then she nodded and left the room.

Close call.

Funny thing was that, only last night, I had even considered having sex with her – the first time we'd have done it for months. Glad I didn't. Truth is, that *everything* has to be right between us before I can have sex with Maggie. The corollary to this is that if *anything* is wrong between us, I'm up for having sex with someone else.

THURSDAY, OCTOBER 28

Had five hundred quid in my pocket and decided to put the *lot* on the red-hot favourite in the last race at Stratford. No favourite had won in any of the previous races and the favourite in the last race was 4–5.

Those are the facts and there were two ways of interpreting them: a mathematician – particularly a Bayesian – would argue that there might be something wrong with the going or the track which caused the better horses to do less well than the nags. An idiot, on the other hand, would contend that the law of averages would be bound to reassert itself eventually and so the favourite should be backed.

So which should I go with: my head (and leave the race well alone or else look for something that links the previous winners and place a small bet on the horse in this race that shares similar characteristics) or my heart (and back the favourite with everything in my pocket)? Well, there's no choice is there? It's *got* to be the favourite, hasn't it? Notwithstanding my aversion to odds-on chances. And yet this aversion is based on the fear of not winning enough money. A return of £355 profit (after tax) is a fine profit. So why not break my no odds-on rule – especially as odds-on shots seem to come in every time when I bet against them?

This was a big race for me. They're all big races nowadays but this was especially important. The difference between (nearly) £900 and nothing is huge. So, having taken the decision to make the bet, I spent the next few minutes before the off convincing myself that this was the best horse in the world and that my bet was dumb only because it was too bloody small. By the time they were under starter's orders, I'd have put £100,000 on if only I'd had it with me.

Fortunately, I didn't because not only did it not win, it didn't even fucking finish.

That does it for me with bloody horses. From now on, I'll only bet on sports where animals aren't involved for at least then I'll have a human – even if it is me – to blame.

FRIDAY, OCTOBER 29

Still pissed off. Broke. Can't afford to have a bet. Can't afford *not* to have a bet.

I've just come home from Jake's stag night. We went to this restaurant in Chiswick that Ben swears is the best restaurant in the entire fucking universe. Because he's such a regular, they've 'given' us the whole place. Except they haven't, which pisses Ben off big time.

There's eighteen of us stag-nighters at a big table and then two tables of four civilians each. And they're not the sort of people who'd want to find themselves caught up in a stag night.

So although the strippers get there at ten, they're not allowed to do their bit until eleven. And I, for one, am glad that I had longer to digest my dinner because I swear that I damn nearly retched when I saw their disgusting bodies. One was fat and flabby and the other was thin and flabby.

I was sitting next to Douglas and a guy named Rick, a friend of Jake's from university days and a good bloke. We, at least, had a giggle. 'Put 'em on, put 'em on, put 'em on!' we chanted as they stripped off. Ben and Jake, at the other end of the table, glared at us but the trollops, prancing up and down the top of the table starkers, didn't give us a second glance: probably thought we were pissed.

And then they offer 'extras'. A tenner from each of us and they'll suck off anyone who wants/needs sucking off. Douglas, Rick and I – as well as a couple of guys from the middle of the table – baulk at the thought of *any* physical contact with these scrubbers but we're overruled and are obliged to cough up.

The girls get under the table and go a-gobbling. A silence falls around the table as each bloke is blown off in turn. The slags *seem* to be swallowing but surely not? A guy named Nick is the first to refuse and gets jeered but he's joined by Douglas, Rick, me and a few others too modest, decent or, indeed, sophisticated. When I refused there was some catcalling from the 'top' of the table but I kept my dignity and merely put up a hand to register my disapproval. I've nothing against paying for sex but a) I don't like doing it in public, b) I don't like doing it with a group of baying men treating women as objects and, most important, c) I don't like doing it with dogs.

On the whole, I'd rather have been playing poker.

SATURDAY, OCTOBER 30

I've just come home from Jake's wedding and, notwithstanding the Prozac, I feel depressed. Losing £400 (plus) on the football this afternoon didn't improve my mood much either. Thing with weddings – rather like Christmas – is that they serve to exaggerate whatever mood you're currently in. So if your own marriage is going swimmingly well, then you'll enjoy the wedding enormously but if it isn't, you won't.

Mine isn't and I didn't.

Not only do I not have a wife who loves me (and whom I love), I didn't even have a wife to take to the wedding. And it was all due to the fact that I *didn't* have a blow job last night!

If I'd had one, then obviously I wouldn't have mentioned anything about blow jobs to Maggie but because I didn't, I thought I'd earn myself some brownie points by telling her about last night with the emphasis on my abstention.

She was shocked. No, not shocked, horrified. She couldn't believe that men she knew had behaved like that. 'I'm not a prude,' she started to say, 'but . . .'

'Why is it that prudes always start sentences by saying "I'm not a prude but . . ."?'

'So you think I'm a prude, do you? You think it's fine for strange women to perform oral sex on strangers, do you?'

I can't remember her being so angry, so confrontational, but instead of calming her down, I found myself taking the piss. 'Come on, Maggie, it's a man's right to choose, after all. *I* didn't because I like a girl to gargle as well as swallow.'

She glared at me and then walked out which didn't bother me much. However, later, when I tried to apologise, she was having none of it. 'You like your *friends*' – she spat out the word – 'so much, you can have them all to yourself. I'm staying here.' And there was nothing I could do or say to get her to change her mind.

So I went on my own and explained Maggie's absence on the babysitter not turning up. No one believed me but then I didn't really give a damn – about anything: Maggie not coming or what anyone else thought about it. Fuck her and fuck them.

SUNDAY, OCTOBER 31

It's the end of the month and I've been doing my sums. I finished the month £5,500 down. I'm £12,400 down on the year.

I'm in deep shit. On the plus side, I've got my salary of about £3,500. I've also got my £5,000 line of credit with the spread-betting firm. Against that, I haven't paid the mortgage for two months (£1,600), there's a pile of unpaid bills – totalling about £2,500 – *some* of which will have to be paid and not only am I right up to the limit on my credit cards but I can't even seem to find the money to pay off the minimums due each month (if only to keep off the credit black-lists). I'm also right up to my overdraft limit at the bank. I suppose I *could* ask the bank to extend my overdraft but it would come with too many strings attached. So, instead, I'm going to take out the biggest unsecured personal loan I can possibly get from one of those companies that advertise on TV and in the papers. It's the only thing I can possibly do that could give me even a *chance* of winning.

MONDAY, NOVEMBER 1

It *looks* like I'm going to be getting £15,000!

I phoned this number in the paper and it was a fucking cinch. They reckon that I'll have no difficulty being accepted because I've got a really good credit rating and no CCJs outstanding.

Apparently, I'll get the forms tomorrow and, if I return them immediately (as if I wouldn't?), I should get acceptance and a cheque for fifteen big ones, within seven working days.

The best part about it is that because it's an unsecured loan, they don't have to register a charge against my house and, therefore, Maggie doesn't need to know anything about it.

TUESDAY, NOVEMBER 2

I'm at the office, minding my own business, chatting to the temp with the foxy smile when I'm summoned to the phone. It's Maggie. My first reaction was surprise: Maggie hardly ever phones me at work. Consequently, my second reaction was panic: had something happened to the kids?

'No,' said Maggie, sharply, 'the children are fine but I am not. I have a bailiff here who says that he has come for three hundred and sixty-three pounds, ninety-four pee or goods to the value thereof and he's got a court order empowering him to do so.'

Damn it. It's my bloody fault for tempting fate by boasting about how I don't have any CCJs. Of course, I didn't say this to Maggie but merely sighed and advised her to pay him. 'It was an oversight, Maggie, I'm sorry,' I added but I found myself speaking to a dead line.

I delayed my return home for as long as possible – well, I knew what to expect and, to be honest, I just couldn't face it – and I hoped that time might dull Maggie's anger.

This seemed like a good tactic when she greeted me with a not unfriendly 'Hi, Steve, your dinner's ready.'

Taking her lead. I smiled at her and pecked her on the cheek. I then dashed upstairs to kiss the children goodnight before returning to the kitchen table to find a plate of what I call 'stew' but Maggie calls 'ragout' and Maggie sitting down opposite the plate in obvious need of offloading her distress. In other words, time for a well-earned bollocking.

But no! Her tone was soft, kind even which, in some ways, I found even more alarming. I'm used to being told off by matriarchal figures. I was raised with a wagging finger and a smacked bottom. I *understand* the short, sharp shock. but Maggie had obviously been reading the latest *How To Make Your Husband Squirm* book (chapter one: Wrongfoot The Bastard) and was approaching me as though I were poorly or something. Maybe she thinks I'm about to have another breakdown? I'm never averse to a bit of sympathy – even if I don't deserve it.

'Steve, I'm worried about you. I think you're going through it at the moment.'

It's money I need, sweetheart, not platitudes. 'Well . . .'

'I've been thinking about this morning.'

I was wondering when you were going to bring that up. All right, it's a fair cop: you've got me bang to rights.

'It's a disease, that's what it is.'

WHAT? What's she on about? What's she *on*?

'Your gambling.'

Oh that.

'I've been reading up about it and talking to the experts at Gamblers Anonymous . . .'

'Wait a second, Maggie,' I said holding up a hand. 'I am *not* a gambler and, if I were, I can promise you that I wouldn't be anonymous about it.'

'The books warned me to expect some aggression when I raised the subject with you.'

'If you think *that* was aggression . . .'

'Steve, listen to me, *I understand*. Gambling for you is like alcohol is to an alcoholic.'

Close, pet, but no cigar. No gin and tonic ever felt as good as bluffing a poker pot; no hangover ever felt as bad as losing by a nose.

'Look, Steve, I have a checklist here.' She brandished a piece of paper as though she were Neville bloody Chamberlain. 'It's from Gamblers Anonymous and it will *prove* to you that you are a compulsive gambler.'

'It can't because I'm not.'

'Steven' – oh-oh – 'you *are*. I'm sorry to hurt your feelings but there's so much more at stake here than your feelings, you know.'

OK, I get it. 'All right then, in the words of Gary Gilmore, "let's do it".'

'Now listen, Steve, you *have* to answer honestly or else there's no point to the exercise.'

I decided that now was as good a time as any to reclaim some lost ground so I raised my voice a little. 'All right, woman, I said I'd cooperate and I will. Just ask me the bloody questions.'

'Have you ever lost time from work or school due to gambling?'

Yes, frequently. 'Ooh, that's a tough question. Can I phone a friend or go fifty-fifty?'

'Steven!'

'The answer is "no". I gamble recreationally – as you well

know – usually on Saturday afternoons or when there's football on the telly in the evenings.'

'Has gambling ever made your home life unhappy?'

I grimaced. 'Not until now.' She glared. 'OK, I guess so.'

'Does gambling affect your reputation?'

No. 'No.'

'Have you ever felt remorse after gambling?'

Whenever I lose – i.e. almost always. 'No. A slight twinge of regret maybe, but never "remorse" as such.'

'Do you ever gamble to get money with which to pay debts or otherwise solve financial difficulties?'

Ha ha. 'That would be an extremely dumb thing to do.'

'Honestly, Steve?'

'Honestly, Maggie.' It *would* be an extremely dumb thing to do. The fact that I'm doing it doesn't render it any less dumb.

'Does gambling cause a decrease in your ambition or efficiency?'

I don't think so. 'No.'

'After losing do you feel you must return as soon as possible and win back your losses?'

Good question. Sometimes. Usually. 'No, not that I'm aware of.'

'After a win, do you have a strong urge to return and win more?'

Is the Pope a Catholic? Still, if I keep on saying no, she won't believe me at all. 'Yes,' I said thoughtfully, 'I should say I do.'

'Have you often gambled until your last pound has gone?'

Only when I lose. 'Oh no. Maybe once or twice but very rarely.'

'Have you ever borrowed to finance your gambling?'

Thousands. Too quickly, I shook my head. Maggie pounced on me. 'Steve, I *know* you have. It's only a few months since we were forced to increase the mortgage, so please don't lie to me. I'm not a fool, you know.' No, Maggie, you're not. You're a dupe but you're not a fool.

'Have you ever sold anything to finance gambling?'

No, not that I'm aware of but it's not a bad idea if push comes to shove. Good old Gamblers Anonymous: what a great source of inspiration they are. 'No.'

'Are you reluctant to use "gambling money" for normal expenditures?'

I am at the moment. 'No.'

'Does gambling make you careless of the welfare of yourself or your family?'

I don't know what to say. 'I don't know what to say . . .'

'Let's answer that as "yes".' I looked – and felt – suitably grim-faced at that.

'Do you ever gamble longer than you've planned?'

Yeah, see question one (whenever I've taken time off work to gamble). 'No.'

'Have you ever gambled to escape worry or trouble?'

Yup. Time for some contrition. 'Not that I'm aware of but I suppose it's possible that I have.' Confess to the lesser crime in the hope of avoiding indictment for the greater.

'Have you ever committed, or considered committing, an illegal act to finance gambling?'

Suicide doesn't count, surely? 'No.'

'Does gambling cause you to have difficulty in sleeping?'

Sometimes. Occasionally. 'No.'

'Do arguments, disappointments or frustrations create within you an urge to gamble?'

Only when they're with you, my petal. 'Nope.'

'Do you ever have the urge to celebrate good fortune by a few hours of gambling?'

And what good fortune would that be? Good opportunity to score some brownie points. 'Well, the answer to that is yes in that I only tend to gamble when I'm in a good mood. You've seen me when I've been really depressed, haven't you, Maggie? I've not been up to switching on the TV to watch the racing, let alone have a bet.'

She looked confused as I intended she should. 'I'm not sure that's the point. Nevertheless, I'll mark that down as a yes.'

'Suit yourself.'

'Finally, Steve, have you ever considered self-destruction or suicide as a result of your gambling?'

Funny you should mention that. For a split second, I thought about . . . but instead, I looked her straight in the eyes as though wrestling with some great inner demon. It'd do her no harm – and me no end of good – for her to think that there was only *so far* she could push me before . . . I sighed. 'No, Maggie, I haven't.'

She held my gaze. I was determined not to look away first as though to do so was to incriminate myself. Eventually, she looked down at her sheet.

'Well, teacher, how did I do?'

She ignored my flippancy. 'By my calculation, you scored six out of twenty. According to Gamblers Anonymous, most compulsive gamblers will answer yes to at least seven of these questions.'

'Good, so that means I'm not a compulsive gambler.'

'Well, not necessarily. A lot depends on how honest you were being.' She halted my attempted protest. 'At any rate, given that even by your own admission you're borderline, I'd be grateful if you could start attending some sessions at Gamblers Anonymous. I've found out the address and time of . . .'

'Whoa, Maggie, not so fast. I took your test in all good faith and I passed.' Now it was my turn to silence her. 'Yes, I like to gamble and yes, I'm prepared to admit it, sometimes I do go too far and that's why we've had a few little financial problems . . .'

'A few?'

'Yes, Maggie. I accept that I might have a bit of a problem.' I'm looking at Maggie's question sheet as I write this and I reckon that if I'd answered her truthfully, I'd have scored about fifteen out of twenty. Thank God she wasn't using a polygraph.

'So what are you going to do about it?'

'I'm going to face up to it and try to overcome it. If you'll help me.' That put the ball back in her court.

'I'll help you but only if you're prepared to help yourself.' Good return, Maggie. Wish I could acknowledge it to you, girl.

I nodded. 'OK.'

'So you're prepared to go to Gamblers Anonymous?'

'I didn't say that.'

'Steve.' She was almost imploring me.

'Look, I'll think about it. I'll check my gambling and I'll think about going to Gamblers Anonymous. That better be all right with you because it's the most I'm prepared to concede.'

I think she knew she'd been beaten but then, for her, maybe even just tackling me about it represented some sort of achievement. 'I've bought a book for you, Steve, it should help you.'

I have it here in front of me now. A little book – approved by Gamblers Anonymous – full of sententious God-bothering sayings like 'Do I trust the infinite Lord rather than my finite self' and 'Have I asked God for strength today?' I really would rather die than surrender myself to pap like that.

WEDNESDAY, NOVEMBER 3

All that palaver with Maggie has, if anything, only confirmed me in my determination to see the bet through to the very end.

Ah, but wait a minute, what about 'the book's' Thought For The Day? 'A one-way street is better than a dead end.' Hallelujah! I've been saved.

FRIDAY, NOVEMBER 5

Before poker, I lit a few fireworks for the kids. Jona enjoyed it – well, at least he stopped twitching while it was going on – and so did his dad. Melanie, meanwhile, has sadly reached the age where she feels obliged to be ever so slightly disdainful towards it all (she learnt that off her *extremely* disdainful 'how can you bear to see your money go up in smoke' mother) and merely watched from the kitchen where she helped prepare the obligatory tomato soup and hot dogs.

The poker (talking of money going up in smoke) was at Douglas's.

Gerard announced – and it was very much done in the style of an announcement – that his first game will be on Sunday.

Ben was having none of it. 'No way am I going to play if we have to give up five per cent of each pot to you, Gerard. We don't do that when we play in our homes.'

Gerard, not unreasonably, pointed out that he'd never been allowed to play at Ben's but also explained that it was impossible for him to charge some people and not others.

'Then count me out,' said Ben.

'Me too,' said Jake.

Peter also made it clear that he wouldn't be coming but, in his case, it was more to do with the fact that playing once a week is enough for him.

This left me and Douglas who both agreed to suck it and see. This seemed to cheer up the never-disconsolate-for-long Bad Man. 'Great! You're really going to be impressed by it all. I've had it done so *professionally*: it's just like Vegas. I've got *three* professional dealers. I've got a waitress – well, my daughter actually – and I've even had my own chips made.'

'Sounds tacky,' commented Douglas.

'Thanks,' said the Bad Man taking this as a compliment. 'Now, boys,' he told us in no uncertain manner, 'the dealers aren't getting paid, so you're expected to tip them every time you win a hand. The waitress . . .'

'Your daughter,' I interrupted.

'Yes, Sylvie, she's also not getting paid, so I shall expect you to tip her as well. But she's happy to provide you with drinks and sandwiches and crisps and things.'

Douglas summed it up. 'Basically, what you're saying, is that however much money we bring along to gamble with, we should bring along *twice* as much for all the extras.'

Gerard smiled: whether out of appreciation of Douglas's 'joke' (well, it was a bit like a joke but without that funny bit at the end that makes people laugh) or because he was pleased at Douglas's grasp of the realities of poker at Gerard's, I couldn't tell.

Jake was a bit bothered about Gerard's daughter being involved in her father's dodgy 'business'.

'Oh it's quite all right,' said the Bad Man blithely, 'she's living with me now so she'll be there anyway.'

'You're going to raise your fifteen-year-old daughter in a casino?' asked Douglas incredulously.

'That's the way it goes,' said Gerard blithely.

Unusually for us, the discussion moved on to the subject of children and their upbringing. Douglas, who's also a single parent, reckons, 'the best way to raise children is within the context of a loving relationship: failing that, within marriage.'

All of this inevitably interrupted the poker but, even so, it was a fine evening. Funny thing was, I lost big time on all the games I called (Follow The Queen, five-card stud and four-card Omaha) but (almost) made up for it on the games I ordinarily dislike (seven-card stud high-low – which always gets Ben singing 'High-low' to the tune of 'Hi-ho' from *Snow White And The Seven Dwarfs* – and seven-card stud with nothing wild). In the end I lost about two hundred.

SATURDAY, NOVEMBER 6

Did some good trades today. Having noticed (in Henry's) that in six of the eight Premiership games, the home teams were odds against to win, I sold the home over away goals for £200 a goal.

In the event, there was actually an equal number of home and away goals so, having sold at 2.2, I made £440.

I also bought total Premiership bookings on the grounds that with so many games tightly poised – in the betting at any rate – there was likely to be quite a lot of hot-headedness. With 10 points for a yellow card and 25 for a red, the spread was 315–325 and I bought at 325 for £20 a point. A couple of sendings-off and three matches in which there were more than six bookings saw the index make up at a massive 390 and so I made a fantastic £1,300.

If I'd only restricted myself to those two trades, I'd have showed a great profit on the day. Unfortunately, some really *dumb* trades on the televised rugby reduced my profit on the day to a (relatively) small £350.

SUNDAY, NOVEMBER 7

I arrived early at Gerard's and got the full personal tour. But first I was obliged to wait for the Bad Man to 'conduct some business'. 'I'll just be twenty minutes,' he shouted from his office.

I told him that that wasn't acceptable and I'd go off and pop in on a friend.

'OK, I'll be five minutes.' Fine.

He took forty minutes.

At least Gerard does a nice line in apologies. In the end, I found *myself* apologising to him for him keeping me waiting.

The offices – such as they are – consist of one large open-plan area stuffed full of cheap desks, chairs and telephones. Gerard's small and functional office is just off this area. The only other upstairs room provides the first indication that all is not as it seems. Directly opposite Gerard's office is the 'boardroom'. Whereas everything else on the ground floor is functional – cheap and plastic – this room is, as Gerard himself put it (again without irony) 'lavishly appointed'. The Wedgwood blue walls are hung with ornately framed hunting prints. There's a huge mahogany table with ten or twelve finely carved chairs around it. Then there's all the paraphernalia that goes with a room like this: the whisky and sherry decanters, the coat and umbrella stand, the matching grandfather clock. It looked so perfect that, inevitably, it looked bogus.

'Do you approve?' he asked me and, once again, I was James Bond in the villain's lair. If only he'd said, 'You have no chance of escape, you understand' or 'Unfortunately your predecessor can not be here with us tonight' or 'Before you die I will tell you my master plan to take over the world.'

The Bad Man's bought himself an Alsatian. 'My family's always kept Alsatians.'

'That just means that your family are as bad as you are, Bad Man.'

Gerard's flat and card room are downstairs and are pretty well what I expected. All subterranean and *bad*. All flash and absolutely *no* taste – although I do have to say that the card room is well equipped even if he's struggling to fit in three tables.

It was only when I actually *saw* the scale of his operation that I felt my first twinges of concern. 'Are you sure about this, Gerard?'

He immediately understood but just shrugged his shoulders. 'It's OK. The police won't do anything. So long as I don't advertise or put a sign up, they're not bothered.'

'But what you're doing is illegal.'

'So I'll get a bridge licence.'

'But you're not playing bridge, you're playing poker.'

'They're similar enough.'

They're not but you can't argue with that and, besides, the door bell was ringing with the first of Gerard's 'guests' or the five percenters as I'm going to suggest we should call ourselves.

I've got to make an early start in the morning, so I only stayed until about eleven before the game(s) had even begun to warm up. However, I saw enough – and was sufficiently impressed – to make sure that, next week, I'll be there for the duration.

I was pleasantly surprised by the other players. Far from being the scuzzbags I'd imagined, they were the same sort of decent blokes, regular guys, I've been playing poker with for the past fifteen-twenty years. Plus Douglas, of course. There was a guy named Joel, however, who had the worst case of obsessive compulsive disorder I've ever seen – certainly at the poker table: he touched wood ten times before *every* deal.

The dealers – Gerard's much-vaunted 'professional' dealers – actually proved to be a godsend. All the usual areas of disagreement – whose deal is it?, who's not anted up?, how much goes? etc. etc. – were entirely avoided and the dealers themselves slotted in to the atmosphere perfectly. The fact that there were three of them and, until 10.30, only one table in play, meant that there was no pressure on them as they could take as many breaks as they wanted or even, as one did, actually play.

The only jarring note as far as the dealers were concerned was sounded by the Bad Man. At the end of *every* hand – Gerard said to the winner, 'Tip the dealer, go on, tip him.' We understood that the dealers were relying on tips – how could we fail to with Gerard (or 'Marcel' as everyone there except for Douglas and I was calling him) reminding us? – but tipping after *every* hand felt like an additional burden (on top of Gerard's five per cent) and robbed the tipper of the spontaneity (and satisfaction) of giving.

The other 'facilities' – the food, the drink and, saints be praised, the air-conditioning, were all first-class and I have to say that, despite our direst fears, Gerard's daughter, Sylvie, looked to be having an enjoyable evening without being in any way morally corrupted.

The poker stakes were a *little* higher than we're used to in our game but certainly no higher than at the casino. Gerard, however, was doing his best to drive up the pots – a) because that's the way he plays and b) because he's on five per cent of every pot.

The players don't mind Gerard's five per cent tax (as Douglas pointed out, 'It adds a whole new meaning to "income tax".') – they're used to it: other illegal games do it and so do casinos in the States. Gerard also limits himself to £30 per pot maximum – not because he's charitable but, again, because it's the norm.

We mostly played high-low (seven-card stud), Omaha, Hold 'Em and Irish. Wild games are out but otherwise it's 'dealer's choice' (i.e. whoever would have been dealing if there weren't a professional dealer present).

At the time I left ('Please don't go, Steve,' wailed Gerard as though I were his daddy going off to war), I was about four hundred quid up – having been as much as five or six hundred down. Fortunately, Gerard is offering credit or, to use the vernacular, 'spotting' people, so there's never any danger of running out of money.

I really enjoyed the evening and, in the words of Douglas MacArthur, 'I shall return.'

TUESDAY, NOVEMBER 9

Hard time from Phil today. He got a call yesterday from the buyer at Adams complaining that I was an hour late for an appointment. Neither of them (neither Phil nor the client) was interested in my (totally fictitious) excuse, the cunts. I was on the verge of telling him to stuff his job but didn't on the basis that why should I do his dirty work for him? Besides, I want as much money (for as little work) as possible before I go.

I was going to have a bet on the horses this afternoon but I'm tired of gifting my hard-earned to the fucking bookies simply because I don't really know what the hell I'm doing. I'm going to save my money for a few big sports bets – spread and fixed odds – and, of course, poker.

WEDNESDAY, NOVEMBER 10

When I returned from work today there was a letter from the loan company notifying me that a payment of £15,000 has been deposited in my bank account. Best of all, there are no repayments to make until February.

Maggie couldn't help but notice my elation. 'You seem very happy.'

'And why shouldn't I be?'

'I thought . . . after our . . . *talk* . . .'

'Oh, that's fine. I took on board everything you said and will act upon it.'

'Really, Steve?'

'You can bet on it.'

FRIDAY, NOVEMBER 12

Funny thing is, for forty-eight hours, I've had fifteen thousand metaphorically burning a hole in my pocket and yet I haven't had a bet – not even put a couple of quid into a fruit machine! It's like when I used to smoke, I'd always smoke *less* if I had a good stock of duty-frees than if I were down to my last packet of ten.

About a third of that money's going to go on bills (red ones only) and the mortgage backlog – if only to keep Maggie off my back – but that still leaves a good ten thou.

Having said that, I didn't go mad tonight at Ben's. I just played my natural game. Of course, all the girls were desperate to find out what had happened at Gerard's (who wasn't present) and so Douglas and I, as heroes returning, didn't disappoint them.

Dulce et decorum est
To play poker at the Bad Man's nest

Everyone – even Nathan and Peter – had a view on the Bad Man and no one seems to give either him or it (the poker game) longer than about three months.

Jake confined himself to the elliptical statement. 'He talks the talk but, when it comes down to it, is he going to walk the walk?' It sounded really wise at the time but now that I actually write it down, I'm not entirely sure what the good doctor means.

Some fun poker but, for me and also I suspect for Douglas too, it felt a bit like a gentle friendly sandwiched between two important Premiership games. I guess I won maybe £100 but it really doesn't matter. Not any more.

SATURDAY, NOVEMBER 13

I selected the three Premiership teams I fancied to win and then, after checking in *The Racing Post*, chose the bookmaker offering the best (overall) odds on the treble.

One bet for £1,000 (plus £90 tax). That's all. Liverpool at 4–5, Leeds United at 10–11 and West Ham United at evens. If it comes off, I will win £6,872.72.

In one sense it's not that different from the bets I used to make at fixed odds covering my downside on the Saturday Shorties. The big difference is that these are three teams that *I've* selected rather than three that have been 'imposed' upon me by a spread-betting firm.

That's not to decry spread betting for it has a useful role to play in, if not offsetting then mitigating the primary fixed-odds bet. In the old days, before 'the bet', I'd often do trebles on the football fixed odds: usually I'd lose (and that's not counting the times when I couldn't resist shoving in a couple of odds-on Scottish teams which would then go on to lose and thus ruin the five-timer) but even when I did, the other two teams in the treble would almost always win.

Which is where spread betting comes in. You can buy (or sell) an individual team with the mini-performances and that's what I've done today. With 15 points for a win, 10 for a draw, 5 for a clean sheet and 10 for each goal (less 15 for a red card), I've bought Liverpool at 31, Leeds at 29 and West Ham at 28 for £100 a point each. Now, I don't mind (or at least I don't mind so much) if all three don't win. I don't even mind if *none* of them win – so long as they score tons of goals when they lose.

Later: it's only money. There's lots more where it came from. I am *not* going to get all down and pathetic about it all because down that road lies ruin. See it in perspective, Steve. No one's died and there are many opportunities for you to win it all back and more. There are still more than six weeks left.

For the record. Liverpool won 2–1, Leeds drew 1–1 and West Ham drew 0–0. So I lost £1,090 on the fixed-odds treble and the spreads made up respectively at 35 (I won £400), 20 (lost £900) and 15 (lost £1,300). That's a total for the day of minus £2,890. Lucky for me that no one got sent off.

SUNDAY, NOVEMBER 14

Dad popped over in the morning. I could tell from his body language that he was itching to ask me about his monthly interest payments. Eventually, he broached the subject in a typically hesitant way. 'Son, um . . . you know that . . . er . . . money I er . . . lent you.'

'Yes.'

'Um, you were paying . . . er . . . me interest . . . um . . . but I haven't . . . er . . . received anything for the past two months.'

Me nonchalant, 'Oh yeah?'

Him flustered, 'No . . . er . . . yes.'

'Well, I'll look into it and get back to you.' That's it, end of conversation. Remembering all those beatings I got, I'm not bothered if I never talk to him again. I don't care if the next thing he hears about me is that I've killed myself, that I've checked out in precisely the same way that Mum did, the way that Mum maybe *had* to.

Off to Gerard's. Told Maggie I had to go to a sales conference. She raised an eyebrow in that unlovely way she has of registering disapproval or disbelief (I can never tell which). So, to gain a little breathing space, I decided to tell her (a little) about our current financial position.

'Now that I've stopped gambling – no, really I have, darling – I've restructured our finances. We – I – were behind on the mortgage: we're not now. As you know, there were piles of red bills: I'm in the process of sorting them all out. The bad old days are gone, I promise you.'

She seemed relieved. She's all right, my Maggie. Wish I didn't have to lie to her.

MONDAY, NOVEMBER 15

I'm writing this having had no sleep for, I don't know, thirty-six hours? Certainly not since yesterday morning.

I'm dead, I'm gone. I've told Maggie I've got a migraine and I'm going to lie down. She's been really kind and has offered me a neck massage and a cold flannel for my forehead.

I lost bigtime. I was up – oh, one and a half thousand – and then I just couldn't stop losing.

Fuck, I think I'm actually getting a headache. I don't know, I just feel so jetlagged. I'd go to sleep right here and now if it didn't mean that I'd wake up at four in the morning and get into a really bad cycle.

Met Caz (short for Cazalet-Thornton – his surname which, as I told him, sounds to me like a Scottish football team). I like him. He's a bit posh but he's one of those guys who just don't give a damn. Him and his mate Johnny.

Typical example: one of the (more staid) players there said, 'I've never been so insulted in my life.'

Caz's reply: 'You should get out more.'

Gerard was absolutely full of it. I honestly don't know how he does it – not more than once at any rate. You have to admire his stamina.

Like last week, he was playing crazily – even when the pot had gone past the point where his five per cent had maxed out. Gerard owning a poker club is a bit like putting an alcoholic in charge of a pub: maximum temptation coupled with maximum opportunity.

What annoyed me about the Bad Man was his reluctance to let me (or, indeed, anyone) go. 'Please stay because otherwise the game's going to fold,' he pleaded with me. At that point (five in the fucking morning), I was only two thousand or so down. Between five and eight (the time I eventually escaped) I managed to lose another six hundred quid.

Once again, his daughter Sylvie was doing the catering. What was OK last week at ten in the evening – even quite charming – was really horrible at three in the morning this week. I felt so bad about it that I actually said something to Gerard. 'Damn it, Bad Man, what's your daughter doing up at three in the morning with school tomorrow?'

'She's earning three hundred quid in tips.'

'But what's that going to do to her value system? And when she does eventually go to sleep, what protection does she have here? What's to stop some creep going into her bedroom?'

'I'd *kill* anyone who even *looked* at her the wrong way.'

'I'm sure you would, but with the best will in the world, there's no telling who she's going to bump into if she goes to the bathroom in the night.'

All he could do was shrug his shoulders but clearly I've given him something to think about.

Whatever else I'm guilty of, at least I know that my daughter's safe at night.

I must stay awake for another few hours even though I'm finding it really difficult to concentrate for long. Christ, I feel ragged. The last time I stayed up *all* night, Melanie was born. She weighed eight and a half pounds. And now I've lost two and half thousand pounds.

TUESDAY, NOVEMBER 16

Another day, another fucking speeding camera. I hate them – and the people whose decision it is to put them up – so fucking much. If only they knew the misery they cause. 'Ah,' they'd say, 'if you only knew the misery that speeding causes. Speed kills, you know.' Sanctimonious gits. No it doesn't. Speed doesn't kill – not *per se* – it's bad driving that kills. Doing 45 in a 30mph zone that happens to drive comfortably at 50 isn't dangerous. On the other hand, doing 25 in a 30mph zone outside a kindergarten as the kids are coming out might very well be. It's all a question of judgement and to punish people – i.e. bloody me – just for getting to work as best they can without doing any harm to anyone else is so fucking unfair.

That's it then, I've lost my job. Without a licence – as I will be when I get my summons and three-point penalty – I'm no use to any company that expects its workers to drive themselves around the country.

I think I'd have probably been caught even if I hadn't been so tired. I got a good night's sleep but I'm still playing catch up. So, though I was concentrating on my driving, maybe I wasn't keeping enough of a lookout for the cameras. Ridiculous.

I didn't tell anyone at work about the speeding camera: it's none of their business. When I get my summons, I'll ignore it and that'll take me past the end of the year at which point either I'll be dead or else I'll be doing something completely different.

The only good thing that happened today was that Jim gave me a tip for Thursday: Carlanda's Hope in the 3.15 at Sedgefield. He told me that, according to his source, 'The trainer *won't* see him lose'.

THURSDAY, NOVEMBER 18

Carlanda's Hope ran in the 3.15 at Sedgefield. There was no ante-post market so, on the basis that the world and his stable lass would be piling in on it, I took the first show of 7–4. Not a great price but with £2000 on the nose, I stood to make £3500 profit less the tax that, foolishly and superstitiously, I declined to pay.

It started the race at 5–4 – having see-sawed with the favourite – which pleased me: it's great to take a price and then watch it come in, like snuggling under the duvet when it's cold outside.

Carlanda's Hope ran a good race but, unfortunately, another horse ran a better one and beat him by four or five lengths. Funny thing is, I don't feel too bad about it. The information came from Jim, who's given me good info in the past and I went in big because it was the right thing to do.

Actually, on second thoughts, I wonder if the info *was* good. 'The trainer *won't* see him lose.' Maybe this is a tragic case of Chinese whispers? The trainer tells someone that he can't be bothered to go Sedgefield because the horse is only going to lose so why bother? This eventually metamorphoses into 'The trainer *won't* see him lose'.

I don't mind the tip not coming in: only about fifty per cent of them seem to; I *do* mind if some idiot got hold of the wrong end of the stick.

FRIDAY, NOVEMBER 19

There was a game (of sorts) at Ben's but I didn't go because a) Gerard's not going to be there, b) Douglas's looking iffy and c) the game's moved on. The other factor was Maggie. Since her 'lecture' I'm meant to have foresworn poker – even though she's under the impression that we only play for small stakes and do other things apart from just play poker (like have a few beers, or watch sport on telly). I got away with going a couple of weeks ago on the basis that they were expecting me. Last week, I told her I was going out for a drink with Douglas (whom she likes – possibly even fancies) but if I were to go out *every* Friday, returning home late, she'd smell a rat.

So tonight I made a big deal of staying in and had a great time. The kids stayed up because there's no school tomorrow and we all had a giggle together.

Melanie wanted to know how her Mummy and Daddy had met. Maggie told her and I found myself softening towards her (Maggie). Where is it written, I wonder, that I can't love my wife?

Jona, who seemed to be taken out of himself by the sheer fun of it all, wanted to know if *we* knew how babies were made. 'Er, yes, darling but do *you* know?'

'If Daddy kisses Mummy's tummy, they get a baby,' he announced authoritatively with just a hint of embarrassment. So *that's* how it's done.

SATURDAY, NOVEMBER 20

Had a feeling that there would be lots of goals in the Premiership today. All right, maybe I didn't: maybe I just *wanted* there to be lots of goals and the wish was father to the thought. Truth is I'm a buyer not a seller. I'd rather feel like I'm *winning* my stake each time a goal's scored rather than losing it.

With remarkable restraint, I made just *one* trade. I bought Premiership goals at 20.5 for £200 a goal.

I sat rooted to the television – or, to be more precise, the teletext – from three o'clock until (nearly) five and I have to say that I have never been more excited in my life.

My maximum downside was £4,100 but, given that I don't think there's ever been a totally goalless Premiership programme, it was realistically limited to about half of that.

By half-time, there had only been five goals and four of those had come in just two of the matches. I had 'won' £1,000 but was still losing over three times that amount.

Things didn't improve much in the first twenty minutes of the second half. I thought that maybe it was the fault of the teletext service-provider in not updating the scores quickly enough (they can be a little lax in the second half of games) but, after flicking channels, it turned out that the problem was the message and not the medium.

Then, suddenly, around the seventieth minute, there was an absolute torrent of goals. I didn't make a note (though I will check in the paper tomorrow) but I wouldn't be surprised if there weren't as many as ten goals scored in a five-minute period.

This was followed by a quarter of an hour of relative drought before a final flourish of goals in injury time.

The actual total was 31 and so I made a profit of £2,100.

MONDAY, NOVEMBER 22

Got Douglas to pick me up to go to Gerard's – a) because, with all my points and a conviction pending, I'm trying to avoid driving at night in case I'm stopped by the police (and I'm not entirely sure I should even be driving at the moment) and b) it makes Maggie think that I'm just going out with a friend.

We got there early enough to find Gerard sprawled out on his settee looking for the life of him just like a beached whale.

'Aha, my friends,' he greeted us. 'So glad you could come. I've just finished playing backgammon. It went on all night' – does the bad man *ever* sleep? – 'and there were twelve players in a *chouette* against me.'

'Why would all twelve want to play against you, Gerard,' I asked.

'Because,' said Douglas, 'they're only seven years old.'

Bigger game; heavier game. Caz was there and so was Johnny. Caz asked me to tell him if ever there was a big private game on: he reckons he's the 'fireman of short-order poker games'.

Gerard was spotting people like he was some kind of money-lender. He was sitting there with a book while he was playing and he was lending money to people – from time to time going into another room where he's got his own free-standing seven-foot-high vault. Meanwhile, with three tables in play, after just a few hours Gerard had collected two and a half grand in 'tax' – though he must have lost nearly as much as that because he was so fucking high.

Almost every hand was Hold 'Em. I'm not a fan. I can never hit the right rhythm for it. For a start, I *never* fold before the flop – not even if I have 2, 7 unsuited – just because I couldn't bear it if the flop then came down, say, 2, 2, 7. Also, although I'm obviously aware of what the nut hand is, I'm never quite sure whether my hand is good *enough* to win. I seem to have a talent for coming second in Hold 'Em hands.

I must have lost sixteen or seventeen hundred pounds by the time we left at two-thirty. Douglas's had enough – and not just for the evening: after losing an undisclosed four-figure sum, Douglas's decided that the Bad Man's game is too heavy for him. 'I've found that when you bleed out of your arse, it doesn't form a scab.'

THURSDAY, NOVEMBER 25

Only realised the other day that I haven't been taking my Prozac for ages. Just forgot all about it. Wonder if that's why I'm feeling so fucking low today? Went out the house (couldn't be bothered to explain to Maggie) but just mooched around. Couldn't even be bothered to have a spiv. Just feel so goddamn listless and cold and apathetic and

FRIDAY, NOVEMBER 26

Felt better this morning. Even made a few work calls. Tried to get hold of Gerard but it turned out to be impossible – especially as I'm *not* prepared to call the premium-rate phone lines in his office (*and* he doesn't do sex chat). Gerard uses all the devices BT possess to hide from people he doesn't want to speak to. Gerard's only available if *he* wants you and then he'll do all the talking. He's jammed on transmit, the Bad Man, that's his trouble.

I'm spending this evening at home like the dutiful husband/father I am. It saves me grief and also *Goodfellas* is on TV again.

SATURDAY, NOVEMBER 27

What do the Yanks call a draw? It's like kissing your sister. That's right. Sorry, Sue, but that's no good to me at the moment.

Maybe it's my own stupid fault for doing so many different trades but I swear that none of them were intended to offset others.

Nor was I just betting for entertainment, to have an interest of a Saturday afternoon. Every trade, every bet, was done in deadly earnest. How was I to know that they'd all effectively cancel each other out and leave me with a zero fucking balance on the day?

SUNDAY, NOVEMBER 28

Just as I was getting the hang of Hold 'Em, along comes a hand of four-card Omaha – my favourite game, for Christ's sake – and fucks me right up the shitter.

I'm playing at Gerard's. Maggie doesn't suspect anything because she doesn't associate Sunday nights with me gambling. There are six of us at the table for this hand: Gerard, Caz, Johnny, Tallesh (the dealer, if that's how he spells his name and if I haven't misheard it) and a couple of guys who Gerard's treating like 'the quality' but who look like typical casino trash to me.

I'm dealt 2, 5, 5, queen – all unsuited. There's a bit of betting before the flop (a bit! – six months ago, what I now think of as a bit would have scared me off at the *end* of a hand) but I just call. The flop is the 2 of diamonds, the 5 of spades and the queen of diamonds. I've got trip 5s and all sorts of prospects. Still, I'm cautious and merely see Gerard's bet of two hundred quid which anyway I suspect is caused by the carbohydrate rush of half a pound of taco chips. Tallesh and the two guys whose names I don't know fold, leaving just four of us in the hand with a healthy-looking pot.

The fourth card is the 8 of clubs which does nothing for me and not much, I suspect, for anyone else. If anyone's actually got the nuts (three queens) they're disguising it mightily effectively. Caz bets a hundred and we all call with varying degrees of enthusiasm. I'm assuming that one of them has got two pairs and the other two are waiting on the flush.

The last card is the jack of hearts. Phew. OK, the nuts is still three queens, followed by three jacks but my three 5s is looking mighty beefy. Sure enough, Caz and Johnny (the latter cursing loudly) fold before anyone even bets but the Bad Man is all but licking his lips. 'One big one,' he declares greedily, pushing (what he claims is) a £1,000 in chips into the middle. He sees me raise my eyebrows. 'Come on, Steve, keep me honest.'

'*Keep* him honest?' I hear Johnny say and I can't help giggling. Why would the Bad Man be asking me to 'keep him honest' unless he was bluffing? Or maybe it was a double bluff? Or a triple bluff? Or a quadruple bluff? Or . . . enough, enough . . . it's better to lose a grand than to lose my mind trying to second/third/fourth guess the Bad Man. Shit, he's probably got a pair – maybe two. Perhaps he was going for the nut flush and can't bear to fold. Who *knows* with the Bad Man?

'OK, Gerard, here's a thousand. What d'you got?'

And blow me down. He's only got trip jacks. I don't fucking believe it. The Bad Man, of all people, being rewarded for staying in. 'I also had straight and flush prospects,' he said in mitigation but I was already starting to tune out. More than two grand on *one* hand. Fuck.

That was it. I smiled at the guys and left with Caz's words ringing in my ears, 'When the going gets tough, Steve goes.' Too fucking right.

MONDAY, NOVEMBER 29

Fuck it. I got a summons for that speeding camera. I hoped that I'd got away with it. Well, that does it, I'm not sending back the form. Why should I? I could be out of the country for all they know. I'm going to leave it till they come after me, till after the end of the year. The way things are going, I ain't gonna need a sodding driving licence.

TUESDAY, NOVEMBER 30

It doesn't matter but I lost about nine grand this month and I'm now £21,500 down on the year. It really doesn't matter because for the purposes of the bet, I can lose by twice that amount or half that amount: it's the same result.

Maybe, like away goals in Europe, it actually *benefits* me to be this far down. This way, I'll be forced to make bigger, much bigger, bets and therefore clear the deficit even quicker.

A couple of big, big winners is all that it takes. I'm going to have to give it *everything*. I've got nothing to lose (except other people's money) and everything to gain (my fucking life).

WEDNESDAY, DECEMBER 1

Every day I don't gamble brings me a day closer to death. Sometimes I wonder how on earth I could ever have conceived of such a ridiculous bet. Sometimes I tell myself that I'll pull back from the brink, that I'll stop short of actually killing myself, that maybe accidentally-on-purpose I'll 'attempt' suicide.

'Attempt suicide.' That's complete bollocks that is. If someone *genuinely* wants to kill themselves, they can and will. A bullet in the mouth, a jump from the top of a tall building, enough pills – and then more – taken somewhere *totally* private (my own preferred method): all of these will lead to death. Except in the 0.01% of cases where the bullet lodges somewhere safe, where a soft-top truck happens to go past the tall building or someone turns up – *completely* unexpectedly – before the pills have taken effect.

I think – I *know* – that if I lost the bet and *didn't* commit suicide then I'd be unable to look myself in the eye again. In other words, if I couldn't face killing myself, then I'd want to die. I've given it a go – I'm *giving* it a go, my best shot – and, if I lose, then I must pay the price. The alternative, to live with no pride or self-esteem, is unthinkable. Besides, if I lose, I intend to lose so big that I couldn't *afford* to stay alive.

FRIDAY, DECEMBER 3

Played poker at Caz's until late this morning.

He lives in a sensational house in St John's Wood that must be worth more than a million. There's a lot of family money there,

I know, because I've heard Johnny teasing him about it, but there's no doubt he also pulls in a big screw from whatever he does in the City.

He also seems to be one of those lucky people who don't need to sleep. He's survived a few marathon sessions at the Bad Man's and I know for a fact that he was still playing at four-thirty this morning when he's due to start work at seven. However, he does have a little help in staying awake: massive quantities of cocaine.

He and the others – Johnny, Richard, a schoolfriend of Caz and Johnny's, Terence, who's unemployed but seems to have plenty of dough and Clive, a surveyor or something – were taking cocaine (or, 'charlie', as they called it) as casually as you like. Not for them the furtive trip to the loo coming out sniffing: no, they just cut it up on mirrors and snorted it *just like that* while playing cards.

I'm not a complete hick: I've taken a bit of speed and smoked my fair share of dope but I've never actually done coke – not because I'm especially law-abiding but simply because the only time I was ever offered any it looked to be seven-eighths rat poison. Tonight, I tried some and it was fucking fantastic. I honestly don't remember feeling so incredibly good. It was like drinking a bottle of champagne without the side-effects of feeling sick or bloated. I really felt as though I could have done *anything* and it didn't seem to hurt my poker playing at all (although that could have had something to do with the fact that we were all taking it). If anything, there was an improvement: I was about four grand down before I snorted anything but ended the evening 'just' three grand down. Clive, meanwhile, seemed to be completely out of his depth. I don't think he helps himself by fawning over Caz so much: as Johnny said to me in a not-so-quiet aside, 'Clive's all over Caz like a cheap suit.' From that moment on, I resolved to be as aloof as possible.

Notwithstanding Caz's undoubted charm, I don't find it hard to keep my distance. He's quite the most degenerate man I've ever met in my life. It's not only the drugs, it's also his 'sexual preferences'. The conversation turned, as it so often does at the poker table, to sex. Terence was describing how he'd had sex with two pregnant women (not women he'd impregnated) and how he longed to have sex with a lactating woman.

Richard and I cringed but Clive checked Caz and Johnny to see their reaction and joined them in nodding approvingly at Terence's sexual adventurousness. 'What's it like, you know, screwing a pregnant woman?' asked Clive eagerly.

'Pretty good,' said Terence.

'Did you get a blow job off the foetus?' asked Caz.

'Yo, Caz,' joshed Johnny, 'I know you like them young but surely not *that* young?'

Caz grinned. 'The younger the better I say. If they bleed, they fuck.'

'Yeah, but come on, Caz,' said Richard who seems a decent bloke, 'some girls start their periods as early as nine or ten.'

Caz stood his ground. 'So?'

'Don't be a cunt, Caz,' said Johnny who, with Richard, is the only person to really stand up to him, 'you *know* that you're just winding them up. How old *is* the youngest girl you've ever had? Go on, break the habit of a lifetime, be honest.'

Caz laughed. 'OK, OK, the youngest would probably be Araminta – you know, Buckhart's daughter – she was, what, *just* thirteen when I had her a couple of seasons ago. And I swear I wasn't her first! But what a top totty: the firmest, pertest little bottom I've ever had the pleasure to fondle.'

I'm no prude but . . . 'Hey, man, that's a bit young, isn't it?'

'Ooh,' Caz and Johnny shrieked together in camp voices, 'get her!'

I found myself out on a limb but I was going to stand my ground. 'Look, I've got a young daughter myself . . .'

Caz didn't seem to be bothered. 'Well, bring her along next time, Steven, and I'll let you know if she's my sort.' The evil bastard. I'd have left on the spot but for the fact that he immediately mollified me by putting his arm round me and telling me not to take everything so seriously. 'I'm just pulling your plonker; you shouldn't believe a word I say.' I still wasn't sure but I have to admit that I felt not a little flattered that he cared enough about my feelings to (sort of) backtrack.

Caz then spoilt it by telling (quite possibly) the worst taste joke I've ever heard – although it was undeniably funny. 'Paedophile takes a girl into the woods. "I'm frightened," she says holding his hand. "*You're* frightened?" replies the paedophile, "I've got to come back on my own".'

Unfortunately, Johnny decided to pick up from where Caz finished by telling us the story (*le mot juste*?) of a friend of his who was in a poker game where one fellow 'won' another fellow's *ten-year-old* daughter.

Sounded like an urban myth to me and I said so but Johnny was adamant. 'Listen, it happened. It was Plinks – Caz, back me up, you know Plinks, he wouldn't lie.' Caz nodded. 'Plinks wasn't involved himself,' continued Johnny, 'but he was definitely there. He said this guy had lost big time but still wanted to carry on. He couldn't give his marker because everyone there knew that he wouldn't be able to honour it. So, in desperation, he offered a night with his daughter – his ten-year-old daughter – in return for a thousand pounds of credit and when he lost, he had to pay up. Or, rather, she did.'

'I don't believe it. I just *don't* believe it,' I said.

'Every man has his price. You just don't *want* to believe it,' said Caz.

'And you *do*,' said Richard to Caz which took my breath away. 'Come on, fellows, let's play cards.'

So that's what we did and very exciting it was too. I'd have enjoyed it even more if I'd won.

SATURDAY, DECEMBER 4

Dad was over. After much clearing of throat, he asked me, ahem, about the interest on the loan. Decided that I'd nothing to lose so I told him that, sorry, I was absolutely wiped out – investments, currency fluctuations, you know the sort of things.

He looked shocked – as well he might – and asked me about the extent of my liabilities.

'Trust me, Dad,' I said, putting a patronising hand on his shoulder, 'you don't want to know.'

He looked worried. For a minute – no longer – I almost felt sorry for him feeling so sorry for me. Is this love? Or is it just vestigial guilt and responsibility? 'What can I do, son?'

'Do you *really* want to know?'

'Yes,' he said hesitantly, then more positively, 'yes, I do.'

'Then can you lend me some more money?'

He looked disconsolate. He looked beaten, like he'd just taken one blow too many. Like I took one blow too many from him. Never forget, Stevie, never forget. 'How about two thousand, son, would that help at all?'

No, not a lot. 'Yeah, that would be fine, Dad.'

Two thousand, huh? I worked my way through *double* that this afternoon. Horses, football, rugby: I don't discriminate. Not any more.

SUNDAY, DECEMBER 5

11.00am. Told Maggie that I've got a very early call in Devon tomorrow and so I'm going to set off this evening and stay at a motel on the way. She gave me a searching look – made me want to quote from her bleeding book: 'The only thing you can bet on is the love of the Lord' – but just said, 'Oh I am sorry, you won't be here in the morning for your birthday. The kids will be disappointed.'

That's a thought. I hadn't exactly forgotten my birthday but it's not been uppermost in my mind. 'Don't worry, darling, I'll make sure I'm home by the time they're back from school and we'll all have a birthday tea. Is that OK?'

'Fine. I'll buy a cake.'

'That's kind of you.' I gave her a peck on the cheek. Nothing unusual but for once she held on to me and before I knew it, we were kissing properly. I was surprised by the intensity of her – not passion – but ardour. Indeed, it was me who broke away first. More like *staggered* away. 'What's all that about?'

Coquettish, flirting. 'Just wanted to remember what it was like.' Then the switch: more serious. 'Be careful, Steve. *Please* be careful.'

MONDAY, DECEMBER 6

I met Gerard's workers this morning. He's Marcel here rather than Gerard which I found confusing. He's got some absolute stunners working for him but there's no question of him having any of them. Not because of his protestations that he's not 'that sort of employer' but because he really is so fat and bloated at the moment that I can't imagine him being able to get it up, let alone any woman fancying him. When I put it to him directly, as in 'Who are you shagging at the moment, Bad Man?', he sniggered, 'I'm still fucking in the dark.'

I'll give the Bad Man one thing, he doesn't flag. Me, I'm absolutely dead but when I left him at eleven this morning, he was still intending to carry on till *tomorrow* morning.

He's also not short of bottle. I wouldn't be running his poker operation – not for all the chips in Monte Carlo. The people he has coming along . . . Gerard marked my card for me while we took a break. 'Look, see that man over there,' he said pointing to a poorly dressed thin man with a sallow face from which was sprouting wisps of hair like adolescent bum fluff, 'he's the UK's premier card-cheat.'

I wasn't going to let Gerard get away with such an extraordinary claim. 'What do you mean "the UK's premier card-cheat"? How do you *know*? Is there some sort of competition, The UK Card-Cheating Championships or something?'

Gerard tried to shush me but I was on a roll. 'No, hang on, Bad Man, why should I keep my voice down? What, doesn't he *know* that he's the UK's premier card-cheat? Does he think that he's just, like, North London's premier card-cheat? Perhaps we should tell him. Maybe you could arrange some sort of award ceremony?'

With his best 'don't mention the war' face on, Gerard attempted to divert my attention from the UK's premier card-cheat by pointing out some other lowlife but I hadn't finished. 'If that guy really is the UK's premier card-cheat, what are you doing allowing him to play here?'

The Bad Man nodded his head vigorously in the way that he

does when he's trying to show that he's on top of a situation. 'It's all right, my dealers are watching him very closely.' I wasn't satisfied and made a mental note to avoid the table where the UK's premier card-cheat was sitting. Gerard continued his guide to scuzzballs. Pointing to a moustachioed type in a check jacket with patched elbows and brown corduroy trousers – almost a caricature of an English prep school teacher – Gerard said, 'That's Rocky, he's a hit man with a temper'. I laughed at this wonderful pen picture – how could I not? – but Gerard was gesturing furiously with his eyebrows to persuade me that this was the truth and to stop me from approaching the hit man with a temper to confirm his occupation. I mean, I've heard of *What's My Line?* but this was ridiculous. 'Are you, by any chance, a baker?' 'No,' says the questionmaster, 'actually he's a hit man with a temper.'

'Remind me not to play at *his* table.' I was rapidly running out of tables. Gerard, on the other hand, hadn't run out of (what he called) 'faces'.

'Now you *will* be impressed,' he said with real pride in his voice. 'That man over there . . .'

'What, the thug with the gold rings sitting two down from the UK's premier card-cheat?'

'Yes, that's right. He's Tony Martins.'

'Good for him. So?'

'Haven't you heard of him?' I indicated I hadn't. 'He's the chief bodyguard to the head of the underworld.'

I was underwhelmed but Gerard had quite enough enthusiasm for the two of us. 'He actually came in here, his boss.'

'Not "the head of the underworld"?' I put it in inverted commas but it went straight over Gerard's head.

'Yes,' he said with something approaching awe. 'He was very nice to me – he shook my hand afterwards.'

Like I say, Gerard's got no lack of bottle but he's not a complete fool. He knows that the more successful he gets, the more, er, 'attention' he'll draw. There are, apparently, other illegal gambling clubs and the owner of one of them has threatened to send down some men with shotguns. Consequently, Gerard has equipped himself with what he calls 'some muscle: a whopping great black guy – you don't mess with him.' Gerard keeps this deterrent hidden until needed but I met him at about three this morning and he is not what one would call undernourished. He is, in fact, a fucking mountain and a tribute to the benefits of steroid abuse. I wouldn't necessarily want to hang out with him but I can certainly see his value as 'muscle'.

There's also another reason for having muscle on the payroll. Gerard has a problem with credit. 'When I spot people,' he explained, 'they only pay me back when they win. The guys who lose take their time. One guy lost twelve and a half thousand, another eight thousand, another five thousand. They don't all pay up.'

I asked him what he intended to do. I didn't tell him that the question wasn't entirely academic.

'If someone doesn't pay? I'll send some people to see them. I have to, otherwise no one would pay me. Look, I'm not the only person these guys owe money to and who do you think they're going to pay if they've got a choice: the man who just asks or the man who sends round the muscle?

'There's another guy, The Turk, who I've got in reserve. He *always* gets paid. The black guy's just hired muscle: the Turk's something else.

'This credit business is a whole lotta problems. I've had my game for four weeks and I've made twenty-five grand profit. Trouble is, I'm still owed thirty. This guy – Tommy – I met him at Ford. He seemed genuine. I let him have fifteen hundred on the books but he's let me down. He's ex-directory but I got his number. I was told not to give him credit because he's known to have gone to the loo in the middle of the game and climb through a window to escape – and the guy's sixty-eight years old, for Christ's sake.'

I watched the Bad Man shaking his head with world-weariness and something else, I don't know, disgust at his own gullibility? 'There's a principle at stake,' I heard him mutter. I was going to taunt him with Murphy's Law ('When someone says, "It's not the money, it's the principle," nine times out of ten it's the money') but, out of deference to Gerard's uncharacteristic, if temporary, low spirits, I didn't. Apart from anything, I don't know when I'll be needing him to 'spot' me.

So far though, I'm OK. I've still got a few bob and I don't know whether it was because of my birthday or what, but I actually finished seven or eight hundred pounds *up*. It's been so long since I last won that I'd almost forgotten how damn good it feels.

Not that that in any way mitigates how fucking *exhausted* I feel right now. I managed to have a shave at Gerard's so I didn't come home looking like a tramp but even so, I must have looked wrecked. I told Maggie that I didn't sleep a wink last night – which, of course, is absolutely true.

It is good to be home in the bosom of my family. Maggie had bought a cake and the kids gave me the birthday cards they'd made for me. I'd have felt choked anyway but, knowing what I do, I have to confess that I had to leave the room to 'wash my face'. Maggie looked puzzled but otherwise seemed pleased by my reaction. Little Jona, whose twitching seems to have abated a little, even gave me a present: his favourite Rugrats character wrapped up in kitchen-roll. Given how much it means to him, it's the most valuable present I've ever received.

TUESDAY, DECEMBER 7

Phil called me in. I thought I was going to get another bollocking – maybe even a formal warning – for 'coasting' and 'not pulling my weight'. Nope, not a bit of it. Instead, he told me I was being 'dismissed' for 'submitting falsified expenses'. Happy Christmas, Phil.

'Hang on a moment,' I said, trying to get used to the idea that I no longer have to kowtow to the creep, 'I haven't been fiddling my exes – at least no worse than anyone else. There's more to it than that.'

The bent bastard played it with a straight bat. 'You had a formal warning,' he consulted his sheet of paper, 'on May the eleventh. In fact, this qualifies as gross misconduct which means that we're not actually legally obliged to give you a formal warning.'

'This isn't about exes, this is about my work rate, isn't it? But that's not a sackable offence, is it? Not without written warnings.'

He put his hands together so that his fingertips met and made a gesture with his mouth which indicated that there might be something in what I said. Then, in a pompous voice as though he were senior management rather than a fucking junior executive. 'You are being dismissed for gross misconduct. Nevertheless, the company' – he tried to make it sound more than the two-bit outfit that he and I know it to be – 'is prepared to be generous. We're going to give you a month's salary in lieu of notice. We're going to pay you for' – again he consulted his sheet of paper – 'four weeks' holiday you haven't taken and we're also going to give you another three weeks' money *ex gratia* because we recognise that it might not be easy for you to find another job before Christmas.' Ah, what compassion. 'The good thing for you is that it's all tax free.'

I felt my eyebrows going up in appreciation and tried in vain to control them. 'Suits me,' I said and then, looking around his office and jerking my head to include the whole of the building, I added, 'I can do better than this.'

'I hope you can,' he said with a false smile and absolutely no sincerity.

We parted company without a handshake. On my way out, Jayne called me over and told me how sorry she was etc. etc. 'You're wasting your breath, honey,' I told her. 'I don't want your sympathy – even if it's sincere.' I stilled her protest. 'No, what I would have liked, what I think I was entitled to, was just maybe a little hint of what Phil was going to do today. So, thanks but no thanks.'

I won't tell Maggie: she doesn't need the hassle. I don't need the hassle. The good thing about my (ex-) job is that, provided I leave the house on the days when she's off work, she won't even know that I've been fired.

WEDNESDAY, DECEMBER 8

Should be feeling pissed off but I have to say I'm not. If anything, I feel relieved, like a weight's been taken off my shoulders.

Decided to go over to see Gerard. Don't mean to be heartless but when I'm with him, I really do know that there's someone worse off than me.

Gerard's in deep doo-doos: his core business is losing money

– and that's (presumably) without having to worry about little extras like paying the bills or the staff. The casino is subsidising the business – i.e. the business is now a front for his casino. He's got a fabulous rent deal but how much longer can he continue to deceive his landlord?

Gerard tells me all this and just as I've composed my face into a suitably glum expression, he changes tack and lets me into his latest coup. He's got himself (what he calls) a 'pigeon'. No, he's not after becoming the Birdman of Pentonville (but give him time), he's got a mark, a patsy, a *victim*. His name's John and he's the decorator doing some work on the flat. I've met the bloke: middle-aged, fat, friendly – looks like Gerard's long-lost brother. Time comes for Gerard to pay him the money he owes – about a grand. Gerard pays it to him in cash – Gerard does *everything* in cash – and then suggests a little poker. John, the poor sap, is only too keen. They sit down together, in the same way that the lamb lies with the lion and, within an hour, Gerard has recovered the whole lot.

This was a week ago. The guy carries on working for Gerard. Three days later, Gerard's due to pay a bill for £1,500 (to cover John and John's men). Once again, Gerard gives it to him in cash and, once again, offers him the opportunity to play some more poker. In a triumph for optimism over experience, John agrees. According to Gerard, John is falling over himself to play.

Incredibly, John starts to win and it ain't no hustle by Gerard, the guy's winning legit. Gerard says he's never seen a streak like it. They're playing six-card Omaha (the Bad Man's favourite) with a stripped deck – i.e. only 8s and above. Gerard gets dealt 8, 9, 10, Q, K, A. Another ace is exposed by mistake and so becomes the 'burnt' card (me, I'd have demanded a re-deal). The flop comes down A, A, K (unsuited – Gerard says that, with six cards and a stripped deck, the suits don't matter unless there's the possibility of a running/royal flush). With a full house of aces over kings, Gerard bets £500 and John calls.

The fourth card is a jack. Later Gerard discovers that John is holding a pair of jacks and so this completes a small house for him of jacks over aces. *Knowing* that he's got the nuts (because of the exposed ace) Gerard bets the pot: one thousand. John, happy as a pig in the brown stuff, calls.

Then the fifth card is turned over: yes, it's the jack. John can't disguise his glee. Gerard folds in disgust that John could stay in just on the offchance of one card – especially given the likelihood that, with six cards dealt, Gerard could have not only the ace (to give him the nuts on fourth street) but also, until it materialised, the fourth jack! But then that's what happens when you're playing against a complete greenhorn: sometimes it's their very lack of knowledge that enables them to win.

Eventually, it took Gerard until five in the morning to win it all back and much more besides. The last hand was the one that did it. Same game. Gerard gets dealt jack of clubs, king of clubs plus a pair of 8s and a pair of 9s. John (it later transpires) is holding jack of hearts, king of hearts, two queens, ace of diamonds and an 8.

The flop comes down 10 of hearts, queen of hearts and the ace of clubs. They've both got straights. There are constant small raises and re-raises until Gerard decides to (try to) scare him off with a bet of a thousand but John sees him.

The fourth card is the queen of clubs. Now it's John's turn to have the nuts: four queens. Having learnt at the feet of the master, he trap-checks, hoping to lure the Bad Man into an injudicious bet but Gerard checks too.

The last card is the 10 of clubs. So Gerard's got the royal flush, the winning hand. John, meanwhile, either unable to see that there's the possibility of a royal flush or ignorant of the precedence of such a hand over four of a kind, thinks *he's* got the nuts. It's a recipe for carnage and so it proves. The two of them raise and re-raise each other until there's nothing left in front of them. They're playing table stakes but John, in the (mistaken) belief that he can't lose, asks if he can dip into his pocket to bet even more. Gerard says, 'You can if you want to but you might get hurt.' Not unreasonably, John takes this 'advice' for typical Bad Man moody and, disingenuously replying, 'I haven't got a very good hand but I'll take that risk,' pulls out (what turns out to be) £1,510 and bets fifteen hundred quid.

Gerard, who *knows* that he's going to win, raises him the final tenner.

With huge excitement, John lays down his queens and goes to rake in the pot. 'Not so fast,' says Gerard, the cartoon-saloon poker baddie, 'my royal flush beats your four of a kind.'

John is, in quick succession, incredulous, appalled, crestfallen. But the Bad Man wasn't finished. 'Then I did something very nice. I gave him back the ten quid I raised him at the end. I don't think it was kind of me to raise that money then.'

Now it was my turn to be open-mouthed. 'Oh so it was all right for you to take thousands off him when you *knew* you had him beaten but not to take the tenner at the end?'

Gerard, his self-image as the Albert Schweitzer of poker barely dented, smiled. 'He only had himself to blame. He was greedy.'

'Maybe he was,' I conceded, 'but don't you feel *responsible* towards him? After all, he's only a decorator and you're taking his wages out of his pocket. Don't you feel a twinge of guilt?'

Silly question really. 'I feel I'm educating him,' replied the Bad Man with a completely straight face. 'Now, with the extra money I won off him, I'm going to buy a motorcycle.'

More fool John then but maybe I'm a bigger fool than him because I allowed Gerard to persuade me to play backgammon with him. Hell, who am I trying to kid? *That's* why I went there in the first place. After just three and a half hours, playing a hundred quid a point, I was down £6,400. What'll he buy with that: a car? I gave him eight hundred in cash – all I had on me – and the rest I put on the slate. So now I've been 'spotted' by the Bad Man. He'll expect paying – even if he does consider me a friend: Gerard would be prepared to fall out with anyone for a lot less than five grand. I just hope I don't get a visit from The Turk.

THURSDAY, DECEMBER 9

I really am fucked. I never thought I'd stoop so low but I phoned Sue and told her that I needed ten thousand – or as much as she could let me have – as quickly as possible. She asked me what it was for. 'I can't tell you,' I said, 'all I can say is that it's a matter of life and death.'

Sue said she'd put a cheque in the post immediately.

FRIDAY, DECEMBER 10

Got phone calls today (on my mobile) from Ben, Jake *and* Douglas all, in their own ways, trying to warn me off Gerard's.

Jake, bless him, was the most concerned. 'Listen, Steve, that game's bad news. Sooner or later, someone's going to come in tooled up and I don't want you to get caught in the crossfire.'

'What a chum you are, Jake.'

'Steve, I'm being serious. What about the money?'

'Aha, so now we come to the rub. Have you been talking with the girls?'

He sidestepped the question. 'Steve, how can you afford to play in that game, week in week out – especially as Gerard says you're losing badly.'

'Gerard's got a big mouth. Besides, I'm not losing badly: I'm losing *well*.' I changed tack. 'You know, Jake, I'm not exactly a kid and I'm definitely not coming on to you guys so why all the concern?' A horrible thought occurred to me. 'You've not been speaking with Maggie, I hope?'

'No, but we are all worried about you. You seem to be on tilt.' I remained silent. 'Come back to our game. Without Gerard it's relatively gentle: no one's going to win or lose much more than about three hundred and at least the money goes around.'

I didn't know how to respond: there's so much I wanted to say. Instead, I mumbled, 'I'd love to, Jake, but it's just too late.'

Jake's right: I *am* on tilt. And which two words invariably follow tilt? Game over.

SATURDAY, DECEMBER 11

Spent the afternoon flicking between the rugby on Sky and the football on teletext. Nothing unusual – except I was losing even more than I normally do.

All of a sudden, Her Maggiesty walks in and switches off the TV. 'That's it, you sodding bastard, you've blown your last chance!'

She was absolutely furious: I can honestly say that I've never seen her so angry and, to be honest, I was more than a little frightened of her. So instead of blustering, I asked what I'd done wrong.

'You've been fucking gambling, you bastard!' I pointed at the children, who'd followed her into the room, as if to reprimand her for swearing in front of them but she just went beserk. 'Don't you fucking *dare* to criticise me and fucking don't think you can hide behind the children. If you loved them, you fucking wouldn't have thrown away all our money!' As someone who is unpractised at swearing, Maggie doesn't do it very well or appropriately.

I tried to stall for time but I could see it was useless. There was, however, one thing I wanted to know. Even with my marriage falling apart, I still needed to satisfy my curiosity. 'How did you find out? I thought I'd been pretty careful.'

She'd been expecting me to deny it or to prostrate myself at her feet or something: she wasn't prepared for my calm admission. It seemed to enrage her still further and she ran over to me screaming, trying to punch me. I fended her off easily by grabbing and holding both of her hands in just one hand. With the other hand, I indicated to the startled, bewildered kids that they should leave the room. 'Mummy and Daddy are just playing,' I told them. They didn't look convinced but hopefully one day they'll come to appreciate my thoughtfulness.

I calmed Maggie down sufficiently to be able to release her. 'You're not as clever as you think you are, Steven Ross,' she hissed. 'It was so *easy*. All I had to do was wire up the old baby alarm in reverse so that it picked up the noise from this room and relayed it to Melanie's room. I put a tape recorder next to the receiver and just before I went out this afternoon, I switched it to record. So there's no point in denying anything cos I've got it on tape, all right? I haven't listened to all of it yet, just enough.' She tried to imitate my voice, '"I'll buy Wasps for a hundred pounds a point." I don't know what it means. What does it mean, Steve? What does it *all* mean?'

I shrugged. 'You're the one who said it was a disease.'

'Don't, just don't. Why couldn't you get a *normal* disease, like multiple sclerosis or muscular dystrophy or something – anything – that didn't make you . . . ?'

'I've lost my job, you know.' I wasn't looking for sympathy or pity: I was merely telling her for the record.

She just nodded. The anger had dissipated leaving only resolution tinged with ruefulness. 'I'm leaving, Steve, and I'm taking the children with me. I'd throw you out but there's no point. You'd only end up on the streets and, anyway, this house doesn't belong to us any more, does it, Steve? It belongs to the bank and whoever else you've borrowed from.'

I admitted it: what was the point in denying it? 'Where will you go?' I asked her. 'I don't know if you believe me but I really *do* care about you and the kids.'

Softly, almost to herself. 'Not enough, Steve, not enough.' She raised her head and looked me in the eyes. There was a sense of purpose I've never seen before. Incredibly, I found myself fancying her. Too fucking late. 'We're going to my mother's house.' I looked surprised. 'You thought that I lost the house when Mum died. No, Steve, I didn't. She was going to take out that mortgage she talked about but she was so worried about me . . .' she started sobbing but successfully composed herself, 'she knew that you were a gambler, she decided that she'd rather have something to leave to me, for my financial security, for the kids, rather than have extra for herself.'

'So you've come into an inheritance, Maggie? I thought you didn't believe in inherited wealth?'

She didn't rise to the bait but just walked out of the room, out of my life.

SUNDAY, DECEMBER 12

So here I am on my tod. I'd feel sorry for myself but the truth is I just feel numb. Can't be bothered to do anything: can't even be bothered to write.

I didn't watch Maggie and the kids leaving yesterday because I couldn't bear to.

That's it.

MONDAY, DECEMBER 13

It's just chips: it's only when you cash out that it's real.

I was at the Bad Man's all night long. Well, I had nothing to go home to. Poor company; good poker. The big hand of the evening (for me anyway) was a game of four-card Omaha – high-low (the Bad Man's contribution). I'm holding ace of diamonds, 2 of diamonds, jack of clubs and queen of spades. There's a bit of betting before the flop which is 8 of diamonds, jack of diamonds and the 4 of hearts. It almost couldn't be better for me: I've got the nut diamond flush covered and, so long as there's *two* more cards under a 9, then I've also got the nut low. Come on, someone, make my day. The guy sitting on my left (the sort of guy you think you know what he does for a living but you don't want to ask) bets a thousand: it turns out that he's holding a pair of kings and wants to scare off the low-ballers in the class. Three of us (including Gerard) call with varying degrees of enthusiasm.

The fourth card is the queen of diamonds. I fucking love it: I've got the ace diamond flush and I'm still in with a chance of the low too. I decide to bet the pot on the basis that, at this precise point in the game, I'm in a no-lose situation: if they all fold, I win the best part of four grand and, if they stay in (on prospects) then, barring something pairing up, I'm going to take even more of their money off them.

I couldn't *quite* manage the pot but anyway went all in for three thousand, six hundred quid. It's just chips: it's only when you cash out that it's real and, besides, it's not a gamble, it's an investment. Seeing the size of my bet and noting the third diamond, Mr Three Kings folds with alacrity. Gerard tells us the story of his life – yawn yawn – concluding with the observation that if he 'had even a *pair* of diamonds in my hand or any two cards lower than a seven, I'd have your arse' and then folds. This leaves just one bloke who's sitting directly opposite me. I don't know him – or anything about him – but he looks OK: certainly not a crook but quite possibly a professional gambler. That's OK: sometimes (and this is one of those times) you play the cards and not the man. He calls. If we weren't playing high-low, I'd be bothered but I have to take him for, say, a king-diamond flush and, almost certainly prospects of ace-2 or ace-3 for the low.

Ordinarily, if we were playing normal (i.e. high only) Omaha, someone would shout out 'on their backs' as there's no more betting but, with high-low and one card to go, there's another layer and, quite possibly, another dimension too.

The final card is the king of clubs. It's a pity that the low is now ruled out but at least nothing paired up. So we're both high and it's time to show our cards. 'The ace flush,' I say with as little triumphalism in my voice as possible. Then, suddenly, before he even puts down his cards, I realise something that I should have seen on fourth street: *I haven't got the nuts – and he has*. Sure enough, he puts down the 9 and 10 of diamonds to make a running flush. How could I not have even seen it? Looking back, maybe I (kind of) did but thought that the 8 didn't stretch to the queen or maybe, unconsciously, I just couldn't believe that anyone could have such fantastic cards. Damn it, even if I had seen the possibility of the running flush, I'd have still bet as I did – especially as people might have stayed in on lowball possibilities. I'd have just felt less like a complete cunt.

It's just chips: it's only when you cash out that it's real. Cash out: cash in – there can be thousands of pounds in just one proposition. I lost seven and a half thousand pounds. Gerard, who at the start of the evening was asking me to pay off what I owe him, agreed to spot me for my losses but I'm obliged to bring along at least ten thousand next time or . . . or, much as the Bad Man (genuinely) likes me, I could be meeting The Turk. I don't know: Sue's ten grand will have cleared in the next day or so. Do I use that to pay Gerard (and therefore get more credit) or do I take it to the casino and play it up to give myself a war chest?

TUESDAY, DECEMBER 14

Today, I was giving some more thought to my 'final music'. I don't know how long it would take me to die but it should be at least an hour from the time I uncork the champagne to when I sink into final oblivion. That would mean about a dozen songs which I could record on to tape and then listen to on my personal stereo.

I'd start with the up-tempo songs and then, as the pills took effect, so too would the slower songs.

'Dancing Barefoot' by Patti Smith
'Like A Rolling Stone' by Bob Dylan
'Walkin' On The Sun' by Smash Mouth
'Rosalita (live version)' by Bruce Springsteen
'Money Don't Matter 2 Nite' by Prince
'Man of The World' by Fleetwood Mac
'The Wind Cries Mary' by Jimi Hendrix
'Don't Worry About Me' by Frank Sinatra
'Gloomy Sunday' by Elvis Costello
'Girlfriend In A Coma' by The Smiths
'Venus (The Bringer of Peace)' from Gustav Holst's *The Planets*

That lot probably wouldn't take up a whole hour so, rather than tape any more *whole* tracks, I'd prefer to pick my favourite *bits* off songs and put them at the top of the cassette.

The intro to The Rolling Stones's 'Gimme Shelter'
The ending of Paul McCartney's 'Maybe I'm Amazed'
The middle eight of Steely Dan's 'Sign In Stranger'
The intro to David Bowie's 'Heroes'
The first verse of Carly Simon's 'The Right Thing To Do'
The last verse of The Beach Boys' 'Heroes And Villains'
The intro to Dave Brubeck's 'Take Five'
The second guitar solo in Dire Straits's 'Sultans of Swing'

The final solo in Pink Floyd's 'Shine On You Crazy Diamond'
The opening clarinet solo of 'Rhapsody In Blue'
The guitar solo in Neil Young's 'Southern Man'
The intro to Hawkwind's 'Silver Machine'
Just the verses of The Beatles' 'I'm So Tired'
The opening of Joan Armatrading's 'Love And Affection'
The middle eight of Joni Mitchell's 'Help Me' (how appropriate)
Precisely one minute forty-one seconds into Santana's 'Incident At Neshabur'

WEDNESDAY, DECEMBER 15

I disdain red bills, I sneer at summonses, I laugh in the face of bailiffs. I'm fucking freewheeling, me.

At least I'm no longer feeling down like I was over the weekend. Truth is I can't afford to but, even so, I'm feeling pretty good. Went back on the Prozac Sunday and, touch wood, it seems to be working its magic again.

I decided to go to the casino with Sue's money rather than repay the Bad Man. I've reached the stage when I *have* to use every penny I can get my hands on for the bet. Yes, I need to keep the Bad Man onside but there's a *possibility* that I can put him off until the New Year whereas it's an absolute *certainty* that there won't be a New Year for me unless I can start winning and ten thousand carefully staked in a casino could make all the difference.

I played roulette and I swear on my children's lives that I didn't do *one* self-indulgent bet.

It was late afternoon and, since I was playing the one-pound minimum table, I was playing (pretty much) on my own. Just me against the casino. I split my money into units of £100 and played a complicated – at least a *more* complicated – progressive system on the even money chances (high/low, odd/even, red/black).

What I did was chart all three even chances and wait until any one of them came up the same three times running. As soon as it did,

I placed a hundred quid on the opposite. So when odd came up three times running, I backed evens; when it was high three times in a row, I went low and when it was black for three goes, I plumped for red. When my bet won, I transferred the profits to a separate pile; when it lost, I doubled my bet. Sometimes, I had three bets running at the same time.

I *thought* that by sticking in the three-times-in-a-row provision, I was mitigating the worst effects of the usual progressive losing system I play but, in the event, I still lost all my money in just a few hours.

The thing was, I did win. After about three hours, I was about £4000 up. If I'd stopped then . . . What I *should* have done was set myself an easily attainable target – like to win two thousand – and then quit when I reached it. But two thousand, four thousand, six thousand wouldn't have been enough. Maybe ten thousand would *just* have been enough.

Knowing when to stop: *that's* discipline – not merely sticking rigidly to one sort of bet. Trouble is, I'm learning these lessons too fucking late. Meanwhile, I'm running out of dough: I've spent the fifteen thousand I got from the finance company, I've spent the 'payoff' (such as it was) from work, I've spent the money Dad 'lent' me and now I've spent the money Sue lent me. I don't know what to do next.

THURSDAY, DECEMBER 16

Applied for loans with three different companies today. Two of them turned me down on the basis that I'm 'over-extended' but the third was prepared to lend me twelve grand. They're charging me a massive 18% but then interest charges don't mean a hell of a lot to me at the moment.

Going to Caz's this evening. At least there, I have a *chance* of winning some money.

FRIDAY, DECEMBER 17

I went to Caz's place to play poker last night. Knowing the money's definitely coming in, I had the confidence to ask for credit on the basis that I could always pay up if I happened to lose. Same crowd – give or take a Hooray Henry – but the evening was totally dominated by something that shocked me (literally) shitless.

Clive, the complete cunt from last time, has, as I thought, got in way over his head. Turns out that he *isn't* a surveyor but a fucking estate agent. I'd have thought that no fate was too bad for such a man but I'd have been wrong.

He's obviously not a very successful estate agent because after losing a big pot (his full house was beaten by a well-disguised running flush in a hand of seven-card stud – nothing wild) to go seven thousand down, he went beetroot red in the face and actually started crying.

Johnny, high from all the cocaine and therefore even more impervious to another human being's misery, actually *laughed*. Caz sniggered but at least had the good grace to try to hide it. Eventually, he asked Clive what the matter was.

Choking back the tears and wiping his eyes like a five-year-old boy who's lost his parents in a busy shopping arcade, Clive said, 'I . . . don't . . . know what to do. I can't . . . afford . . . to lose so much.' His speech was punctuated by sobs. 'I . . . owe money to . . . so many . . . other people.'

Caz was now more alert but still seemingly emotionless. 'What about your parents?' he asked him carefully.

Clive stopped crying long enough to answer that his father was dead and his mother lived on a widow's pension.

'Sell the car, I say,' declared Terence, thumping the table. Johnny endorsed this with a 'Hear, hear!'

'Can't, it's a company car.'

Caz subtly indicated to Johnny and Terence that he was in charge. 'You must have *something* worth – what is it – seven thousand?'

More sobs from the wretched Clive. 'No, nothing. I don't even have the money to get home tonight.' I noticed his Adam's apple bobbing up and down and, from then on, couldn't take my eyes off it.

Caz went into a huddle with Johnny and Terence and then emerged with a gleam in his eyes. 'Clive . . .' Sobs from Clive. Caz's voice no louder but harder and with more authority. 'Stop snivelling, man.'

Clive looked up – in surprise more than anything – but he did indeed stop snivelling.

'How much is your pride worth, Clive?' Clive looked suitably mystified by Caz's question but I experienced a wave of nausea. Clive looked blank. 'Come on, man, you owe us seven thousand pounds. How are you going to pay up?'

'I told you. I don't know.'

'Precisely. So how much is your pride worth? Seven thousand?'

'What do you want me to do?'

'That's better.' A glance over to Johnny for 'moral' support. 'What we want you to do to "discharge your obligations to us" is very simple. We require you to consume a portion of your own excrement.'

Clive looked bewildered, horrified. 'What?'

'You heard him,' said Terence, smiling, 'he wants you to eat your own shit.'

I glanced over at Richard, whom I'd marked down as a decent guy, but he was just nodding his head as if to signify assent. The others were all laughing, smiling and very excited. No one's face expressed anything approaching sympathy, empathy or pity.

More tears from Clive but now they were the tears of conquest and humiliation. 'What, now?'

'Yeah,' roared Johnny. The others cheered him on.

'Wait a second,' said Caz, taking a look in my direction. 'Are you in on this, Steve?'

'What do you mean?'

'You have to pay an equal share if you want to see the entertainment.'

Even if I could have afforded to, I would have declined; even though I couldn't have afforded to, I would have paid good money *not* to watch. 'No thanks, I'm not such a shit.'

'Ooh,' shrieked Johnny and Terence, 'get her! She's got feelings!'

'Just leave the room,' said Caz to me. Then he changed his mind. 'No, on second thoughts, you stay here. The rest of you come with me to the den.'

Out they all trooped. I think Caz even put his arm around Clive's shoulders as though he were a friend or something.

I heard laughter but nothing else. Part of me was obviously appalled. Part of me – a very small part, I'm proud to say – was fascinated: if only by the logistics. Then another part of me still rationalised it thus: no one forced Clive to gamble so heavily; no one actually *forced* him to eat his own shit. They're giving him £7,000 for the 'privilege' of watching him do it. Evidently, that's how much his pride is worth. How much is mine worth? More than seven thousand? Yes, at the moment at least. But how much more? It's like that old gag about the man offering a woman a pound to sleep with him. She refuses on the grounds that she's not a prostitute. So he offers her a million pounds and she willingly accepts. 'Right then,' he says, 'we've established that you're a whore: now all we're doing is haggling over the price.' What's my price? I honestly don't know. I just hope I never get to find out.

When the guys returned (minus Clive whom I heard leaving although, understandably, he didn't come into Caz's dining-room to say goodbye to me), they were still wide-eyed. A couple of them – including Terence but not, surprisingly, Richard – looked, I don't know, ashamed of themselves. Well, maybe not ashamed but at least a little embarrassed to see me, to look at each other. They'd obviously agreed – tacitly, I guess – not to talk about it. Maybe, they were still bothered by the thought of me sharing their 'entertainment' even after the event: rather like satellite TV doesn't allow terrestrial TV even a minute's highlights of a major boxing fight. Didn't bother me: notwithstanding my curiosity, I can live very happily without knowing *any* of the gory details.

Funny thing was, I went on to play some really disciplined poker after that. I don't know if it had anything to do with Clive or the fact that I wasn't taking (much) cocaine, but I was in real control of myself once he left – as though I didn't want to find myself in his position. I left at five this morning having won just over £1,000. Not a huge amount but better – *much* better – than eating my own turds.

Looking back on last night and this morning after a few hours' sleep, I've got a little distance on Clive and his shit. Life was just *waiting* for Clive to come along and be dumped upon: he was a victim looking for an accident. Me? I'm a fortnight away from two hundred grand.

SATURDAY, DECEMBER 18

Noon. I was going to do some serious spread-betting this afternoon but it seems that I'm way past my limits. Apparently, the £2,300 I lost yesterday afternoon selling the favourites at Uttoxeter has taken me over the top.

In the absence of the twelve grand I'm getting from the loan company, I'm a bit boracic but I've still got the grand I won at Caz's so fuck them, their spreads, their trades and their credit facilities.

9.00pm. I split the thousand into four lots of £250 and then visited four different (independent) betting shops where I gambled £250 at each (I even won at 11–10 in one race before gifting it back in the next) and then asked for some credit on the basis that I'd left my wallet and credit cards at home.

Three of the four shops turned me down flat but one, in Fulham, let me have a monkey on tick – just like that. Unfortunately, the horse I put it on – a 9–4 favourite running at Ascot – got beaten by a short head and so not only did I do my money but now I have to avoid Fulham.

I suppose I could always get some money on tick at Henry's but not enough, not nearly enough.

SUNDAY, DECEMBER 19

I'm in limbo at the moment. I want to gamble – I *need* to gamble – but I just don't have the necessary funds. I know I've got twelve grand coming in but until then . . .

I'm going to Gerard's tonight. Win, lose or draw – well, certainly lose or draw – I'll borrow even more money than I need for the game.

MONDAY, DECEMBER 20

I can't believe it. I'm sitting in Gerard's club, I'm maybe eight K down but, like, it's only five in the morning and there's hours, days, to go. I'd even intended to have a kip in one of the Bad Man's bedrooms so that I could return to the fray refreshed.

Suddenly, crash bang boom, and the police – wielding serious batons and wearing ridiculously over-the-top body armour – are screaming at us: 'This is the police!' Oh, so that's who you are: I thought you were the pizza-delivery boys. It is, of course, a fucking raid.

Not content with booking motorists for breaking the speed limit, it transpires that the police have decided to do something to halt the scourge of illegal gambling – as if we were harming anyone. Thinking about it later, especially after some sleep, I realised that they were prompted to do this by one of Gerard's rivals/enemies/marks. It's hard to know where to start: basically the list is as long as anyone who's ever known him.

He, of course, has been arrested. Douglas, who I spoke to just twenty minutes ago (the jungle drums obviously beat out the news) reckons that Gerard will go down for this big time. In Douglas's words, 'by the time Gerard gets out of prison, he'll be Gabby Hayes.'

I gave a false name but, anyway, the police didn't want to nick me. Nevertheless, I'm down. I hate to be egocentric about this and

I'm truly sorry for the Bad Man but I was banking on being able to borrow off him. What the hell will I do now?

It would be a bit of a result if I could now simply write off the (several, several) thousands I owe the Bad Man but, unfortunately, he's been obliged to assign – i.e. sell – his debts as he in turn needs money to pay his own debts and to cover his arse over the next few weeks. Prison, as he knows only too well, is expensive if you need protection and, notwithstanding his prowess at martial arts (which we only have on Gerard's authority) and the fact that he will inevitably end up back at Ford where everyone's on best behaviour, Gerard is going to need all the help he can get if he's to survive two weeks in a holding jail.

Poor old Gerard. Poor old me.

TUESDAY, DECEMBER 21

The twelve grand cleared my bank account this morning. I cashed it out early this afternoon and went to the casino. By eight o'clock this evening, I had *lost the lot*.

It honestly wasn't my fault. OK, so it was, like, *my* fault (as opposed to anyone else's) but I really did play it by the book: I *only* played blackjack and I played it properly and methodically. I played a simple one, two, three (hundred) pyramid staking plan, doubling down on ten and eleven only (plus 9 against the dealer's 4, 5 or 6) and only splitting 8s and aces (plus 9 against the dealer's 9) and *always* drawing on sixteen and below against the dealer's 7 or above and always sticking on twelve or better against the dealer's 6 or below. Most important, I had a specific target of what I was looking to win – a very reasonable, gettable ten thousand – so my upside was protected. And even then, after all that, I lost *everything*.

WEDNESDAY, DECEMBER 22

Morning. I must find money. This is beginning to obsess me to the exclusion of everything else – even the children who I saw this morning (*they're* missing Daddy even if Maggie isn't).

Maurice (Morris? I don't know – he's a bloke I met at the Bad Man's) reckons that he can 'source immediate cash advances' but we're talking exorbitant rates of interest: i.e. a loan shark.

I've always wondered at the mentality of people who could even *contemplate* going to a loan shark but now I'm one of those people and it doesn't seem quite so crazy after all. Where else can someone like me in my current position – no job, no savings, credit all used up – get money?

Afternoon. I phoned Maurice/Morris and within an hour – *an hour* – I had ten grand in my sweaty paws. I have to pay back fifteen grand (i.e. ten plus fifty per cent interest) within two weeks or else pay it off at a grand a week for twenty-five weeks. 'And those are bleeding good rates, my son,' said Maurice/Morris who, for all I know, could very well be the loan shark himself instead of the middle-man. He also warned me not to default on the loan 'or else things could get a little nasty.'

I'm going to the casino as I still think it offers me the best chance of winning some serious dosh.

Evening. Fuck, fuck, FUCK. I am feeling sick to my stomach. In fact, I was retching in the casino before staggering into a taxi with just the cab fare to get home.

I've done the *whole* ten grand. I can't believe how quickly it goes. I was up three or four grand. I would have stopped there if only I didn't need to win so much more. *So* much more.

That's it. I honestly don't think I can recover from this position. I'm closer and closer to death.

I don't regret it though. The only *fears* I have are logistical ones. Truth is, I can't wait to get it over with.

THURSDAY, DECEMBER 23

I'm amazed at my resilience. Last night, I was out for the fucking count. This morning, I was totally determined to do whatever I could to raise funds. So much so, I did something awesomely dumb. I went up to Oxford Street and got credit cards from three different stores. It took me nearly four hours but it got me three, four and five thousand pounds' worth of credit.

Unfortunately, this credit couldn't take the form of cash so I just bought things I knew I could pawn – basically, watches and men's jewellery – at the cheapest possible prices. Then I went to a pawnbroker's – an upmarket pawnbroker's – I'd passed by dozens of times and pawned the lot for five thousand. In cash.

I took this money and went straight to the casino which was just opening and, after checking with the manager, put the lot on black. I chose black because it includes all my favourite, 'lucky' numbers – 4, 8, 11, 26, 29 and 33.

It came up red.

Thing is, if I had won, would I have left it on? If so – and I think I would – for how many goes? Until I had doubled my money? Quadrupled it? Or until I had won 'the bet'? Wish I'd had the chance to find out.

SATURDAY, DECEMBER 25

Could sit here feeling very sorry for myself. Here I am, deprived of my children etc. Woe is me. But that's to be just like those blokes I found myself despising at Ford. Instead of thinking about the effect of their incarceration on their loved ones, they merely wallow in self-pity: you can see it in their eyes.

Well, like those cons, I'm entirely responsible for my own situation and it's Jona and Mellie I feel sorry for, not their cunt of a father. I feel slightly less sorry for Maggie: she has some choice in the matter but the kids have absolutely none.

Dad phoned this morning: ostensibly to wish me Happy Christmas but really to see if I was OK. He was sweet, kind, considerate. Maybe, I've been too hard on him: he raised me the only way he knew. Perhaps he was fucked up in his turn? I don't know. I'll leave instructions for him to be repaid.

What with all these debts and loans that'll have to be repaid out of the insurance money, there won't be that much left over for Maggie and the kids. Even so, there'll be a damn sight more than if I don't kill myself.

MONDAY, DECEMBER 27

This is my last year, my last month, my last Monday on earth and there's so many things I haven't done. But my biggest regret doesn't concern Maggie or the kids or my family or Cathy or my work or the bet but something more intangible. When I embarked on the bet, I obviously hoped to win but I thought that, if I lost, I'd gain something in the days leading up to my death: I thought that I'd have an *epiphany*, that I'd get some sort of insight into life and the meaning of life. But no, if anything, I understand less with each passing day.

TUESDAY, DECEMBER 28

I'm resigned to it now. I'm £95/96,000 down on the year and there's just no way I can win enough to claw myself back into the black.

I'm going to do it on Friday. I've got it all planned. I'll say goodbye to the kids in the morning. I'll take the pills in the afternoon and then, listening to my music, just drift off into oblivion. That's it. There's nothing else after that. Heaven and Hell are just stories to encourage/frighten kiddies, big and small. The truth is much more banal: death is the end, a full stop, nothing remains except other people's memories. Nothing. As it happens, I positively embrace nothingness and look forward to entering the void of death. It's so much *easier* than life.

I was going to phone Cathy. I always promised myself I would, at the end, in the hope that she might say something encouraging to 'stay my hand'. I won't bother. She wouldn't do or say anything to stop me and, besides, I really don't *want* to be discouraged.

The condemned man enjoys – *enjoys!* – a final poker game tonight. I'll get some credit off Caz. If I win, I'll try to play it up in the two/three days I've got left. If I lose, then Caz can go sing for it. To be fair to him, I'm pretty sure that when he finds out I've killed myself, he won't hound my family for the money: not because he's compassionate or anything but because – and I think I've read him right – he'd consider it uncool.

WEDNESDAY, DECEMBER 29

5.00am. I've got all the pills in front of me and I'm going to take them. It's only a matter of time. If not now, then later or tomorrow.

I'm shaking, I'm crying. I've already taken thirty milligrams of Valium and washed it down with a large whisky but it's having no effect. Fuck, I'm so frightened – not of death: no, the thought of that is my one source of comfort – of going beserk, crazy, demented. I honestly believe that my head could explode any second and I can't stand it.

I want to kill myself. I've said it so many times but now I'm ready. I want to kill myself: it's my mantra, the only thing that can keep me sane.

No one could blame me for going mad since only an insane man could possibly be sane after what I've been through.

I want to scream but I'm worried that if I start I'll never stop. So I'm letting it out bit by bit by shaking and shaking and retching but there's so much that needs to come out. It's like a pressure cooker. I can feel all the tension and horror at the top of my skull. Any minute now my brains will be on the floor. But I won't have died. I'll still be conscious enough to *know*.

That's bollocks. Once the brain goes, everything goes. I must control myself. I have to stay sane if I'm going mad otherwise I'll go mad.

I'm so scared of myself.

When they used to hang, draw and quarter a man, they'd take out his innards and show them to him. I don't want to see them.

I have to write down what happened. If I write it all down, I'll be able to read it and then it won't have happened to *me*. It'll be a story and I can close the book and walk away. What I can't do is go to sleep even though I haven't slept since Monday and my eyes are closing. Sleep will mean that I wake up and I can't do that.

It started off as a lark. One of the guys – Terence – got a six-pack of lager and shook up one of the cans. Really shook it up, like it was going to explode. He shuffled (what he called) the 'death' can into the other five. Then he challenged another guy to pick a can at random and open it in his ear. 'It's like Russian roulette,' he said. I remember that. 'It's just like Russian roulette.'

The guy did it and then another guy did it and then Johnny had a go and got a right earful and everyone laughed and he did too and I think some guys were betting on it but I'm not sure who. I do know that Caz and I weren't involved. I know that because he was looking at me as though I don't know. 'Are you queer for me?' I asked him and he just said, 'Maybe' and I said, 'It'll take a lot more than cocaine' and we laughed and then the other guys joined us. 'It's like Russian roulette,' said this guy again.

Then Caz said, 'What's wrong with real Russian roulette?'

A couple of people looked puzzled but I could tell from their glances that Johnny had caught his drift. Caz looked from Johnny to me and then back again. 'Knew a chap once who played Russian roulette. They had to redecorate the ceiling afterwards.'

'Your ceiling looks like it could do with some refurbishment already,' added Terence.

Caz looked at Terence and Johnny then, like a computer mouse dragging a cursor, he 'drew' their eyes to meet mine. I found myself looking from one to the other to the other. And then Richard was brought into the loop so it started to feel like a fucking court-martial. 'Hey, what's up, guys?' But by then I knew. Least I think I did.

'How much would it take, Steve?'

'How much would what take?' Now, I was definitely playing for time.

Caz went immediately to the point. 'For you to play Russian roulette. One shot from a six-chamber revolver with just one chamber loaded.' I remember now the word that really made me feel sick to my stomach was 'play'.

'Just one shot,' said Johnny.

I've suddenly thought: maybe the whole lager-can stunt was intended to set me up. I don't know, maybe they've had this in mind for *weeks*.

Suddenly, I could see an opportunity opening up for me. I was breathing hard but thinking clearly. '*They don't know about the bet!* They *mustn't* know about the bet. They mustn't know that they're throwing me a lifeline. Certain suicide on Friday against five chances in six of survival now. How much am I down? Best part of a hundred grand? OK, deep breath. Be calm, state your price and stand by it. They can guess that I need money but they mustn't know how badly.

'I'll do it. For one hundred thousand pounds.' Then a wonderful thought occurred to me. 'To be paid to my family if . . .' and I let my words trail off.

'A hundred thou?' shrieked some oaf, 'I wouldn't do it for a hundred million!' Johnny shushed him before going over to Caz to confer. Terence and Richard joined them.

'We'll give you fifty,' said Caz.

Looking back, this was my biggest gamble of the evening. 'No,' I said, 'it's a hundred thousand or you can get yourself another idiot.'

'Ah, but Steve,' said Johnny genially, 'we've watched you gamble like a lunatic the past two months. You've put us all to shame. It has to be you, old boy. No one else would do.'

'Then pay me what I ask. I'm only valuing my life at six hundred thousand. How much do you value your life at, Johnny?' Johnny conceded the point by nodding his head so I turned to Caz. 'And what about you, Caz?'

Caz shot me a look of such condescension that, even now, even after what happened, fills me with nausea and said, 'A lot more than that.' He then barked out the names of all the other players, starting with Johnny. One by one, they all said 'Yes'. Richard – 'decent' Richard – was almost salivating at the prospect.

Caz, in command and totally businesslike, sent Johnny to fetch a revolver from his bedroom and took out a Mont Blanc fountain-pen to write me a cheque.

'My surname's Ross,' I said trying to be helpful.

'Do you want me to make it out to you or to your wife? Or is that tempting fate?'

I felt another wave of nausea sweep over me but I was determined not to show it or, indeed, anything. I might very well die but I was determined that they wouldn't get their money's worth in terms of watching me squirm. So I replied, in a similarly matter-of-fact tone, 'Put down Ross for the time being. Afterwards, you can write Steve or Maggie.'

He looked impressed and, I have to admit, there was a (tiny) part of me that felt bucked. Then Johnny walked in with a gun in one hand and a bullet in the other.

I had difficulty in catching my breath and I didn't even *try* to swallow. Caz held up the gun and the bullet for all to see. He broke open the gun, put the bullet in one of the chambers and closed the gun again. Then he gave the chambers a hard spin. I tried to follow the course of the bullet but, of course, it was impossible.

I was ready or as ready as I could ever be. One thing above all else was buoying me up: the thought that they didn't *know* that my downside was limited to just three days' of life and that my upside was not just a hundred grand but life itself. Just the knowledge of what I stood to gain was helping to make the whole experience bearable.

And then, just as I was about to pick up the gun, something happened that was so horrible, so *evil* that I must write it down quickly or I'll start shaking again and will have to stop altogether.

'Hang on a mo,' brayed Terence, 'aren't we going to have a bet on this?'

'Of course!' said Johnny. The others all agreed.

I thought I'd have a heart attack on the spot. *They were going to bet on me!* I'm hyperventilating even now just at the thought of it.

Caz, whose eyes never left my face, said, 'You seem to be

bothered, Steve? What's the point of playing roulette without having a bet on it.'

That did it. I threw up on the spot. Caz's was the first face I saw when I'd finished. No sympathy, no pity, not even any disgust: just mild distaste. 'I'll deduct the cost of having my carpets cleaned from your cheque.' Laughter. 'So who's betting what? I'll offer sixty thousand to ten that he dies.'

'I'll have some of that,' said Johnny, looking at me. 'Steve's not the lucky kind.' Clearly, it wasn't enough for me to lay my life on the line for their amusement, they must torment me first.

More bets were struck along the same lines. Then there were what Caz called the 'speciality bets'. Johnny bet ten grand that I'd 'honk again' before shooting. Caz gave him 6–4 and I remember Johnny triumphantly telling anyone who was prepared to listen that 'the double chunder is on the cards' and Richard replying, 'Don't you mean "on the carpet"?' Terence had fifteen thousand at evens that I'd bottle it or 'accidentally-on-purpose miss'. One guy – I think his name was Bennett – wanted to bet that I'd turn the gun on Caz – in the same way that Robert De Niro did to his captors in *The Deer Hunter*. I don't know if anyone took the bet or not but it's perfectly possible that they did.

I didn't throw up again – I'm glad to say that Johnny lost his bet – having started to experience a sense of alienation, of tuning out. I tried to hang on to it but, as I did so, it disappeared like mercury through cupped hands. In any event, Caz's authoritative tone would have jerked me back to awful, horrendous spine-chilling reality. 'Pick up the gun and pull the trigger.'

They say that just before you encounter death, your whole life flashes before you. It's not true – at least it wasn't for me. As I raised the gun to my head, all I can remember thinking is 'I thought my whole life was going to flash before me so where is it, what's happening?' My hand dropped to my side.

'Pick up the gun!'

'Pull the trigger!'

'*Squeeze* the trigger!'

'Do it, you cunt!'

'Come on, don't fuck around, Steve!'

Then, suddenly, out of nowhere, a picture of Mellie and Jona came into my mind. 'I want to live! I want to live! I WANT TO LIVE!' And then it was me urging me to pull the trigger. 'Do it, Stevie, there isn't a one in six chance of dying, *there are five chances in six of living!* The sooner you squeeze the trigger, the sooner you can get on with *life*! This gun isn't going to kill you, it's going to save your life!'

Unexpectedly, I felt light-headed, even serene.

'Look,' said someone, 'he's smiling.' And now it was *their* turn to be horrified as I calmly raised the gun to my ear and squeezed the trigger. Nothing. Pure nothing. Well, just a click. I looked around the room and saw disappointment, shock, anger etched on their faces. Me, I felt numb.

'Fuck!' screamed Johnny.

'Hooray,' shouted someone else who'd obviously 'backed' me.

Caz looked disappointed as though he hadn't had his money's worth but, ever the 'gentleman' (or at least that's his self-image), he added my first name to the cheque.

As soon as he handed it over, I ran out of the door to the sound of cheers, jeers and catcalls. I was obviously this week's Clive but I'm sure there are plenty more – especially if the price of humiliation remains so high.

Once outside on the street, I thought I might throw up again but after a little retching, nothing came up. I hailed a taxi and . . . well, here I am now with a cheque for a hundred thousand in my shirt pocket. I've only taken it out to check it nineteen times. I'll pay it in as soon as the bank opens.

Funny thing is, I've stopped shaking. I've stopped sobbing. I'm OK. I feel . . . normal, on an even keel. I no longer want to end it all. Maybe the Valium worked. No, it's more than that. I think that writing it all down helped even more than I thought it would. There are some good things for me to hold on to – especially that moment of yearning I experienced for Mel and Jona.

I'm going to the bank as soon as it opens and then I'm going to bed but before I do anything, there's one thing I've *got* to do and that's to throw away *every* fucking Valium in the house.

THURSDAY, DECEMBER 30

The madness is over. I didn't 'win' the bet: I survived it. Besides, like an anarchist in a court of law, I no longer recognise the bet or grant it any significance. My children have got their father back and I've got a life or, at least, the chance of one.

I'm not sure I'll ever get over the horror of Tuesday night but I have to learn to *live* with it, with myself. If I was humiliated then so were they and, in a sense, they're victims too, if only of their own perversion.

As long as I live, I'm never going to bet again. I feel sick at the thought of it. I don't need Gamblers Anonymous. An alcoholic who nearly drowns in a vat of whisky doesn't need Alcoholics Anonymous; a smoker who's had a lung removed due to cancer doesn't need nicotine patches; a drugs courier who survives a condom of heroin bursting in his stomach doesn't need a methadone prescription.

Maybe that was the point of the bet: to end the lunacy one way or the other. I couldn't have carried on with it, that's for sure. The one thing I do know is that I would have killed myself if I'd lost. Just to get it over with.

Maggie's wrong: it's not a disease, it's not an illness – it's a madness. If it's an addiction at all, it's not to gambling but to that adrenalin rush that accompanies it. I realise now that cutting down my gambling (both in terms of frequency and staking) – as I originally intended to do if I 'won' the bet at the start of the year – would be impossible. In gambling at all, I would be priming myself for something that I could never hope to deliver: the buzz. Sooner or later, if only to test myself, I'd increase the stakes or the frequency and I'd be back where I started.

I paid the money into the bank and I'll clear every single card, loan and debt and then make a fresh start. I'll get a new job: not as a salesman but as a teacher. I was a good teacher and teaching is a decent, worthwhile thing to do. I *know* I'll be fine when I get back in the classroom. After last Tuesday, nothing will ever scare me again.

I'd also like to try to make a fresh start of it with Maggie. She's not the love of my life but I do love her and she is the mother of my children. Maggie is a constant (not that I should treat her as such) in all of our lives and although she has her faults, the worst thing about Maggie has always been *me*. If she's a drudge, it's only because I turned her into one. If I can learn to value her – and to demonstrate that value to her – then we can make it work.

This time last year I couldn't wait to start the bet. Now . . .

FRIDAY, DECEMBER 31

I phoned Maggie this morning. I told her that I've finished gambling for ever, that I'm going back to teaching and that it's time for her and the children to come home. Maggie knows me better than anyone and she can tell that I'm genuine. I didn't tell her about the bet and I wasn't going to tell her about Tuesday but, in the end, I had to give her a potted version – if only to explain how I'm able to clear all the debts.

There were no conditions, no dire warnings and no lecture. They would have been superfluous and Maggie is an adult who doesn't go in for score-settling. All she asked me for was 'a little respect'. Neither of us said, 'I love you' although there is plenty of affection on both sides but I think Maggie would prefer deeds to words. She'll get them.

I've spent the past few hours reading my diary from beginning to end. None of those things happened to me, did they? I always thought that a man was the sum total of his experiences but I find it almost impossible to relate to mine.

I've gained nothing except just maybe, a little wisdom. I've also learned that taking control of my life means accepting that I've sometimes got to cede control in some areas. *I* set the bet and its parameters: where was it written that I had to carry on staking so much money? I was doing it for my habit, for my addiction. I wasn't chasing money so manically for the bet but because I got a massive rush from being so close to the edge. The trick is not to try to replace it but to accept that it can't be replaced and to live without it. Reckon it's 6–5 that I'll make it.